Structural Mechanics Software Series

Volume III

Structural Mechanics Software Series

Volume III

Edited by
N. Perrone
W. Pilkey

Technical Editor
B. Pilkey

University Press of Virginia
Charlottesville

THE UNIVERSITY PRESS OF VIRGINIA
Copyright © 1980 by the Rector and Visitors
of the University of Virginia

First published 1980

ISSN: 0146-2059
ISBN: 0-8139-0857-4

Printed in the United States of America

PREFACE

In this, the third volume of this series of books, the scope of material covered has been broadened to include reviews of computational mechanics technology, as well as reviews and summaries of available programs, and information on and access to structural analysis and design computer programs. Once again, leading authorities list and critically review public and commercial programs available on large, mini, and desk computers. These are in-depth assessments intended to assist the readers in selecting the best program for solving their particular problems. Precise information is given on how to acquire or gain access to each program mentioned.

Information is also given on a wide range of abstracting services that are available and of possible interest to the structural mechanics community. Both commercial on-line sources of these multiple data bases and custom ordered sources are covered.

There is a library of selected programs available on a nationwide commercial computer network. In Volume I, the programs documented were BOSOR4, GIFTS, TOTAL, BEAM, BEAMSTRESS, and SHAFT. In Volume II, the programs documented were SAP V, UCIN, WHAMS, DISK, TWIST, GRILL, and TABS 77. Updates to SAP and BOSOR are included in this volume. A GIFTS/ SAP interface is also presented. It is necessary to contact individuals described in the availability information section in the first chapter with regard to questions concerning the programs.

Potential contributors of survey articles for subsequent volumes are urged to communicate their interests in outline form to the editors. In particular, articles related to microprograms for new computer systems are also welcome.

The programs of the Software Series Library and the descriptions presented in this volume are being made available without any representation or warranty of any kind. The editors and publisher, therefore, assume no liability of any kind arising from the use of these items.

The editors acknowledge the financial support of the Department of Mechanical and Aerospace Engineering of the University of Virginia.

We also appreciate the assistance of E. Campbell and C. Ripley.

August 1979

Nicholas Perrone

Structural Mechanics Program
Office of Naval Research,
Code 474
800 N. Quincy St.
Arlington, Virginia 22217

Walter D. Pilkey

Applied Mechanics Division
Department of Mechanical and
Aerospace Engineering
University of Virginia
Charlottesville, Virginia 22901

CONTRIBUTORS

Otis H. Burnside
Southwest Research Institute
San Antonio, Texas   78284

T. Y. Chang
Department of Civil Engineering
University of Akron
Akron, Ohio   44325

Eugene D. Denman
Electrical Engineering Department
University of Houston
Houston, Texas   77004

Lawrence L. Durocher
Mechanical Engineering Department
University of Bridgeport
Bridgeport, Connecticut   06602

Billy Fredriksson
Linkoping Institute of Technology
Department of Mechanical Engineering
S-531 83 Linkoping
Sweden

Robert Greif
Department of Mechanical Engineering
Tufts University
Medford, Massachusetts   02155

Ronald L. Huston
Department of Engineering Analysis
University of Cincinnati
Cincinnati, Ohio   45221

Dennis C. Krinke
Loc. K16-15
Boeing-Wichitta
Wichitta, Kansas   67202

Jaroslav Mackerle
Linkoping Institute of Technology
Department of Mechanical Engineering
S-581 83 Linkoping
Sweden

Douglas P. Neary
Department of Civil Engineering
University of Maryland
College Park, Maryland   20742

Frederick C. Nelson
Department of Mechanical Engineering
Tufts University
Medford, Massachusetts   02155

Ahmed K. Noor
George Washington University Center
NASA Langley Research Center
Hampton, Virginia   23665

J. Padavon
Department of Mechanical Engineering
University of Akron
Akron, Ohio   44325

Coda H. T. Pan
Shaker Research Corporation
Ballston Lake, New York   12019

Barbara F. Pilkey
Applied Mechanics Division
University of Virginia
Charlottesville, Virginia   22901

F. Everett Reed
Littleton Research and Engineering Corp.
Littleton, Massachusetts   01460

David R. Schelling
Department of Civil Engineering
University of Maryland
College Park, Maryland   20742

Robert J. Stango
Department of Theoretical and Applied
   Mechanics
University of Illinois
Urbana-Champaign, Illinois   61801

Wallace B. Wright
Arthur D. Little, Inc.
20 Acorn Park
Cambridge, Massachusetts   02140

CONTENTS

Part I

SOURCES OF INFORMATION AND PROGRAMS

Library of Available Software Series Programs

INTRODUCTION

The following programs were documented in previous volumes as part of the library of the Software Series computer programs.

SAP V
UCIN
WHAMS
DISK
TWIST
GRILL
TABS 77
BOSOR
GIFTS
PREMSAP
BEAM
BEAMSTRESS
SHAFT

Some of these programs can be accessed on United Computing Systems (USC), a participating computer network. Usually, connection to the computer requires only a local telephone call. UCS should be contacted directly for information on using the programs on their system. Appropriate addresses are listed in this chapter. For information or assistance in using the programs on the network, please contact the local UCS representative.

PROGRAM AND DOCUMENTATION AVAILABILITY

Programs Documented in Volume II of the Software Series

SAP V

SAP V is a general three-dimensional, linear, static and dynamic, finite element structural analysis program. The elements available in the program are:

    1. Three-dimensional truss element
    2. Three-dimensional beam element
    3. Plane stress membrane element (quadrilateral or triangular)
    4. 2D quadrilateral or triangular element for plane strain or plane stress membrane axisymmetric solid
    5. 3D solid (eight-node brick)
    6. Thin plate and shell element (quadrilateral or triangular)
    7. Boundary element
    8. 8 to 21 variable-number-nodes thick shell and 3D element
    9. General element (read-in stiffness matrix element)
   10. 3D straight or curved pipe element

For dynamic analysis, there is a choice among:

    1. Eigenvalue and eigenvector solution only
    2. Forced dynamic response by mode superposition
    3. Response spectrum analysis
    4. Direct step-by-step integration
    5. Frequency response analysis using mode superposition

Network Availability
  UCS
Technical Manual
  None
User Documentation
  Contained in Volume II of the Software Series
Program Availability
  SAP Users Group
  Dept. of Civil Engineering
  University of Southern California
  University Park
  Los Angeles, California   90007
  Phone: (213) 741-5508

The cost of the tapes is $1000. This price also includes the manual and updates on the program for a one-year period.

Technical Problems in Using the Program Contact
  SAP Users Group

UCIN

The purpose of UCIN is to study the dynamics of crash victims. The model
consists of 12 rigid bodies representing the human limbs together with a
vehicle cockpit. The twelve bodies of the model are connected together
with ball-and-socket joints.

Technical Manual
  Available at no cost from
  R. L. Huston
  Dept. of Engineering Science
  University of Cincinnati
  Cincinnati, Ohio 45221
User Documentation
  Contained in Volume II of the Software Series
Program Availability
  The program is available for the cost of the tape, or free if a tape is
  sent to
  R. L. Huston
  at the address above.

  The cost of a new tape is approximately $15.

Technical Problems in Using the Program Contact
  R. L. Huston
  Phone: (513) 457-6131

WHAMS

WHAMS is a program for the nonlinear, transient analysis of two-dimensional
and axisymmetric three-dimensional structures and continua. Both material
nonlinearities and nonlinearities arising from large displacements are
treated by the program. Large strains can also be treated within certain
restrictions.
     The program is based on a finite element format, so that it has great
versatility in modeling complex shapes and boundary conditions. Both
constant strain and higher-order continuum elements as well as bending
elements are included. In addition, the user may add his own element for
special applications.

Network Availability
  UCS
Technical Manual
  Not yet available
User Documentation
  Contained in Volume II of the Software Series
Program Availability
  T. Belytschko
  Dept. of Civil Engineering
  Technological Institute
  Northwestern University
  Evanston, Ill. 60201

The price for the tape and all updates for one year is $300.
CDC and IBM versions are available

Assistance in Using the Program on the Network
  Contact the local network representative.
Technical Problems in Using the Program Contact
  T. Belytschko
  Phone: (312) 492-7270

DISK, TWIST, GRILL

The program DISK is for the thick elastic solids problems of disks,
cylinders, and spheres. These members can be formed of layers of different materials with arbitrary mechanical or thermal loading and boundary
conditions.
    For a disk it calculates the radial displacement, the radial force
per unit circumferential length, and the tangential force per unit radial
length for static and steady state conditions. The natural frequencies
and mode shapes are found for radial vibrations. The disk is based on a
plane stress assumption. Both applied loadings and responses are axially
symmetric.
    For the cylinder, DISK calculates the radial displacement, radial
stress, tangential stress, and axial stress for static and steady state
conditions as well as the natural frequencies and mode shapes of radial
vibration. The underlying theory for the cylinder employs a plane strain
assumption. Applied loadings must be axially symmetrical. The calculated
responses are also axially symmetric.
    In the case of the sphere, the radial displacement, radial stress,
and tengential stress are found for static and steady-state conditions.
Also, the natural frequencies and mode shapes are calculated for radial
vibration. The applied loading and the resulting responses are spherically
symmetric.
    The program TWIST is for the torsional analysis of simple and complex
torsional systems. It calculates the angle of twist and the twisting
moment for static and steady-state conditions. The natural frequencies
and mode shapes are computed for three torsional vibrations. The torsion
system can be formed of segments with any loading, gears, branches,
foundations, and boundary conditions. When applied to extension systems,
TWIST finds the axial displacement and force for static and steady
state systems. Also, the natural frequencies and modes of longitudinal
vibration can be calculated. The extension system can be a sequence of
springs and masses or a bar of uniform segments with arbitrary loading,
foundations, and boundary conditions.
    The program GRILL handles the static analysis of uniform grillages
subjected to uniform, hydrostatic (ramp), and concentrated forces. It
calculates deflections, slopes, bending moments, and shear forces, In
establishing a model, either set of beams of a gridwork may be designated
as the girders; the other set is the stiffeners. In GRILL, the stiffeners
are simply supported while the girders may be fixed, simply supported,
or free ends. Any number of concentrated forced may be placed on the
grillage at the intersections of the stiffeners and girders. Only one
of each type of the distributed loads (uniform or hydrostatic) may be
placed on a parituclar grillage.

Network Availability
  UCS

Technical Manual
   Available from the Structural Members Users Group
   These programs belong to a collection of a dozen programs,
   three of which were documented in Volume I of the Software Series.
   The technical manuals for all of the programs cost $50.
User Documentation
   Contained in Volume II of the Software Series
Program Availability
   A tape or deck of the program can be purchased from
   The Structural Members Users Group
   P.O. Box 3958, University Station
   Charlottesville, Virginia 22903
Assistance in Using the Program on the Network
   Please contact the local representatives of the network.
Technical Problems in Using the Program Contact
   The Structural Members Users Group
   Phone: (804) 296-4906

TABS 77

TABS 77 is a special purpose computer program for the elastic three-
dimensional static and dynamic analysis of frame and shear wall buildings.
For buildings with rigid diaphragms (in-plane), which can be approximated
by independent frames and shear walls, the program is very economical
and easy to use as compared to a general purpose three-dimension
structural analysis program.

Network Availability
   UCS
Technical Manual Availability
   National Information Service Earthquake Engineering (NISEE)
   College of Engineering
   337 Davis Hall
   University of California
   Berkeley, California 94720
   Phone: (415) 642-5113

   The price of a manual is $10.00

User Documentation
   Contained in Volume II of this Series
Program Availability
   National Information Service Earthquake Engineering

   The cost is $125, including manuals.

Assistance in Using the Program on the Network
   Please contact the local representatives of the network.
Technical Problems in Using the Program Contact
   For problems arising using the documentation presented in Volume II
   contact
   A. Habibullah
   Computers/Structures International
   Oakland, California
   For problems arising using a purchased deck, or tape, contact NISEE.

Programs Documented in Volume I of Software Series

BOSOR4

This is a program for the stress, stability, and free vibration analysis
of segmented, ring-stiffened, branched shells of revolution and prismatic
shells and panels. BOSOR4 performs large-deflection axisymmetric stress
analysis, small-deflection nonsymmetric stress analysis, modal vibration
analysis with axisymmetric nonlinear prestress included, and buckling
analysis with axisymmetric or nonsymmetric prestress.

Network Availability
  United Computing Systems
  University Computing Company
  TYMSHARE
  McDonnell-Douglas Automation, Huntington Beach, Calif.
  Control Data Corp., Rockville, MD.
  Westinghouse Electric, Pittsburgh, PA.
  Information System Design, Oakland, Calif.
  Boeing Computer Service, Seattle, Wash.
  Det Norski Veritas (Norway)
  CNES (France)
  CERN (Switzerland)
  Aeronautical Res. Inst. of Sweden (FFA) (Sweden)
  CTR (Italy)
  Matematischer Beratungs and Programmierungsdienst (West Germany)
Technical Manual
  Use the one in Volume I of the Software Series. No other technical
  manual is adequate.
User Documentation
  Volume I of the Software Series
Program Availability
  CDC and UNIVAC versions are available from
  D. Bushnell 52-33/205
  Lockheed Missiles and Space Co.
  3251 Hanover St.
  Palo Alto, CA 94304
IBM and VAX versions of the program can be purchased from
  V. Weingarten
  Dept. of Civil Engineering
  University of Southern California
  University Park
  Los Angeles, California 90007

  The price is $600.

Assistance in Using the Program on the Networks
  Please contact the local representatives of the networks.
Technical Problems in Using the Program Contact
  D. Bushnell
  Lockheed Missiles and Space Co.
  Palo Alto Research Lab.
  3251 Hanover St.
  Palo Alto, California 94304
  Phone: (415) 493-4411 Ext. 45491 or 45133

GIFTS

This is a finite element program with advanced interactive graphics pre-
and postprocessors. It has the capability of model generation, display,
editing, and verification. Output displays include displacements and
stresses. Static analyses are performed using a library of elements
suitable for trusses, frames, shells, and elasticity problems.

Network Availability
  UCS
Technical Manual
  Included with the purchase of the program tape
User Documentation
  Documentation is in Volume I of the Software Series and is also included
  with the purchase of the program tape.
Program Availability
  A tape of the program can be purchased from
  H. Kamel
  Dept. of Aerospace and Mechanical Engineering
  University of Arizona
  Tucson, Arizona 85721

The pricing schemes for the program and membership in the GIFTS User's
Group (GUG) are:

GIFTS 4A, for U.S. user, unsupported	$ 600.00
U.S. Government agency, latest standard GIFTS	
version, unsupported	950.00
U.S. Government agency, latest special version	1250.00
U.S. GUG member, Initiation fee	1250.00
Yearly subscription	2000.00
Foreign user, Initiation fee	1500.00
Yearly subscription	2000.00

Assistance in Using the Program on the Network
  Contact the local representatives of the network.
Technical Problems in Using the Program Contact
  H. A. Kamel

PREMSAP

This is a format-free, interactive, prompting input preprocessor for the
SAP program. PREMSAP avoids formatted input card preparation. It has
nodal point and element mesh generating features.

Network Availability for PREMSAP Coupled to SAP IV
  MERIT/TELENET
  Chairman
  Dept. of Naval Architecture & Marine Engineering
  University of Michigan
  445 West Engineering Building
  Ann Arbor, Michigan 48109
  Phone: (313) 764-6470
Technical Manual
  Available from M. Kaldjian with the purchase of the card deck

User Documentation
  Contained in Volume I of the Software Series or available from
  M. Kaldjian with the purchase of the card deck
Program Availability
  Card deck of the program can be purchased from
  M. Kaldjian
  Dept. of Naval Architecture & Marine Engineering
  University of Michigan
  Ann Arbor, Michigan 48109

  The price is $250, including manuals.

Assistance in Using the Program on the Network
  M. Kaldjian
Technical Problems in Using the Program Contact
  M. Kaldjian
  Phone: (313) 764-9317

BEAM, BEAMSTRESS, SHAFT

The program BEAM is for the flexural analysis of simple and complex beams.
It calculates the deflection, slope, bending moment, and shear force for
static and steady-state conditions. The critical axial load and mode
shape are found for stability. The natural frequencies and mode shapes
are computed for free transverse vibrations. The beam can be formed of
segments with any mechanical or thermal loading, in-span supports, foundations, and boundary conditions. The user can include any or all of bending, shear deformation, and rotary inertia effects.
      The program BEAMSTRESS is for determining the section properties and
stresses in an arbitrary homogeneous or composite cross section of a
straight bar. Properties include cross-sectional area, centroid, moments
of inertia about any axes, polar moment of inertia, radii of gyration,
angle of inclination of principal axes, principal moments of inertia,
location of shear center, shear deformation coefficients, torsional constant, and warping constant. For composite cross sections, these cross-
sectional properties are calculated as modulus, weighted properties. The
stresses include normal stresses due to bending moments, axial forces,
and constrained warping and shear stresses due to torsion, tranverse shear
forces, and constrained warping.
      The program SHAFT is for the flexural unbalanced response and criti-
cal speed of a rotating shaft with no cross-coupling coefficients in the
bearings. For unbalance problems, it calculates the component and
resultant deflection, slope, bending moment, shear force, and their corresponding phase angles along the shaft. The critical speeds are found
for a rotor with or without damping in the bearings. The corresponding
mode shapes are also printed out. The shaft can be formed of lumped or
continuous mass segments with foundations, any boundary conditions, and
any distribution of unbalanced masses. The user can include any or all of
bending, shear deformation, and rotary inertia effects.

Network Availability
  UCS
Technical Manual
  Available from The Structural Members Users Group
  These programs belong to a collection of a dozen programs. The
  technical manuals for all of the programs cost $50.

User Documentation
  Contained in Volume I of the Software Series
Program Availability
  A tape or deck of the program can be purchased from
  The Structural Members Users Group
  P.O. Box 3958, University Station
  Charlottesville, Virginia 22903

  The price is $750 for all twelve programs, although programs may
  be purchased individually.

Assistance in Using the Programs
  Please contact the local representatives of the network.
Technical Problems in Using the Program Contact
  The Structural Members Users Group
  Phone: (804) 296-4906

PARTICIPATING NETWORK

United Computing Systems (UCS)

Local Offices:

Suite 775
2300 North Mayfair Road
Wauwatosa, Wisconsin 53226
Phone: (414) 475-9392

Suite 204
5410 Gamble Drive
Minneapolis, Minnesota 55416
Phone: (612) 545-6999

Suite 1850
Two Pennsylvania Plaza
New York, New York 10001
Phone: (212) 563-8484

1767 Morris Avenue
Union, New Jersey 07083
Phone: (210) 964-6050

Jamestown Executive Center
3005 N.W. 63rd Street
Oklahoma City, Oklahoma 73116
Phone: (405) 843-9784

Suite 104
3919 Westerly Place
Newport Beach, California 92660
Phone: (714) 752-9551

Suite 111
930 Woodcock Road
Orlando, Florida 32803
Phone: (305) 896-3710

Suite 2026
2 Pennsylvania Center Plaza
Philadelphia, Pennsylvania 19102
Phone: (215) 568-6300

15436 N.E. Bellevue-Redmond Rd.
Redmond, Washington 98053
Phone: (206) 747-8981

Bldg. 1, Suite 106
5825 Glenridge Drive, N.E.
Atlanta, Georgia 30328
Phone: (404) 256-3610

36 Washington Street
Wellesley Hills, Massachusetts 02181
Phone: (617) 237-2910

Suite 1016
150 North Wacker Drive
Chicago, Illinois 60606
Phone: (312) 782-0865

Two Commerce Park Square
23200 Chagrin Boulevard
Beachwood, Ohio 44122
Phone: (216) 464-9205

P.O. Box 781
Delaware, Ohio 43015
Phone: (614) 548-6371

525 Hearst Building
3rd & Market Streets
San Francisco, California   94100
Phone: (415) 495-6850

Suite 410
101 Continental Boulevard
El Segundo, California   90245
Phone: (213) 640-0891

Suite 101 West
7750 Clayton Road
Clayton, Missouri   63117
Phone: (314) 781-0123

Suite 518
1000 Ashley Drive
Tampa, Florida   33602
Phone: (813) 223-3921

Suite 165
710 Lakeway
Sunnyvale, California   94086
Phone: (415) 542-8600

Suite 213
3725 National Drive
Raleigh, North Carolina   27612
Phone: (919) 711-**4946**

6626 Convoy Court
San Diego, California   92111
Phone: (714) 292-9824

Suite 200
4801 W. 110 Street
Overland Park, Kansas   66211
Phone: (913) 341-9330

Suite 404
16 East 16th Street
Tulsa, Oklahoma   74119
Phone: (918) 582-7291

Suite 250
7700 Leesburg Pike
Falls Church, Virginia   22043
Phone: (703) 821-1022

Suite 1020
Bow Valley Square 1
P.O. Box 9235
Calgary, Alberta
Canada   T2P 2W5
Phone: (403) 265-4926

Suite 1112, Twin Towers South
8585 Stemmons Freeway
Dallas, Texas   75247
Phone: (214) 638-8260

Suite 20C
2460 West 26th Avenue
Denver, Colorado   80211
Phone: (303) 458-8001

799 Main Street
Hartford, Connecticut   06103
Phone: (203) 522-3534

Suite 346
4544 Post Oak Place
Houston, Texas 77027
Phone: (713) 622-5351

Updates to Library Programs: Introducing SAP6

a GIFTS/SAP Interface, and BOSOR5

INTRODUCTION

Brief descriptions and some background of the most recent versions of
SAP, GIFTS, and BOSOR are given in this chapter. Documentation for
earlier versions of these programs is provided in Volumes I and II of the
Structural Mechanics Software Series. See Chapter 1 for availability
information on the programs.

SAP

Overview

Since the original development of the general purpose structural analysis
program, SAP [1], in 1970, by E. L. Wilson, the program has been modified
by many researchers to solve a wide variety of structural analysis problems.   The most recent modifications made to the SAP program transform
it into a user-oriented design program for the linear dynamic and static
analysis of large complex structures which is called SAP6, version 2.
     Version 1 of the SAP6 program was essentially the FESAP [2] program
combined with capabilities taken from the SAPV [3] program. The FESAP
program was a modified version of SAP that was donated to the SAP Users
Group by the Babcock and Wilcox Company. All the capabilities presently
in the SAPV program have been added to SAP6, version 2. This program
also contains many new capabilities which were not previously available
in either FESAP or SAPV. Throughout this paper, the name SAP6, version 1
will be used for the FESAP program.

SAP6, Version 1 [2]

The SAP1 program was obtained from the University of California-Berkeley
in December 1970 and converted to an IBM 360/44 computer version. One
serious program deficiency was that the program had only an execution

mode, which makes input data checking very difficult. The generation of
nodal coordinates was limited to equal increments along a straight line.
Generation of element descriptions was limited to a single row array of
elements, and each type of element required a different format. The
lack of a bandwidth minimization routine resulted in excessive execution
times. There was a relatively small problem capacity for a given amount
of available core memory. The program could not handle thermal transient stresses, and no graphics capability was available.

The SAP program was modified by Babcock and Wilcox to change the
input formats and location within the program. The majority of the
input required by SAP6 is now input into a separate module of routines
that perform the required generation of the mathematical model. The
input is separated into data sets which begin with an eight-character
alphanumeric instruction card and terminate with a blank card. All data
sets for a given problem begin with an instruction card that has the
alphanumeric NEW-PROB and the problem's input is terminated with the
instruction EXECUTE. Data sets between these cards can be inserted in
almost an arbitrary order.

Typical alphanumerics are NODE-INP, ELEMENTS, MATERIAL, and BEAM-
TYP, which respectively require nodal input description, element
description, material property constants, and beam properties.

Within each section of the input many of the parameters are initialized to appropriate values. For example, all nodes are initially constrained and located at the center of the nodal coordinate system and
only nodes for which coordinates are specified by the user are activated.
All element numbers are initialized as blank elements, which are ignored
by the program during execution. The generation of nodal coordinates may
be done in Cartesian, cylindrical, or spherical coordinates about either
the global or any user-specified local coordinate system. In addition,
curvilinear, quadratic surface, or quadratic volume coordinates may be
generated using an isoparametric scheme similar to that described by
Zienkiewicz [4]. A refinement factor can be used to alter the nodal
spacing during generation.

The original SAP concept of grouping elements of the same type has
been replaced with a standardized element input description which allows
a unique element for every element. Each element is described by the required number of nodes, element type number, and four element-dependent
variables indicating entries in tables of materials, thicknesses, beam
properties, etc. Row and column arrays of element-nodal descriptions can
be generated by specifying only two opposite corner element descriptions.
This can be expanded into the generation of layers of solid continuum
elements by the additional specification of the number of layers.

The description of nodal constraints is simplified by using alphanumerics to describe the desired constraints. For example, to con-
strain rotations on a node the user specifies the constraint FIX NE for
no rotation. The Cuthill-McKee [5] bandwidth minimizer was also incorporated into the program in order to increase the size of the problem
that can be handled by the program and to decrease computer time. The
renumbering is internal to the program.

The program can output information for mesh plotting, deformation,
and stress plots. The information can be fed into other postprocessor
programs to reduce the results into useful stress data required by
various regulatory agencies.

The analyst has the option of requesting the mode of operation in which
the input data are read in and verified. If an input error is detected
during a requested execution, the program automatically reverts to the
read data only option.

The problem capacity was increased by overlaying the program and packing several integer words into real words in various vertical locations.

The program was modified to include thermal transient temperature inputs and temperature-dependent material properties. The temperature-dependent material properties are available in the form of polynomial functions derived from user-supplied temperature-dependent material tables.

On the CDC 7600 version of the program, parallel processing is possible. Several machine-dependent subroutines [6] were inserted in critical locations in various solution routines to take advantage of this feature. The use of these routines greatly reduced execution times.

The three-dimensional brick element was modified in the same way used by Arendts [7] in order to increase the thermal stress accuracy by including incompatible modes. The elbow element, the determinant search eigensolver, the subspace iteration eigensolver, and the direct integration dynamic analysis capabilities were removed from SAP IV [8] and added to SAP6.

A six-node constant strain wedge or prism element was added to the element library. In addition, the 3-8 node isoparametric planar element and the 8-20 node isoparametric solid element from NONSAP [9] were added to the element library. These elements were modified to include thermal and pressure loading, and also to permit degeneration to a 6-node linear strain triangle and a 15-node linear strain wedge by inserting the correction terms derived by Newton [10].

Limited restart capabilities have been added to the program. The user can save the generated geometry and then request the analysis to stop after calculating the element stiffness, load, mass, and stress matrices. These matrices can be saved and used in a later run, such as a subsequent eigenvalue and eigenvector frequency calculation. An eigenvalue-eigenvector restart tape can be saved for later use in calculating more eigenvalues and eigenvectors if required for a modal time history response or response spectrum analysis.

The equation solver in SAP6 has been changed to an active column solver. A modified version of the routine SLOWR, developed at UC-Berkeley [11] is contained in the program. A comparison of CPU time between the row solver and the column solver in SAP6 can be found in Table 1. For problems where the bandwidth varies significantly, sizable reductions in execution times can be realized.

The "super element" method [12] of static substructuring was also added and the program has been set up to allow the use of substructures which are portions of other substructures. This feature allows the use of multileveled substructures.

Program Development at University of Southern California [3]

In 1973, the CDC version of SAP IV was received from UC-Berkeley and was converted to operate on an IBM 300/158 computer. The program was introduced to students at U.S.C. and used to solve undergraduate and graduate class problems. The program was also used as a research tool at U.S.C. in a number of funded and unfunded research projects.

The program was modified to include a postprocessor graphics subroutine which could activate either a Calcomp or SC 4020 plotter. This subroutine plots the undeformed and deformed shape of a structure, and also the vibration and buckling mode shapes.

The Cuthill-McKee [5] bandwidth minimization subroutines was added to the program, allowing the user to number the structure in any manner he wishes. He can then indicate by an input parameter to the computer that bandwidth minimization is desired. The bandwidth minimization is then activated, and the node points are renumbered to give bandwidth minimization. The structural problem is then solved using the new node point numbering system.

A general 48 x 48 finite element was added to the program to allow the inclusion of the effect of structural components which could not be determined from the finite elements available in the program.

Geometric stiffness matrices for plate and beam elements were added to the program to consider the effect of external loading on the natural frequencies of the system. Bucking is obtained by increasing the loading until a zero frequency value is obtained.

A frequency response analysis in which mode shapes and frequencies computed for dynamic analysis can be used to calculate the response to steady-state, variable frequency, sinusoidal base motion was added to the program.

A response spectrum analysis option which combines modal shapes for the dynamic response analysis to satisfy the N. R. C. Regulatory Guide Requirement 1.92 was also added to SAP6.

Further SAP6 Developments

On March 1, 1979, version 2 of the SAP6 program was released. In this version, additional restart capabilities were introduced, as well as rotational inertia effects. Rotating disks, shafts, and turbine blades can be analyzed with this added option.

An eight-node isoparametric element for plane stress, plane strain, and body of revolution problems was added to the program. This element can be used for stress, vibration, and buckling problems. Thick or thin shells can be analyzed using the shell of revolution element. The geometric stiffness matrix for this element was also added to the program.

The subspace iteration eigenvalue subroutine in the program was modified so that it could be utilized to solve truss, beam, and plate buckling problems. The body of revolution element utilizes this eigenvalue routine to determine the buckling loads of shells of revolution.

The beam element was modified to include a rigid beam offset option, and also to allow the user to directly input pressure and concentrated force and moment loadings that allow the program to internally calculate the fixed end forces and moments. An added rigid beam finite element can connect one or more dependent nodes to an independent node. The program was also modified to calculate rigid body modes and the dynamic response, including the effect of rigid body modes.

Modifications were made to include dynamic substructuring by the Guyan decomposition method. The eigenvalue routines were modified to accommodate a full mass matrix. The pre- and postprocessor graphics subroutines were modified to operate with Tektronix scopes as well as Calcomp and SC 4020 plotters. A new interactive graphics pre- and postprocessor program is also available.

SAP6 Pre- and PostProcessors

It is essential for a finite element program to have companion programs for preprocessing of the finite element model and postprocessing of the output. SAP6 presently contains internal mesh generation capabilities. Curvilinear, quadratic,or quadratic volume coordinates can be generated using an isoparametric generation scheme.

An interactive mesh generation scheme is presently being developed to use a tablet digitizer in conjunction with a Tektronix scope to generate and check a complex structural model quickly. This program will become part of the SAP6 package once it is completed.

Since many structural problems require the calculation of thermal stresses, SAP6 has a companion heat transfer program called TAP6. This program has steady-state or transient analysis capabilities. The TAP6 program is a thermal analyzer program which usually uses a coarser grid than the structural analysis model. Once the temperature time history is known, at the thermal control points, a curve fit subroutine then determines the temperature time history at each structural node and places the results on disk in anticipation of the thermal stress calculations.

SAP6 Availability

SAP6 is a proprietary program and is presently operational on IBM and CDC computers. The IBM version of the program is written in double precision. The SAP6 program is also operational on the DEC VAX 11/780 minicomputer. The program can be obtained from the SAP Users Group headquartered at the University of Southern California. Inquiries should be directed to:

SAP Users Group
University of Southern California
Dept. of Civil Engineering
Los Angeles, CA 90007
(213) 741-5580

The program is also available for use on a time-sharing basis on the UCS network.

SAP6 Comparisons

It is very difficult to compare computer programs since elements, equation solvers, and eigenvalue routines are constantly changing within programs. Therefore, interpretations of any comparisons are not always valid. In 1977, the Babcock and Wilcox Company compared FESAP (SAP6, version 1) [2] with ANSYS, MARC,and NASTRAN. These results were indicated in the previous statements. The first comparison concerns SAP6 with a row equation solver, SAP6 with the column solver, and SAP 1. The problems were all run on the CDC 7600. The first problem is a planar geometry of seven rows of 249 quarilateral elements, for a total of 1743 elements and 2000 nodes. The nodes were deliberately numbered in the long direction to give a nearly uniform high bandwidth. The second problem was also a planar problem with 72 rows of eight columns of quadrilateral elements modeled in a V-shaped geometry, which would have a semi-bandwidth of 22 equations; but three elements were added across the V to give it locally high bandwidths of 253, 613, and 973. There was a total of 579 elements and 657 nodes. SAP6 and SAP 1 both had blank common sizes of 40,000 words. Table 1 gives results for the two programs.

Table 1   Comparison of SAP 1 and SAP6

Problem 1 3749 deg. of freedom 504 semi-bandwidth	No. of Matrix Blocks	Matrix Assembly Time (sec.)	Equation Solver Time (sec.)	Disk I/O Million Words
SAP 1	97	14.64	777.8	78.96
SAP6 (row solver)	97	12.84	142.14	29.28
SAP6 (column solver)	89	12.12	127.24	55.20
Problem 2 1295 deg. of freedom 973 max semi-bandwidth				
SAP 1	65	6.30	50.42	87.0
SAP6 (row solver)	64	5.70	35.95	2.27
SAP6 (column solver)	2	0.44	0.87	0.39

The second comparison problem has a three-dimensional geometry with 670 hexahedron elements, 968 nodes, 409 semi-bandwidth, and 2706 degrees of freedom. The problem has been run on several revisions of SAP6 as well as on the NASYS and MARC programs. Table 2 gives the results of the comparisons. Accuracy comparisons were made, but all three programs gave similar results and they will not be reported here.

The third comparison is a simply supported, flat, rectangular plate problem that was run as an additional comparison between SAP6, ANSYS, and NASTRAN. The comparison problem was done both statically and dynamically (ten frequencies and mode shapes) with the plate modeled with 100 and 1000 elements. For the 100 plate static problem SAP6 and ANSYS compared favorably with the theoretical answers, and NASTRAN deviated significantly more from the theoretical answer. The three programs gave nearly the same results for the 1000 plate static problem. The comparisom for the two problems is given in Table 3. The comparisons were all run on the CDC 7600 computer.

Conclusions

SAP6 has been developed into a user-oriented design program. It is not intended to be a program that can perform every type of analysis that is ever required but, instead, an easy-to-use, efficient design tool for the large majority of structural analyses which require linear static or dynamic analysis. The program has been heavily used for a very wide variety of structures. Its development is not complete; and the SAP6 program will continually be improved, updated, and corrected by the SAP Users Group.

GIFTS

Overview

The GIFTS 4A package was released in 1976. Since then the program has

Table 2   Comparison of SAP6, ANSYS, and MARC

Program	Element Type	Program Revisions	Year	Computer	Total CPU Time (sec.)
SAP6	5	4	1973	CDC 6600	1015.07
SAP6	5	14	1974	CDC 7600	171.43
SAP6	5	20	1975	CDC 7600	75.05
SAP6	5	22	1977	CDC 7600	58.44
ANSYS	STIF45	UP-165	1975	CDC 7600	180.34
MARC	7	G.1	1975	CDC 7600	133.37

Table 3   Comparison for SAP6, ANSYS, and NASTRAN

Program	Analysis	Elements	Average Percent Deviation from Theoretical Frequencies	I/O Megawords or Million Words	CPU (sec)
ANSYS	Static	100	N/A	0.303	11.156
SAP6	Static	100	N/A	0.188	7.453
NASTRAN	Static	100	N/A	1.176	13.974
ANSYS	Static	1000	N/A	1.204	252.015
SAP6	Static	1000	N/A	2.927	76.727
NASTRAN	Static	1000	N/A	6.764	110.040
ANSYS	Guyan Reduction	100	2.60	0.553	17.572
SAP6	Subspace Iteration	100	1.05	1.523	14.758
NASTRAN	Inverse Power	100	0.53	4.818	31.222
ANSYS	Guyan Reduction	1000	1.05	4.244	308.020
SAP6	Subspace Iteration	1000	0.09	15.787	151.756
NASTRAN	Inverse Power	1000	0.62	48.830	310.606

been widely distributed, enhanced, and improved. A users group described in the chapter on Users Groups in this volume has been formed and is self-supporting, so that no further support is required from ONR for maintenance and distribution. The following paragraphs are a description of the current status of the program and future plans of expansion for GIFTS.

GIFTS Changes, Additions, and Future Plans

There have been major improvements to the program since 1976; these are incorporated in version 4B. These improvements include:

  a. Addition of axisymmatic solids analysis capability
  b. Implementation of the solids model and load and boundary conditions preprocessors
  c. A generalized Lagrange constraint capability, and the implementation of some specific types allowing inclined boundary conditions, a beam joint release, prescribed displacements, and rigid links.
  d. Computation and display of residual forces as a check on solution accuracy
  e. Pre- and postprocessing of higher order elements

After many delays, GIFTS 5 was released in May 1979. The first release, version GIFTS 5.0, primarily involves a change of the data base to accommodate expanded capabilities and new program interfaces. In addition, the following improvements are included:

  a. Improvements of command structure, allowing multiple commands and data lines on a single physical line, minimum segment decoding, and alphanumeric mode switch
  b. Improvement of stiffened plate and surface loading commands.
  c. Unification of the data base for solids, plates, shells, trusses, and frames
  d. Distribution of "Pre-converted" GIFTS 5 programs. Many, but not all, computer models and operating systems will be included. It would be overly optimistic to assume that all user conversion efforts will be alleviated; however, the majority of the necessary work will hopefully be eliminated.

Many GIFTS additions and improvements, already operating in a special in-house version (GIFTS 4C), have been held up in anticipation of the release of GIFTS 5. It was decided that these would be incorporated into version 5.1, released in August 1979. Among the improvements are:

  1. Arbitrary beam cross section, in open or closed polygonal form
  2. Distributed beam loads, as well as load, shear force, and bending moment diagrams
  3. Higher order triangle and quadrilateral membrane and axisymmetric elements
  4. Thermal stress capability for all supported elements
  5. Extensive use of the cursor in selecting the point and element for information purposes, as well as in model editing

Plans are already underway for the release of GIFTS 5.2. This release will include, among other things: two-dimensional digitizing program, designed as a preprocessor for BULKM; computation of solid models; transient response by model superposition; and more program interfaces.

Other items whose exact date of release is still open include: three-dimensional digitizing; solids postprocessing; more cursor functions; use of new minicomputer hardware, such as superminis, array processors, and dynamic display devices; an interface to a color graphics program; and a double precision version of GIFTS.

Program Interfaces

GIFTS has been designed as both an interactive analysis package and a pre- and postprocessor for other standard finite element programs. Many interfaces have been written, or are in the process of being written, by various GIFTS Users Group members as well as at the University of Arizona. Most GUG members are willing to share their interfaces with other members, and GUG is in the process of collecting and distributing such interfaces. Various interfaces are described below on a program-by-program basis.

Interfaces between GIFTS and other analysis programs take the form of two new GIFTS modules per program which are called in the usual manner. The initial response takes the form of a job name request. Subsequently the interface module asks specific questions to the user in a self-prompting mode. Through these questions additional key information, needed by the specific program, is obtained. Apart from knowing the name of the module, little documentation is necessary, except perhaps for that necessary to understand the program to which it is interfaced. With the exception of the PIGSAP program, two modules are necessary for each program (say XYZ). The first module, GFTXYZ, creates an input file to the analysis program. A batch job can then be submitted by the user. Upon completion of the analysis, the analysis program creates one or more standard output files. The second module, XYZGFT, reads results and inserts them into the GIFTS data base in preparation for postprocessing by GIFTS.

SAP 4 (Module name: PIGSAP)

An interface has been developed at Ruhr-Universität, Bochum, West Germany. It transmits data from the GIFTS data base to a SAP input file. After the SAP job is completed, PIGSAP may be called again to transmit the results back to the GIFTS data base. The interface was developed on a PRIME minicomputer. It is now being tested on the UCS network of Cyber computers. It is available (as is) to GUG members.

ANSYS (Module name: GFTANS)

A one-way interface has been written and run on the ECLIPSE computer, and is now also operational on the UCS network. Presently only preprocessing is possible, but a postprocessing interface (ANSGFT) is anticipated in the near future.

STAGS

STAGS is a nonlinear structural code developed at Lockheed, Palo Alto. The Office of Naval Research funded a joint project between Lockheed and the University of Arizona, of which a GIFTS/STAGS interface was a by-

product which will be made available. GFTSTA has passed preliminary
tests at the University of Arizona.

NASTRAN

Several users have been developing NASTRAN interfaces of varying sophistication. None of these interfaces has, as of yet, been delivered
to the University of Arizona, although acquisition is anticipated
soon and installation on UCS is expected shortly thereafter.

MOVIE-BYU

An interface for GIFTS to the MOVIE-BYU program, a hidden line and surface package supporting both storage tube and color graphics terminals,
is being tested at the University of Arizona. The interface will be
available to GUG members.

Miscellaneous Programs

There are also several interfaces to other program being developed by GUG
members. They will be made available as they are received. Two in
preliminary stages of development at the University of Arizona are to
the program DAISY, a proprietory linear FEM program developed primarily
with funding from the American Bureau of Shipping, and to the program
NONSAP, a nonlinear structural analysis program.

Difficulties in Maintaining Program Interfaces

There are several difficulties that one must contend with in maintaining
the various program interfaces:

    a. The interface must relate data between two continually changing
programs. Changes to the program should be reflected in the interface,
thus presenting a maintenance problem.
    b. The interfaces should be made available on a myriad of different
computer systems, preferably as many as there are machines on which GIFTS
runs. Additionally, there are many combinations of computers on which
the combined GIFTS-interface-solution routine can exist (i.e., GIFTS
and solution on same computer, GIFTS on mini, solution on maxi). When
an interface is received from a GUG member, it is usually written specifically for one computer system. This version is immediately made
available, as is, to other GUG members; other machine versions may be
produced and made available if feasible.
    Because of these problems, it is understandable that the GUG support
of program interfaces will generally not be up to the level of the support
provided for the GIFTS modules. Although there is a serious effort being
made to keep all interfaces current and debugged, a certain amount of
user expertise is required.

Availability of GIFTS Versions

The following versions of GIFTS are available to Gifts Users Group members:

    CDC
      NOS operating system (up to Update #7)
      SCOPE operating system (up to Update #7)
      UCS: United Computing System (up to Update #7)
    DEC
      DEC-10: TOPS-10 operating system (up to Update #5)
      PDP-11: RT-11 operating system (up to Update #3)
      PDP-15: DOS operating system (not updated)
    DATE GENERAL
      Eclipse: S/230 AOS operating system (current)
    PRIME
      Prime: (up to Update #5)
    AHMDAHL
      MTS: Michigan Terminal System (up to Update #4)
    IBM
      A version suitable for MVS/TSO.

BOSOR

Overview

BOSOR4 [13-23] was developed in 1972 to perform stress, buckling, and modal vibration analysis of ring-stiffened, branched shells of revolution loaded either axisymmetrically or nonsymmetrically. Complex wall construction is permitted in the analysis. The program can handle 1500 degrees of freedom in nonaxisymmetric problems, and 1000 degrees of freedom in axisymmetric prebuckling stress analysis. A maximum of 20 fourier harmonics are allowable per case. The program was updated most recently in 1979.

    BOSOR5 performs stress and buckling analysis of ring-stiffened, branched shells of revolution that are loaded axisymmetrically. In addition, it can handle layered walls with different elastic-plastic-creep properties in each layer. Prebuckling deformations are axisymmetrical; buckling may be either axisymmetric or symmetric. This program does not supersede BOSOR4. It was initially developed in 1974, and its most recent update was in 1979.

    For the sake of comparison and clarification an outline of pertinent information describing BOSOR4 and BOSOR5 follows.

BOSOR4

Keywords: shells, stress, buckling, vibration, nonlinear, elastic,
    shells of revolution, ring-stiffened, branched, composites,
    discrete model
Method: Finite difference energy minimization; Fourier superposition
    in circumferential variable; Newton method for solution of nonlinear
    axisymmetric problem; inverse power iteration with spectral shifts
    for eigenvalue extraction; Lagrange multipliers for constraint con-
    ditions; thin shell theory
Restriction: 1500 degrees of freedom (d.o.f.) in nonaxisymmetric
    problems; 100 d.o.f. in axisymmetric prebuckling stress analysis;
    maximum of 20 Fourier harmonics per case; knockdown factors for
    imperfections not included; radius/thickness should be greater

than about 10.
Input: Free-field input. Required for input are shell segment geo-
        metries, ring geometries, number of mesh points, ranges and incre-
        ments of circumferential wave numbers, load and temperature dis-
        tributions, shell wall construction details, and constraint con-
        ditions.
Output: Displacements and stress resultants or extreme fiber stresses,
         buckling loads, vibration frequencies; list and plots
Hardware: UNIVAC 1108 or 1110, CDC 6600 or 7600, IBM 360 or 370, VAX;
           SC4020 and CALCOMP plotters
Run Time: Typically a job will require 1-5 minutes of computer time.

BOSOR5 [24-32]

Keywords: Shells, stress, buckling, nonlinear, plasticity, creep,
           shells of revolution, ring-stiffened, branched, discrete model
Method: Finite difference energy minimization; trigonometric variation
         in circumferential direction; Newton method for solution of non-
         linear axisymmetric problem; inverse power iteration with spectral
         shifts for eigenvalue extraction for bifurcation buckling; Lagrange
         multipliers for constraint conditions; thin shell theory; isotropic
         strain hardening; subincremental method for evaluation of plastic
         and creep strains.
Restrictions: 1000 degrees of freedom (d.o.f.) in axisymmetric pre-
               buckling stress analysis; 1500 d.o.f. in nonaxisymmetric bifur-
               cation buckling analysis; knockdown factors for imperfections
               not included; radius thickness should be greater than about 10.
Documentation: BOSOR5 User's Manual [24] and 9 journal articles with
                numerous examples (References [25-33])
Input: Required for input are shell segment geometries, ring geo-
        metries, number of mesh points, ranges and increments of circum-
        ferential wave numbers, load and temperature distributions, shell
        wall construction details including stress-strain curves for
        materials, and constraint conditions. BOSOR5 is divided into three
        executable modules, a preprocessor for which most of the input is
        prepared, a main processor with restart capability, and a post-
        processor.
Output: Displacements and stress resultants; stresses and strains
         through the thickness at each nodal point for user-selected load or
         time steps; buckling modes; list and plots
Hardware: UNIVAC 1108 or 1110, CDC 6600 or 7600, IBM 360 or 370;
           SC4020 and CALCOMP plotters
Run Time: Typically a job will require 1-10 minutes of computer time.

Availability

Both programs are available from the developer in CDC and UNIVAC in versions. Contact:

        David Bushnell, 52-33/205
        Lockheed Missiles & Space Company, Inc.
        3251 Hanover Street
        Palo Alto, CA 94394
        Tel: (415) 493-4411, Ext. 45491 or 45133

The IBM version of the programs is available from

Prof. Victor Weingarten, Dept. of Civil Eng., University of Southern California, University Park, Los Angeles, CA 90007

The cost for BOSOR4 is $500. BOSOR5 costs $600.
In addition, the programs can be run through numerous data centers and networks worldwide.

Acknowledgment

The help of V.Weingarten, H. Kamel, and D. Bushnell, who supplied the information for this chapter,is greatly appreciated.

REFERENCES

1 Wilson, E. L., "SAP - A General Structural Analysis Program," SESM Report 70-20, Dept. of Civil Engineering, University of California, Berkeley, 1970.
2 Van Fossen, D. B., "FESAP - A Design Program for Static and Dynamic Structural Analysis," Second SAP Users Conference, University of California, June 23-24, 1977.
3 Weingarten, V. I., "SAP Development at U.S.C.," Second SAP Users Conference, University of Southern California, June 23-24, 1977.
4 Zienkiewics, O. C., and Phillips, D. V., "An Automatic Mesh Generation Scheme for Plane and Curved Surfaces by Isoparametric Co-Ordinates," International Journal for Numerical Methods in Engineering, Vol. 3, 1971, pp. 519-28.
5 Cuthill, E. H., and McKee, J. M., "Reducing the Bandwidth of Sparse Symmetric Matrices," Procedures of the 24th National Conference ACM, 1969, pp. 157-72.
6 Tuttle, P. G., "The CDC 7600 as a Parallel/Vector Computer: Lawrence Livermore Laboratory Vector Library," Babcock & Wilcox Report NPGD-TM-311, Dec. 1974.
7 Arendts, J. G., "SAP Program Eight-Node Brick Element Thermal Strain Improvement," presented at the First SAP User's Conference, University of Southern California, June 7-11, 1976.
8 Bathe, K. J., Wilson, E. L., and Peterson, F. E., "SAP IV - A Structural Analysis Program for Static and Dynamic Response of Linear Systems," University of California, Berkeley, EERC Report No. 73-11, April 1974.
9 Bathe, K. J., Wilson, E. L., and Idding, R. H., "NONSAP - A Structural Analysis Program for Static and Dynamic Response of Nonlinear Systems," SESM Report No. 74-3, University of California, Berkeley, Feb. 1974.
10 Newton, R. E., "Degeneration of Brick-Type Isoparametric Elements," International Journal of Numerical Methods in Engineering, Vol. 7, No. 4, p. 579.
11 Stock, D. J., "Symmetric Linear Equation Operations without Rows," graduate student report, University of California, Berkeley, Spring, 1974.
12 Egeland, O., and Araldsen, P. O., "SESM-69 - A General Purpose Finite Element Method Program," Computer and Structures, Vol. 4, No. 1, Jan. 1976, pp. 41-68.
13 Bushnell, D., et al.,"BOSOR4 - Program for Stress, Buckling, and Vibration of Complex Shells of Revolution," Structural Mechanics

Software Series, Vol. 1, ed. N. Perrone, and W. Pilkey, University Press
of Virginia, Charlottesville, 1977, pp. 11-143.
    14 Bushnell, D., et al., "Thin Shells," Structural Mechanics Com-
puter Programs, Surveys, Assessments, and Availability, ed. W. Pilkey,
K. Saczalski, and H. Schaeffer, University Press of Virginia, Charlottesville, 1974, pp. 277-358.
    15 Bushnell, D., et al., "Finite Difference Energy Models versus
Finite Element Models: Two Variational Approaches in One Computer
Program," Numerical and Computer Methods in Structural Mechanics, ed.
N. Perrone, Robinson, and Schnobrich, Academic Press, New York, 1973,
pp. 291-336.
    16 Bushnell, D., et al., "Evaluation of Various Analytical Models
for Buckling and Vibration of Stiffened Shells," AIAA J., Vol. 11, No. 9,
1973, pp. 1283-91.
    17 Bushnell, D., et al., "Nonsymmetric Buckling of Cylinders with
Axisymmetric Thermal Discontinuities," AIAA J., Vol. 11, No. 9, 1973,
pp. 1292-95.
    18 Bushnell, D., et al., "Stress, Stability, and Vibration of Com-
plex, Branched Shells of Revolution," Computers & Structures, Vol. 4,
pp. 235-399.
    19 Bushnell, D., et al., "Local and General Buckling of Axially Com-
pressed, Semi-Sandwich, Corrugated, Ring-Stiffened Cylinder," J. Spacecraft and Rockets, Vol. 9, No. 5. May 1972, pp. 357-63.
    20 Bushnell, D., and S. Smith, "Stress and Buckling of Nonuniformly
Heated Cylindrical and Conical Shells," AIAA J., Vol. 9, No. 12,
Dec. 1971, pp. 2313-31.
    21 Bushnell, D., et al., "Stress Buckling and Vibration of Prismatic
Shells, AIAA J., Vol. 9, 1971, pp. 2004-13.
    22 Bushnell, D., et al., "Analysis of Ring-Stiffened Shells of Re-
volution under Combined Thermal and Mechanical Loading," AIAA J., Vol. 9,
March 1971, pp. 401-10.
    23 Bushnell, D., et al., "Analysis of Buckling and Vibration of Ring-
Stiffened, Segmented Shells of Revolution," Intern. J. Solids and Struc-
tures, Vol. 6, Feb. 1970, pp. 157-81.
    24 Bushnell, D., et al., "BOSOR5 - A Computer Program for Buckling
of Elastic-Plastic Complex Shells of Revolution Including Large Deflec-
tions and Creep," Vol. I: User's Manual, Input Data, LMSC-D407166;
Vol. II: User's Manual, Test Cases, LMSC-D407167; Vol. III: Theory and
Comparisons with Tests, LMSC-D407168, Lockheed Missiles & Space Co.,
Sunnyvale, California, Dec. 1974.
    25 Bushnell, D., et al., "BOSOR5 - Program for Buckling of Elastic-
Plastic Complex Shells of Revolution Including Large Deflections and
Creep," Computers and Structures, Vol. 6, 1976, pp. 221-39.
    26 Bushnell, D., et al., "A Strategy for the Solution of Problems
Involving Large Deflections, Plasticity and Creep," International Journal
for Numerical Methods in Engineering, Vol. 11, 1977 pp. 683-708.
    27 Bushnell, D., et al., "Bifurcation Buckling of Shells of Revolu-
tion Including Large Deflection, Plasticity, and Creep," Intern. J. Solids
and Structures, Vol. 10, 1974, pp. 1287-1305.
    28 Bushnell, D., and Galletly, G. D., "Comparisons of Test and
Theory for Nonsymmetric Elastic Plastic Buckling of Shells of Revolution,"
Intern. J. of Solids and Structures, Vol. 10, 1974, pp. 1287-1305.
    29 Bushnell, D., et al., "Buckling of Elastic-Plastic Shells of Re-
volution Discrete with Elastic-Plastic Ring Stiffeners," Intern. J. of
Solids and Structures, Vol. 12, 1976, pp. 51, 66.

30 Bushnell, D., et al., "Nonsymmetric Buckling of Internally Pres-
surized Ellipsoidal and Torispherical Elastic-Plastic Pressure Vessel
Heads," Journal of Pressure Vessel Technology, Vol. 99, 1977, pp. 54-63.
31 Bushnell, D., and Galletly, G. D., "Stress and Buckling of
Internally Pressurized Elastic-Plastic Torispherical Vessel Heads -
Comparisons of Test and Theory," Journal of Pressure Vessel Technology,
Vol. 99, 1977, pp. 39-53.
32 Bushnell, D., and Lagae, G., "Elastic Plastic Buckling of
Internally Pressurized Torispherical Vessel Heads," University of
Ghent, Nuclear Engineering and Design, Vol. 48, 1978, pp. 405-14.

Computerized Sources of Abstracts of the Engineering Literature

Barbara F. Pilkey

University of Virginia

INTRODUCTION

Because of the mushrooming number of computers owned by government, schools, and industry and the even greater number and variety of programs available for the computers, many groups and dissemination centers have been initiated so that software can be shared, distributed, and maintained. These organizations differ in their membership structure and/or their dissemination goals. By participating, a user may be able to have access to needed software at a reasonable cost, and thus eliminate the need to duplicate work that has already been done. Included in the following list are cooperative users groups and software dissemination services.

AASHTO Committee on Data Processing

Contact: Mr. Kenneth Close, HMS-40
          Federal Highway Administration
          400 7th Street, S.W.
          Washington, D.C. 20590

     In 1973, the American Association of State Highway and Transportation Officials established the Committee on Data Processing to replace the AASHTO Committee on Computer Technology.
     The purposes of the committee are: to develop, improve, and promote the use of data processing techniques in transportation engineering, management, and fiscal control; to investigate advances in the use of computers in allied fields; to promote the application of appropriate new methods to transportation programs; and to keep current a catalog of computer programs applicable to the transportation field and to disseminate this information to member departments. The committee has compiled and distributed Computer System Index, a catalog of programs developed by AASHTO members. Through this index, members are able to exchange knowledge, programs, and experience. The exchange is between user and originator, and the user's experience is not passed back to the committee

or other members.

Aerospace Structures Information and Analysis Center (ASIAC)

```
            ASIAC
Contact:    AFDL-FBR
            Wright-Patterson AFB
            Dayton, Ohio  45433
```

The Air Force Flight Dynamics Laboratory sponsors ASIAC as a central agency to collect and disseminate information on aerospace structures, including structural software. ASIAC services are available to government agencies and to their contractors upon written request with a valid need. A newsletter is published containing topics of interest to the structures community. For specific information, contact Mr. Gordon R. Negaard at (513) 255-6688.

Automated Procedures for Engineering Consultants (APEC)

```
Contact:    Mrs. Doris J. Wallace
            Executive Secretary
            Automated Procedures for Engineering Consultants
            Grant-Deneau Tower, Suite M-15
            Fourth and Ludlow Streets
            Dayton, Ohio  45402
```

APEC is a nonprofit association primarily consisting of engineer/ architect firms, but including utility companies, manufacturers, construction firms, universities, and governmental agencies interested in the practical application of computer technology to building design. Its primary efforts have been in the fields of mechanical and electrical engineering, but activities are currently under way to serve and provide an effective interface with structural and architectural disciplines.

APEC member firms pool resources (through membership fees, annual dues, and software license fees) and engineering talent and experience (through committee efforts) to produce practical software for the benefit of their members. Software development is undertaken by contract with software firms.

Other than actual software development and support, typical projects include the Computer Aided Building Design System (CABDS) study, a feasibility report on a Structural Executive System, and the development of APEC Program Standards in improved software effectiveness and portability.

All software products remain as APEC property and are released in source form to member licensees under a computer Software Licensing Agreement (for nondisclosure purposes).

COMMON

```
Contact:    Mr. Robert G. Bostrom
            Administrative Director, COMMON
            435 N. Michigan Avenue
            Chicago, Illinois  60611
```

COMMON, a users group for IBM computers, was formed in 1962. Its membership consists of users of System 3, 1130, 1800, DOS OS, and System 7. The principal objective is to advance the effective usage of equipment among users of IBM computers and data processing machines. The organization promotes the free interchange of information about the machines and techniques of use.

Programs contributed by members are listed in their magazine CAST, with descriptions of the programs and information on obtaining the programs distributed to the membership as a program library service.

Computer Software Management and Information Center (COSMIC)

Contact: Mr. Harold Hale, Director
          COSMIC
          112 Barrow Hall
          University of Georgia
          Athens, Georgia   30602

The Computer Software Management and Information Center (COSMIC), an integral part of the National Aeronautics and Space Administration's Technology Utilization Program, has been operated by the University of Georgia since its beginning in 1966. COSMIC functions as the collection, evaluation, and dissemination center for over 1500 computer programs developed by NASA, NASA contractors, and other agencies.

Program areas include engineering, manufacturing, transportation, communications, natural resources, energy conservation, information management, and of course, computer technology. For example, COSMIC is the dissemination point for NASTRAN, NASA's Structural Analysis program. First developed for space vehicles, NASTRAN is used by industry to design automobiles, aircraft, oil drilling towers, and much more.

Further information on COSMIC and available programs may be obtained by contacting a COSMIC representative.

Cooperating Users of Burroughs Equipment (CUBE)

Contact: Mr. Thomas S. Grier
          CUBE Secretary
          Burroughs Corporation
          Second Avenue at Burroughs
          Detroit, Michigan   48232

CUBE was founded because of the need of computer users to exchange ideas as well as software and to communicate among themselves and with the vendor. The common link shared by CUBE members is their use of computers manufactured by Burroughs Corporation. Users of all Burroughs computers, B1700/B1800 through B7800, are eligible to join CUBE.

Program exchange among CUBE members takes two forms. For users of the smaller and medium systems, the catalog of abstracts provides the name and address of the originating member to contact for further discussion and negotiation at the time of the exchange. For users of the larger systems (B6700 through B7800), tapes of the desired programs may be obtained by sending scratch tapes and postage to the CUBE librarian. The programs were donated by members and are available only to other CUBE members. The library of programs consists of mathematical subroutines, some language enhancements, and various data processing and accounting routines.

Digital Equipment Computer Users Society (DECUS)

Contact: Digital Equipment Computer Users Society
            Office of the Executive Director
            One Iron Way
            Marlboro, Massachusetts 01752

     DECUS was established to advance the effective use of DIGITAL
computers; it is a voluntary, nonprofit users group, supported in part
by Digital Equipment Corporation. Membership in DECUS is voluntary, and
no membership fee is charged. In addition to the office in the United
States, DECUS maintains offices in Australia, Canada, and Switzerland.
As of January 1979, the DECUS Program Library contained 1500 active
software packages. These programs are available to members for a nominal
service charge. Information on membership and available programs may
be requested from the office of the executive director.

Federal Agencies Computer Time-Sharing System (FACTS)

Contact: Mr. Henry A. Borger
            Program Manager
            Federal Construction Council
            Building Research Advisory Board
            2101 Constitution Avenue, N.W.
            Washington, D.C. 20018

     FACTS, a main mechanism of a program for facilitating the use of
computers in federal construction agencies, is an extensive library of
fully validated, easily utilized computer programs dealing with a wide
variety of construction related engineering problems. The library is
available for use by all federal construction agencies, through remote
terminals.
     The aim of this effort is to solve the two major problems that lead
to the underutilization of computers by federal construction agencies.
The two problems are:

     1. that engineers at most agencies have far too few programs of
proven validity available to them.
     2. that most programs available in the agencies are written in such
a way that they can be used only by engineers who have extensive knowledge
of computers or only after the using engineer has been given detailed
instructions on the use.

     The solutions to these problems are respectively:

     1. pooling the programs already available in the various agencies
into this consolidated interagency library of programs and subsequently
initiating a coordinated interagency effort to develop new programs.
     2. using the library system developed by the U.S. Army Corps
of Engineers that employs programs in which documentation is an inherent
part of the program.

     Work associated with the development, adaptation, refinement, and
validation of computer programs is carried out on a voluntary basis by
participating federal agencies. Work associated with the development of
the executive programs for the FACTS library (i.e., the computer programs
that serve as librarian) and the preparation of manuals on writing pro-

grams for the library and on using the library is carried out by the Office, Chief of Engineers, U.S. Army Corps of Engineers. The library of the General Services Administration (GSA) will be made available to federal agencies through the Center's time-sharing system identified as RAMUS, Remote Access Multi-User System, and the entire program is coordinated by the Federal Construction Council. FACTS has been in operation since July 1974, and there are currently 75 programs in the library; all these programs have been validated and have the documentation as an inherent part of the program.

The programs in the FACTS library cover a wide variety of subjects dealing with construction engineering; however, the majority deal with hydraulics. Since FACTS is an interactive time-sharing system, no programs are included in the library that require a substantial amount of input data or generate extensive output.

Federal agencies can gain access to FACTS merely by becoming RAMUS subscribers. For details, agencies should write to the General Services Administration, Automated Data and Telecommunications Service, 1776 Peachtree Street, NW, Atlanta, GA 30309.

GENESYS Limited

Contact: Laurence N. Beckreck
           Sales Manager
           Genesys Limited
           Lisle Street
           Loughborough
           Leicestershire
           LE11 0AY
           England

GENESYS Limited is a software-sharing organization sponsored by the National Research Development Corporation of the United Kingdom government and is self-supporting. Its function is to provide a public service based on the GENESYS software. This service falls into three parts:

1. Coordinate development of the library
2. Distribute and maintain completed subsystems
3. Promote use and advise users

GENESYS is a master program designed to be as machine independent as possible. This master program performs two types of operations. For the programmer developing a subsystem it provides facilities through which a set of commands may be defined to allow users to call up individual program modules of a subsystem. The commands provided for the subsystem form a problem-oriented language. GENESYS also translates the modules of the subsystem from the source language called GENTRAN into FORTRAN, tailored to fit the particular configuration of the run time computer. GENTRAN is almost identical to FORTRAN IV without any statement for reference to peripheral devices. Programmers write GENTRAN modules assuming the availability of an infinitely large core storage, but are provided with a number of optional statements which override the software virtual storage providing this facility.

The total size of GENESYS is approximately 11,000 FORTRAN statements and can run on the following types of computers: ICL 1900, ICL System 4, IBM 360 series, Honeywell 200 series, CDC 6600, and UNIVAC 1108. Machine requirements vary from machine to machine from 64K 24 bytes of central memory and magnetic tapes, or one disc, upwards.

GIFTS User's Group (GUG)

Contact: H. A. Kamel
            Aerospace and Mechanical Engineering
            University of Arizona
            Tucson, Arizona

The GUG users group has a international membership, encompassing
people in universities, federal agencies, the military, and industry, who
use the graphics-oriented finite element program GIFTS. GUG members
are supported through regular updates and have the right to free telephone consultation. Exchange of information, program innovations, and
enhancements between GUG members is encouraged and implemented through
the Interactive Graphics Engineering Laboratory at the University of
Arizona. Modest membership fees are charged so that GUG can be self-
supporting. The program, GIFTS, is in the public domain.

Highway Engineering Exchange Program (HEEP)

Contact: Mr. James W. Dahlen
            Seattle District
            Corps of Engineers
            P. O. Box C-3755
            Seattle, Washington 98124
            (206) 764-3742

HEEP was organized with the objectives of promoting the free exchange of computer programs and related concepts among its membership
and increasing the effectiveness of computer usage and development.
Membership is held by state and provincial highway and transportation
departments, major city and county road departments, federal agencies,
and institutions of higher education. Associate membership includes
civil engineering consultants and equipment and software vendors. The
objectives of HEEP are primarily promoted by one national meeting and
four to six area meetings held each year; however, the active membership
varies depending on agency-imposed travel restrictions.
    There is no HEEP library. To accomplish the goal of information
interchange, HEEP has cooperated with the AASHTO Committee on Data Processing in publishing a Computer System Index. Any cross-agency development efforts have been carried out primarily by individual agencies
cooperating together. The AASHTO index can be obtained ($10.00 prepaid,
plus $1.25 postage and handling) from

        American Association of State and Highway and
          Transportation Officials
        444 North Capitol Street, N.W., Suite 225
        Washington, D.C. 20001

Honeywell Large Systems Users Association (HLSUA)

Contact: HLSUA Assoc.
            815-15th Street, N.W.
            Suite 511
            Washington, D.C. 20005

The HLSUA was organized to stimulate the development of and to disseminate information concerning techniques for the preparation and operation of electronic data processing systems for Honeywell computers. The organization operates primarily as a working group concerned with operating systems, program languages, computer utilization, and operational problems of the member organizations.

ICES Users Group

Contact: Frederick E. Hajjar
Executive Director
ICES Users Group, Inc.
P. O. Box 8243
Cranston, R.I. 02920

The ICES Users Group is a nonprofit, professional organization formed in 1967 for the purpose of free exchange and public dissemination of technological information pertaining to the ICES family of computer programs, the most important of which is STRUDL. The ICES Users Group conducts semiannual meetings, discussion groups, forums, panels, lectures, and other similar programs and publishes the ICES Journal, which contains conference papers, information on ICES activities, publications, and information on ordering programs. Currently, the group has 525 organization members; among these are 375 private industrial organizations, 90 universitites and colleges, and 60 state and federal government agencies. Information about the ICES group can be obtained through the executive director or through the ICES Distribution Agencies in Atlanta, GA., Ispare, Italy, and Tokyo, Japan.

International Computer Programs, Inc. (ICP)

Contact: International Computer Programs, Inc. (ICP)
9000 Keystone Crossing
Indianapolis, Indiana 46240

ICP is a private company involved in many software dissemination activities. They deal primarily in aiding commercial software companies with preparing and selling their programs. Among their publications is the ICP Software Directory,which contains a section on Manufacturing and Engineering. The directory consists of abstracts of computer programs that can be purchased or leased. Each abstract contains a description of the program along with complete details of its availability. Since the Directory accepts abstracts free of charge from anyone, it contains an interesting array of structural mechanics programs, many of which are not listed elsewhere.

National Energy Software Center

Contact: Margaret Butler, Director
National Energy Software Center
Argonne National Laboratory
9700 S. Cass Avenue
Argonne, Illinois 60439
(312) 972-7250

The National Energy Software Center collects, reviews, tests, maintains, and distributes a software library which was developed to meet the needs of the Department of Energy and the U.S. Nuclear Regulatory Commission. The library presently consists of over 850 computer programs, systems, models, and data compilations; approximately 57 of the computer codes relate to structural analysis and engineering design. An organization may become affiliated with the Center as a registered installation, or it may purchase single software packages on a one-time basis. Inquiries concerning the available programs and the procedures for obtaining them should be directed to the Center.

National Information Service for Earthquake Engineering (NISEE)

Contact: NISEE / Computer Applications
           519 Davis Hall
           University of California
           Berkeley, California 94720
           (415) 642-5113

NISEE/Computer Applications is a service offering a means by which computer programs related to earthquake engineering can receive wide distribution among both the engineering profession and the academic community. Its activities include dissemination of brief documentation newsletters about recent computer programs and distribution of programs. Program user documentation and a source deck are sent when a program is ordered through NISEE. The distribution is unlimited; royalty or development charges are not allowed; and the programs which are purchased should not be resold for direct profit.

SAP Users Group

Contact: Michele Raeburn
           Dept. of Civil Engineering
           University of Southern California
           Los Angeles, California 90007

This university group distributes the IBM version of many of the NISEE (Berkely) programs. They also distribute BOSOR4 and 5, general shell of revolution programs. Their most popular programs are SAPV, SAP6, TABS and ETABS, and NONSAP, all available in IBM and VAX versions. Their research is presently focused on improving SAP6, a program performing static and dynamic analysis of structural systems with accompanying plot generation capabilities. SAP6 is available in IBM, CDC, and VAX versions.

SHARE

Contact: SHARE, Inc.
           Triangle Universities Computation Center
           P. O. Box 12076
           Research Triangle, N.C. 27709

This organization, formed in 1955 as an IBM 704 Society, has incorporated into its family of machines the scientific computers from the IBM

700-7000 series and, since 1964, the larger systems from the 360 and
370 lines.

The principal purpose of SHARE is to foster research and development and the exchange and public dissemination of data pertaining to
computer science in the scientific tradition. To achieve these ends,
SHARE: (1) conducts meetings, discussion groups, forums, panels, lectures, and other similar events; (2) publishes through its SHARE secretary the results of its research, and other publications as appropriate, and makes such publications available to the interested public on
a noncommittal and nondiscriminatory basis; and (3) establishes and
continually improves standards for communicating computer science research results and programming information to interested members of the
public.

SHARE currently has over a thousand members and a program library of
more than a hundred programs contributed by member installations. The
programs are available to members at distribution cost.

Society for Computer Application in Engineering, Planning and Architecture, Inc. (CEPA)

Contact: Patricia C. Johnson
Executive Director, CEPA
358 Hungerford Drive
Rockville, Maryland 20850
(301) 762-6070

CEPA, a nonprofit organization formerly known as Civil Engineering
Program Applications, was founded in 1965 by a group of civil engineers.
Its principal objective is to further the effective application of computers in civil engineering, planning, architecture, and related fields.
To this end, CEPA provides a means for the exchange and cooperative
development of computer programs and systems pertaining to civil engineering, planning, and architecture.

Membership is open to organizations and/or individuals utilizing
computers in the practice of civil engineering and related fields and
subscribing and contributing to the cooperative purposes and efforts
of CEPA.

One of the important facilities offered by CEPA to its membership is
the program library. This library presently consists of more than 400
programs, contributed by members and classified generally under Geometry/
Highways, Bridges, Buildings, Sanitary/Hydraulics, Traffic/Transit,
Geotechnical, Graphics, Management, and Electrical. Typical of the programs included are those in geometry and alignment areas. In structural
areas, the library includes bridges, retaining walls, and project management programs.

Members obtain programs based on a point system similar to a bank
account. Members are credited with points when a program is contributed,
debited points when they request a program. In operating the program
library CEPA acts as broker between members in providing information
on program availability and in keeping an account of point balances.
The cost associated with program acquisition is a matter of concern
between the owner of the program and the requester. Should a member
run out of points, they may be purchased from CEPA, with the funds going
to CEPA's general operating fund.

The Structural Members Users Group

Contact: The Structural Members Users Group
           P.O. Box 3958, University Station
           Charlottesville, Virginia 22903

The Structural Members Users Group distributes and maintains computer
programs for the static, stability dynamic response, and stress analysis
of structural members and mechanical elements. The programs are available on such national networks as UCS, or they can be purchased for use
on an in-house computer. These are generally analysis programs for
classical structural members with arbitrary mechanical or thermal loading.
The members can be of variable cross section with any in-span supports,
foundations, and boundary conditions. Composite cross sections can be
handled. The member can be modeled with either a continuous or a lumped
mass. Static and steady-state displacements and forces, natural frequencies and mode shapes, and buckling loads are calculated. The programs
apply to beams, torsional systems, extension systems, cylinders, thick
spheres, torsion of thin-walled beams, strings, sectional properties,
stress analyses, rotating shafts, circular plates, rectangular plates,
gridworks, and discs. These are small, efficient, easy-to-use FORTRAN
programs with versions available for all major computers. Pre- and postprocessors permitting interactive use of the programs are available. The
programs can be used in batch or time-sharing form with fixed, free, or
prompted input formats.

Users Group for CDC 6000 Series Machines (VIM)

Contact: Mr. Thomas Burt
           Fluor Corporation
           3331 Michelson Dr.
           Irvine, California 92730

VIM is an organization for users of large-scale CDC Computer systems.
It currently has 320 institutional members around the world. Control
Data Corporation maintains a centralized library of programs; it dis-
seminates programs to members upon request at no charge. To provide
information on software in the library, it publishes a program catalog
once a year. The programs in the library are contributions from users
and Control Data Corporation. For better communication among users, VIM
publishes a monthly newsletter and holds conferences twice a year.
      Plans for the future include the publication of a catalog, The
VIM Software Directory, which will abstract programs available from
members and information on how to obtain them. Many of these programs
will be available for a nominal fee from the source instead of from CDC.
This new cataloging system will probably supersede the present system.

Wang Systems Users Society (WSUS)

Contact: William P. Poticha
           Executive Director
           Wang Systems Users Society
           One Industrial Avenue
           Lowell, Massachusetts 01851

The primary objective of this group is to advance the effectiveness of utilization of systems manufactured by Wang Laboratories, Inc. Membership is open only to those with Wang equipment. Several hundred programs are maintained and distributed.

Program Dissemination Centers and Users Groups

Barbara F. Pilkey

University of Virginia

INTRODUCTION

It is now possible to do information searches either on-line, by belonging
to a national or international interactive information retrieval service,
or by requesting a search to be done by any one of several appropriate
organizations which have access to one or more data bases. There are
three major interactive networks on this continent which provide on-line
access to many varied data bases. All require that the user supply his
own terminal. The information requested can be printed either on-line
or on the service's terminals and mailed to the user within 24 hours.
The computer-connect hour charges depend partly on how many hours
of use there are per month, but there are also royalty charges (on
an hourly basis) which depend on the data base accessed, and a charge
per record for each abstract or citation printed off-line. There are
communications charges also.
   A literature search via computer, whether done interactively or
through a custom-ordered search by competent technically oriented people,
is much more efficient, comprehensive, and cost-effective than a search
done by a secretary.

COMMERCIAL SERVICES THROUGH WHICH MULTIPLE DATA
BASES ARE AVAILABLE ON-LINE

The following is a list of three major commercial services through which
the customer can have access to a variety of data bases. Each service is
described, and then the data bases available on-line through the service
are listed and described.

DIALOG

Address: Lockheed Information Systems
           Orgn. 5208, Building 201

3251 Hanover Street
Palo Alto, CA 94304
(800) 277-1960 Continental U.S.
(800) 982-5838 in California
(415) 493-4411 outside U.S.A.

This system has no initiation fees and no minimum monthy charges. At
the present time there are 81 data bases on-line, of which they say 22 are
of interest to people working in some phase of transportation. Of these
22 data bases, eight would probably be of some interest to people concerned
with technical and engineering information. These eight are listed below,
along with a short description of what is available in the data base and
the rates for both on-line usage and for off-line printouts.

COMPENDEX

Coverage: January 1970 - present
File size: 700,000 records, monthly updates
Prepared by: Engineering Index, Inc., New York, N.Y.
Description: The COMPENDEX data base is the machine-readable version of
    the Engineering Index (Monthly/Annual), which provides the engineering
    and information communities with abstracted information from the
    world's significant engineering and technological literature. The EI
    data base provides worldwide coverage of approximately 3500 journals,
    publications of engineering societies and organizations, papers from
    the proceedings of conferences, and selected government reports and
    books.
Cost: $65 per on-line computer hour
       10¢ per full record printed off-line

COMPREHENSIVE DISSERTATION ABSTRACTS

Coverage: 1861 - present
File size: 600,000 citations, monthly updates
Prepared by: Xerox University Microfilms, Ann Arbor, MI
Description: COMPREHENSIVE DISSERTATION ABSTRACTS is a definitive subject,
    title, and author guide to virtually every American dissertation
    accepted at an accredited institution since 1861, when academic doc-
    toral degrees were first granted in the United States. In addition,
    CDA serves to disseminate citations for thousands of Canadian disserta-
    tions and an increasing number of papers accepted in institutions
    abroad. Professional (e.g., M.D., L.L.D.) and honorary degrees are
    not included. All subject areas are covered.
        Individual degree-granting institutions submit copies of dis-
    sertations or lists of dissertations completed to University Micro-
    film International (UMI). Citations for these dissertations are in-
    cluded in the data base and in University Microfilms International
    printed publications: Dissertation Abstracts International (DAI),
    American Doctoral Dissertations (ADD), and Comprehensive Dissertation
    Index (CDI).
Cost: $55 per on-line computer hour
       12¢ per full record printed off-line

CONFERENCE PAPERS INDEX

Coverage: 1973 - present
File size: 580,000 records, monthly updates
Prepared by: Data Courier, Inc., Louisville, KY
Description: CONFERENCE PAPERS INDEX provides access to records of more
than 100,000 scientific and technical papers presented at over 1000
major regional, national, and international meetings each year.
CONFERENCE PAPERS INDEX provides a centralized source of information
on reports of current research and development from papers presented
at conferences and meetings; it provides titles of the papers as well
as the names and addresses (when available) of the authors of these
papers. Also included in this data base are announcements of any
publications issued or planned for issuance from the meetings and of
available preprints, reprints, abstract booklets, and proceedings
volumes as well as dates of availability, costs, and ordering information. Primary subject areas covered include the life sciences,
chemistry, physical sciences, geo-sciences, and engineering.
Cost: $75 per on-line computer hour
15¢ per full record printed off-line

INSPEC

Coverage: 1969 - present
File size: 1,160,000 citations, monthly updates
Prepared by: The Institution of Electrical Engineers, Savoy Place,
London WS2R OBL, England
Description: The Science Abstracts family of abstract journals, indexes,
and title bulletins commenced publication in 1898. Today it forms
the largest English-language data base in the fields of physics,
electrotechnology, computers, and control. The on-line INSPEC file
corresponds to the printed Physics Abstracts, Electrical and Electron-
ics Abstracts, and Computer and Control Abstracts. Foreign language
source material is also included, but abstracted and indexed in
English.
Journal papers, conference proceedings, technical reports, books,
patents, and university theses are abstracted and indexed for inclusion in the INSPEC data bases. The total number of journals
scanned is approximately 2000; over 200 of these are abstraced
completely.
Cost: $55 per on-line computer hour
10¢ per full record printed off-line

ISMEC

Coverage: 1973 - present
File size: 82,500 citations, monthly updates
Prepared by: Data Courier, Inc., Louisville, KY
Description: ISMEC (Information Service in Mechanical Engineering) indexes
significant articles in all aspects of mechanical engineering, production engineering, and engineering management from approximately 250
journals published throughout the world. In addition, books, reports,
and conference proceedings are indexed. The primary emphasis is on
comprehensive coverage of leading international journals and conferences on mechanical engineering subjects. The principal areas covered

are mechanical, nuclear, electrical, electronic, civil, optical,
medical, and industrial process engineering; mechanics; production
processes, energy,and power; transport and handling; and applications
of mechanical engineering.
Cost: $75 per on-line computer hour
       15¢ per full record printed off-line

NTIS

Coverage: 1964 - present
File size: 695,000 citations, biweekly updates
Prepared by: National Technical Information Service, NTIS, U.S.
              Department of Commerce, Springfield, VA
Description: The NTIS data base consists of government-sponsored research,
    development, and engineering, plus analyses prepared by federal
    agencies, their contractors, or grantees. It is the means through
    which unclassified, publicly available, unlimited distribution reports
    are made available for sale from such agencies as NASA, DDC, DOE,
    HEW, HUD, DOT, Department of Commerce, and some 240 other units.
    State and local government agencies are now beginning to contribute
    their reports to the file.
        The NTIS data base includes material from both the hard and soft
    sciences, including substantial material on technological applications,
    business procedures, and regulatory matters. Many topics of immediate
    broad interest are included, such as environmental pollution and con-
    trol, energy conversion, technology transfer, behavioral/societal
    problems, and urban and regional planning.
Cost: $35 per on-line computer hour
       10¢ per full record printed off-line

SCISEARCH

Coverage: January 1974 - present
File size: 2,060,000 citations, monthly updates
Prepared by: Institute for Scientific Information, Philadelphia, PA
Description: SCISEARCH is a multidisciplinary index to the literature of
    science and technology prepared by the Institute for Scientific Infor-
    mation (IST®) It contains all the records published in Science
    Citation Index (SCI®) and additional records from the Current Contents
    series of publications that are not included in the printed version
    of SCI. SCISEARCH is distinguished by two important and unique
    characteristics. First, journals indexed are carefully selected on
    the basis of several criteria, including citation analysis, resulting
    in the inclusion of 90 percent of the world's significant scientific
    and technical literature. Second, citation indexing is provided,
    which allows retrieval of newly published articles through the sub-
    ject relationships established by an author's reference to prior
    articles. SCISEARCH covers every area of the pure and applied sci-
    ences.
        The ISI staff indexes all significant items (articles, reports
    of meetings, letters, editorials, correction notices, etc.) from about
    2600 major scientific and technical journals. Beginning January 1,
    1976, all items from Current Contents - Engineering, Technology, and
    Applied Science have been included each month. This expanded cover-
    age adds approximately 58,000 items per year to the SCISEARCH file.

Cost: $70 per on-line computer hour
       10¢ per full record printed off-line

SSIE CURRENT RESEARCH

Coverage: last two years, e.g., 1977 - present
File size: 253,000 citations, monthly updates
Prepared by: Smithsonian Science Information Exchange, Washington, D.C.
Description: SSIE (SMITHSONIAN SCIENCE INFORMATION EXCHANGE) CURRENT
     RESEARCH is a data base containing reports of both government and
     privately funded scientific research projects, either currently in
     progress or initiated and completed during the most recent two years.
     SSIE data are collected from the funding organizations at the
     inception of a research project and provide a source for information
     on current research long before first or progress reports appear in
     the published literature. SSIE CURRENT RESEARCH encompasses all
     fields of basic and applied research in the life, physical, social,
     and engineering sciences.
          Project descriptions are received from over 1300 organizations
     that fund research including federal, state, and local government
     agencies; nonprofit associations and foundations; and colleges and
     universities. A small amount of material is provided from private
     industry and foreign research organizations, while 90 percent of the
     information in the data base is provided by agencies of the federal
     government.
          Research projects in SSIE CURRENT RESEARCH include work in pro-
     gress in the electronics, physics, materials science, engineering,
     and mathematics.
Cost: $90 per on-line computer hour
       20¢ per full record printed off-line

                              ORBIT

Address: System Development Corporation (SDC)
          2500 Colorado Avenue
          Santa Monica, California   90406
          (213) 829-7511

          and

          7979 Westpark Drive
          McLean, Virginia   22101
          (703) 790-9850

          also

          (800) 352-6689 in California
          (800) 421-7229 continental USA except California

     There are no start-up fees or minimum charges if you wish to use this
service. The data bases available through SDC in many cases overlap those
available on the DIALOG system. The technically oriented data bases are
listed below, along with pertinent information which is unique to this system. Data bases not available from the DIALOG system are abstracted.

COMPENDEX

Coverage: January 1970 - present
Cost: $65 per on-line computer hour
         $0.10 per full record printed off-line

Conference Papers Index

Coverage: 1973 - present
Cost: $70 per on-line computer hour
         $0.15 per full record printed off-line

INSPEC and INSP6976

Coverage: INSPEC: 1970 - present
           INSP6979: 1969-1976
Cost: $45 per on-line computer hour
         $0.10 per full record printed off-line

ISMEC

Coverage: 1973 - present
Cost: $65 per on-line computer hour
         $0.12 per full record printed off-line

NTIS

Coverage: January, 1970 - present
Cost: $45 per on-line computer hour
         $0.08 per full record printed off-line

SAE Abstracts

Coverage: January, 1965 - present
File size: Approximately 800 citations per year
Prepared by: Society of Automotive Engineers, Inc.
Description: Worldwide coverage of papers concerned with self-propelled
     vehicles gathered from industry, government, and academic sectors
     as well as research and private organizations. Subject coverage in-
     cludes aircraft, missiles and spacecraft, ground support equipment,
     passenger cars, military equipment, aircraft propulsion, electric
     vehicles, energy conversion, fuels and lubricants, manufacturing and
     production, transportation systems, emissions, safety, noise, manage-
     ment, testing,and instrumentation.
Updating: Quarterly, approximately 200 citations
Cost: $80 per computer-connect hour
         $0.15 per citation for off-line printing

Safety Scientific Abstracts

Coverage: 1975 to present
File size: Approximately 15,000 citations per year
Prepared by: Cambridge Scientific Abstracts
Description: Broad, interdisciplinary coverage of literature related to
the science of safety; a relatively new field devoted to identifying,
evaluating, and eliminating or controlling hazards. Major subject
categories are: general safety, industrial and occupational safety,
transportation safety, aviation and aerospace safety, environmental
and ecological safety, and medical safety. Topics covered include:
pollution, fire, waste disposal, prediction and reporting of natural
disasters, legislative regulations and their impact, urban development,
radiation, drug dosages, criminal acts (e.g., arson, child abuse),
epidemics, pesticides, education, prevention, and psychological factors
related to safety.
Updating: Bimonthly, approximately 3000 citations
Cost: $75 per computer-connect hour
$0.15 per citation for off-line printing

SSIE

Coverage: Fiscal year 1974 to present date
Cost: $110 per on-line computer hour
$0.25 per full record printed off-line

BRS

Address: Bibliographic Retrieval Services, Inc.
Corporation Park, Bldg. 702
Scotia, New York 12302
(518) 374-5011

This is a relatively new data base service, which was started in 1975.
The on-line searching capabilities are the current three- to five-year portions of the data bases. Earlier years will searched and processed off-
line at the user's request, and be available for on-line printing the next
day. This service has no unique data bases available. Data bases of
interest to engineers and other technically oriented people are:

Comprehensive Dissertation Index
INSPEC
NTIS

Additional Data Bases and Custom Search Services

What follows is a list of individualized or custom data search services.
Some of these may overlap the sources available on the interactive services described in the previous section, but in this section information
is given on how each service will do a personalized search for a customer.

TRIS (Transportation Research Information Service)

This data base was loaded onto a computer by Battelle-Columbus and was
maintained and updated by Battelle until it was turned over to the Department of Transportation on April 6, 1979. The system will probably be made
publicly available on DIALOG, the Lockheed System, but final arrangements
have not yet been completed. It has not been decided how or if custom
searches will be done. It should be noted, however, that TRIS is one of
the bases searched by the Railroad Research Information Service when they
do their custom searches. For further information about TRIS and its present status and availability, contact

>   Don Johnson
>   Information and Management Branch
>   Research and Special Programs Administration
>   U.S. Department of Transportation
>   Washington, D.C. 20590
>   (202) 426-0975

NTIS (National Technical Information Service)

NTIS will do a custom search of its own data base if a customer requests
one. The charge is $100 per search and includes up to 100 abstracts. The
search is screened by someone in the appropriate field to remove false
hits. The services are available to anyone.
       NTIS can also be searched through the data base services of DIALOG,
ORBIT (SDC), and BRS.
       For a custom search, or more information, contact

>   National Technical Information Service
>   U.S. Department of Commerce
>   5285 Port Royal Road
>   Springfield, VA 22161

or call:

>   (703) 557-4642 and ask for Mr. Ed Lehman

SSIE (Smithsonian Science Information Exchange)

This data base consists of résumés of current and past technical research
projects sponsored by the Smithsonian and other government branches.
The information is available on-line through DIALOG and ORBIT (SDC). The
SSIE will do custom searches with specialists checking the validity of
the search, for $60. This fee gives up to 50 projects, each described
and summarized on a single sheet. Additional hits can be had for $0.25
each (if they exist).
       For more information contact

>   Smithsonian Science Information Exchange (SSIE)
>   Smithsonian Institution
>   1730 M St., N.W.
>   Washington, D.C. 20036
>   (202) 381-4211

RRIS (Railroad Research Information Service)

This is a computer-based information service operated by the Transportation Research Board with financial support from the FRA. RRIS can give engineers and researchers rapid access to information about ongoing and completed railroad related research activities.

The information in RRIS covers a broad range of problems of planning, building, maintaining, and operating rail transporation systems. A file is maintained of current research projects giving the project description, objectives, sponsor, principal investigator, and other information. Abstracts of pertinent technical papers published after 1973 are in the RRIS file. Descriptions of computer programs from railroads and other sources (such as AAR) are stored in AAR files. There is a large file of information pertaining to foreign rail technology in the files, also. They also have access to the NTIS data base and the Engineering Index Citations.

The basic charge for doing a search is $50, plus $0.25 per printout page, which includes screening of the search by subject experts who work for the RRIS. Requests may be made by phone, mail, or visit.

RRIS also prints the Railroad Research Bulletin biannually. This abstract bulletin contains all of the new references that have been placed in the RRIS magnetic file during the preceding six months. Annual subscriptions to the Bulletin are accepted.

For more information contact

Mr. F. H. Houser, RRIS Manager
RRIS
Transportation Research Board
2101 Constitution Ave., N.W.
Washington, D.C. 20418

or call: (202) 389-6611

Part II

REVIEWS AND SUMMARIES OF AVAILABLE PROGRAMS

Multipoint Boundary Value Problems

Eugene D. Denman

University of Houston

INTRODUCTION

The solution of problems in structural mechanics may require a software program or code to compute the solution to a set of ordinary
differential equations with values of the dependent variables specified at certain points. If the end points of a beam have a specified
deflection (or slope), then the problem is classified as a two-point
boundary value problem; if the deflection (or slope) has been specified at several points along the beam, the problem is a multipoint
boundary value problem.

This chapter will briefly describe the mathematical methods for
solving such problems and provide information on the availability of
software for solving two-point and multipoint boundary value problems.
The information on availability will be as complete as possible, and
include programs that are documented in the literature and known to
the writer. The major sources of the information given in this
chapter were from the recent conference on Working Codes for Boundary
Value Problems [1], at the University of Houston in May 1978, and
from commercial time-sharing computer firms such as University Computing Corp. (UCC), United Computing Services (UCS), and Control Data
Corp. (CDC). In addition, several computer library service listings
were examined for available programs. The search was not an in-depth
one, and there are other codes than those described herein. The codes
described will probably solve the majority of problems that are of
interest to researchers in structural mechanics.

METHODS OF SOLVING BOUNDARY VALUE PROBLEMS

Consider a set of n first order differential equations of the form

$$\underline{y}'(x) = a(\underline{y}(x),x) \qquad x_0 \le x \le x_f \tag{1}$$

where $\underline{y}(x)$ is an nxl vector and x is the independent variable. It has been assumed that a system of higher order differential equations can be reduced to the form of Eq. (1). The boundary conditions may be specified in several forms:

$$\underline{y}_i(x_k) = C_i, \ i=1,2...n \ \text{ with } x_k \text{ a fixed point in } x_0 \leq x \leq x_f \qquad (2a)$$

$$\underline{y}_r(x_0) = C_1, \ \underline{y}_s(x_f) = C_2 \ \text{ with } r + s = n \qquad (2b)$$

$$B_1\underline{y}(x_0) + B_2\underline{y}(x_f) = C \qquad (2c)$$

or with other linear and nonlinear constraints. The solution of (1) must satisfy the boundary constraint, which generally means that the proper[1] initial condition, $\underline{y}(x_0) = \underline{z}$, must be found.

Since the initial condition $\underline{y}(x_0) = \underline{z}$ is not completely specified, the computational procedure must be adaptable in that the algorithm computes new estimates z_i of $\underline{y}(x_0)$ from the computed solutions $\underline{y}(x,\underline{z}_i)$. Two solution procedures will be described; one requires the integration of the differential equations with an initial estimate of $\underline{y}(x_0) = \underline{z}_0$ with an algorithm to update the estimate. The shooting, superposition, and invariant imbedding methods use this procedure. The second computational procedure to be discussed is algebraic. The differential equations are replaced by difference equations with the boundary constraints included in the algebraic structure. Finite difference and spline algorithms fall into the algebraic class. Although both methods require algorithms for solving algebraic equations, the two procedures will be referred to as the integration algorithms and the algebraic algorithms for want of better terms.

The differential equation given in (1) must be satisfied with the boundary constraints which will be denoted by the general function $b(\underline{y}(x_k;\underline{z}_i), \ x_k) = 0$, where x_k denotes the points at which the function is known with $x_0 < x_1 < x_2 < x_3 ... x_f$ which are interior points in $x_0 \leq x \leq x_f$. The first step in the integration algorithms is to select an initial condition $\underline{y}(x_0) = \underline{z}_0$ and compute $\underline{y}(x;\underline{z}_0)$ for x. The initial condition chosen should, if possible, lead to a bounded solution for $\underline{y}(x,\underline{z}_i)$ although such a selection of $\underline{z}_0$ may be difficult. The computed solution $y(x;\underline{z}_0)$ is then used to correct $\underline{y}(x_0) = z_1$ so that the updated value $\underline{y}(x_0) = \underline{z}_1$ is closer to the true value than was $\underline{z}_0$. The procedure is an iterative algorithm which will converge to the approximate solution $\underline{y}(x)$ with $\underline{y}(x_0;\underline{z}_i) = \underline{z}_i$ and satisfy the boundary constraint equation $b(\underline{y}(x_k;\underline{z}_i),x_k) = 0$.

A direct application of the procedure given above is the shooting algorithm. The procedure can be summarized as follows: a) select $\underline{z}_0$ and compute $y(x;\underline{z}_0)$ for $x_0 < x < x_f$; b) use the constraint equation $b(y(x_k;\underline{z}_i),x_k) = 0$ to compute $\underline{z}_1$ with $y(x;z_0)$; c) repeat the procedure until the boundary equations are satisfied. Quasi-linearization or some other optimization algorithm will be used in b) to find $\underline{z}_i$ if $b(y(x_k;z_i),x_k)$ is nonlinear.

------

[1]The initial condition $\underline{y}(x_0)$ may not be unique for a nonlinear system.

The superposition algorithm is similar to the shooting method with the exception that other functions are introduced. Let $\underline{y}'(x)$ be a nonlinear function, then Eq. (1) can be written as:

$$[\underline{y}^{i+1}(x)]' = \frac{\partial a[\underline{y}^i(x)x]}{\partial x} \underline{y}^{i+1}(x) + \{a[\underline{y}^i(x),x] - \frac{\partial a[\underline{y}^i(x),x]}{\partial x} y^i(x)\} \quad (3)$$

which is a Taylor series expansion about the solution $\underline{y}^i(x)$. Equation (2) is now used in an iteration scheme; a solution $\underline{y}^i(x)$ is assumed to be known; and $\underline{y}^{i+1}(x)$ is then computed. The linearized first-order differential equation can then be written as

$$[\underline{y}^{i+1}(x)]' = J[\underline{y}^i(x),x]\underline{y}^{i+1}(x) + B[\underline{y}^i(x),x] \quad (4)$$

The general solution to Eq. (4) is given by

$$\underline{y}^{i+1}(x) = Y[\underline{y}^i(x),c]\underline{y}^{i+1}(x_0) + P[\underline{y}^i(x),x] \quad (5)$$

where $Y[y^i(x),x]$ is the fundamental solution matrix to

$$Y'[\underline{y}^i(x),x] = J[\underline{y}^i(x),x]Y[\underline{y}^i(x)x] \quad Y[\underline{z}_i,x_0] = I \quad (6)$$

and $P[\underline{y}^i(x),x]$ satisfies

$$P'[y^i(x),x] = J[y^i(x),x]P[y^i(x),x] + B[y^i(x),x] \quad (7)$$

with $P[\underline{z}_i,x_0] = 0$. The boundary condition equation $b[\underline{y}^i(x_k;z_i),x_k] = 0$ is then used to find the initial condition update vector $\underline{z}_{i+1}$.

Linear problems characterized by the inhomogeneous equation

$$y'(x) = A(x)y(x) + B(x) \quad (8)$$

are in the form of (4) and no linearization is necessary. The computational procedure follows the same lines as for the linearized system equation.

Finite difference and finite element algorithms are available; these algorithms in general are algebraic algorithms. A brief discussion of each will be given so that the user will have a superficial knowledge of what computations are involved in the codes. Let Eq. (1) be the differential equation for a linear system and suppose that $x_0 \leq x \leq x_f$ is divided into N + 1 equal segments h. The function $\underline{y}'(x)$ can then be approximated by

$$\underline{y}'(x_j) = (\underline{y}_{j+1} - \underline{y}_{j-1})/2h \qquad j = 1,2...N \quad (9)$$

and Eq. (1) then becomes

$$\underline{y}_{j+1} - \underline{y}_{j-1} = 2h \cdot a(x_j)y_j \quad (10)$$

To simplify the explanation of the algorithm, let $y(x_0) = c_1$ and $y(x_f) = c_2$; then a set of algebraic equations of the form

$$y_2 - y_0 = 2ha(h)y_1$$
$$y_3 - y_1 = 2ha(2h)y_2 \tag{11}$$
$$\vdots$$
$$y_{N+1} - y_{N-1} = 2ha(Nh)y_N$$

can be written. Since $y_0 = c_1$ and $y_{N+1} = c_2$, Eq. (11) defines a set of algebraic equations in y_j which can be solved by standard algebraic methods.

The method can be extended to nonlinear boundary value problems by linearizing the differential equations as discussed previously. Multipoint boundary value problems with simple interior and boundary constraints can be solved by defining y_j at the given points. The computational procedure will then be iterative; y_j is computed from y_j^i, etc.

Finite element methods[2] are closely related to the finite difference methods. A function $s(x)$ such as a cubic polynomial in x or a set of orthogonal functions is chosen to closely approximate $y(x)$ over a finite range of x. These functions are used to obtain a set of algebraic equations that are solved to find $y(x)$ subject to the boundary constraint equation $b[y(x_k), x_k] = 0$.

The essential subprogram to any boundary value problem is an efficient code to solve linear and nonlinear algebraic equations. In addition to this requirement, the algorithm by which the initial estimates are updated should converge to the correct initial value. This requirement is necessary for the integration algorithm since improper initial conditions can lead to machine overflow in some problems.

Readers interested in all aspects of boundary value problem codes should obtain a copy of the proceedings of the Working Conference on Boundary Value Codes [1], University of Houston, May 1978, to be published by Springer-Verlag. The Proceedings should be available in late 1979.

BOUNDARY VALUE PROBLEM CODES

Numerous boundary value codes have been written and are available for solving boundary value problems. The list of programs given is not complete since full information was not available for some codes and codes may exist that are known to the writers. Table 1 gives a list of known codes, the method utilized for solving the problem, and the source (originator) of the codes. The methods of solution have been briefly described in the previous section.

---

[2]Also referred to as collocation or spline methods.

In addition to the above codes which are available as stand-alone programs, at least one other boundary value code is available to time-share customers of CDC and UCS computer services. The program is an integral part of the PROSE library, a general purpose higher level language. No details can be given on the code or cost since a request for information from PROSE, Inc. was not answered. The addition of this language to a computer center library is probably not justifiable for the purpose of solving boundary value problems. Users having access to CDC or UCS services should consider the language as there are additional codes in this package which may be of value for structure problems.

Table 1

CODE	METHOD	AUTHORS (SOURCE)
SUPORT[2]	Superposition-orthonor-malization	Staff (SANDIA)
SUPORQ[2]	Superposition-orthonorm-linearization	Staff (SANDIA)
INVIMB[4]	Invariant imbedding	Staff (SANDIA)
MSHOOT[4]	Multiple shooting	Staff (SANDIA)
DDO3AD[1]	Multiple shooting	Harwell
PASVA3 (DDO4A/AD)	Finite difference	Pereya-Lentini (Harwell
QUASII[3]	Superposition-lineari-zation	Childs, et al. (Texas A&M)
SDVP[5]	Multiple shooting	Staff (JPL)
COLSY[3]	Collocation	Ascher, et al. (U of British Col)

1. Available from NAG - Harwell.
2. Contact source for availability.
3. Contact authors for availability.
4. Codes in advanced states of development but not necessarily available as a thoroughly tested code.
5. Under development. No information available.

CODES

Program SUPORT

Author(s): Staff, Sandia Laboratories
Contact for Information: Dr. Mel Scott
                          Sandia Laboratories
                          Albuquerque, N. M. 87115
                          Phone: (505) 264-5678
Type of Problems: Linear two-point, boundary value; first order ordinary
    differential equations
Method: Superposition and orthonormalization
Documentation: Program listing includes user information.
Hardware: CDC 7600
Language: FORTRAN
Availability: Sandia Laboratories for nominal cost

Program SUPORQ

Author(s): Staff, Sandia Laboratories
Contact for Information: Dr. Mel Scott
                          Sandia Laboratories
                          Albuquerque, N. M. 87115
                          Phone: (505) 264-5678
Type of Problems: Nonlinear two-point boundary value; first order
    ordinary differential equation
Method: Quasilinearization with superposition and orthonormalization
Documentation: Program listing includes user information.
Hardware: CDC 7600
Language: FORTRAN
Availability: Sandia Laboratories for nominal cost

Program INVIMB

Author(s): Staff, Sandia Laboratories
Contact for Information: Dr. Mel Scott
                          Sandia Laboratories
                          Albuquerque, N. M. 87115
                          Phone: (505) 264-5678
Type of Problems: Linear two-point boundary value; first order ordinary
    differential equation
Method: Riccati transformation and invariant imbedding
Documentation: Program listing includes user information.
Hardware: CDC 7600
Language: FORTRAN
Availability: Sandia Laboratories for nominal cost

Program MSHOOT

Author(s): Staff, Sandia Laboratories
Contact for Information: Dr. Mel Scott
                          Sandia Laboratories
                          Albuquerque, N. M. 87115
                          Phone: (505) 264-5678

Type of Problems: Nonlinear two-point boundary value; first order
    ordinary differential equations
Method: Multiple shooting
Documentation: Program listing includes user information.
Hardware: CDC 7600
Language: FORTRAN
Availability: Sandia Laboratories for nominal cost

Program: PASVA3 (DD04A/AD)

Author(s): Lentin and Pereyra
Contact for Information: Professor V. Pereyra
                          Escuela de Computacion
                          Univ. Central de Venezuela
                          Apostade 59002
                          Caracas, Venezuela
Type of Problems: Nonlinear two-point boundary value; first order
    ordinary differential equations
Method: Finite difference
Documentation: Program listing provides user information, also [1].
Hardware: Transportable
Language: FORTRAN
Availability: Harwell Library
               Computer Science and Systems Div.
               AERE
               Oxfordshire, OX 11 ORA
               England

Program DD03AD

Author(s): Staff, Harwell
Contact for Information: Harwell
                          Computer Science and Systems Div.
                          AERE
                          Oxfordshire, OX 11 ORA
                          England
Type of Problems: Nonlinear two-point boundary value; first order
    ordinary differential equations
Method: Multiple shooting
Documentation: Harwell Library catalog and program listing
Hardware: See Harwell Library catalog for Information.
Language: FORTRAN
Availability: Harwell Library

Program QUASII

Author(s): S. B. Childs et al.
Contact for Information: Professor S. B. Childs
                          Industrial Engineering Dept.
                          Texas A & M University
                          College Station, Texas
                          Phone: (713) 845-5531
Type of Problems: Nonlinear two-point boundary value; first-order

ordinary differential equations
Method: Superposition - linearization
Documentation: Report available from Professor Childs and [1]
Hardware: Contact Professor Childs for information.
Language: FORTRAN
Availability: Contact Professor Childs.

Program COLSY

Author(s): U. Ascher et al.
Contact for Information: Professor R. D. Russell
                              Department of Mathematics
                              Simon Fraser U.
                              Burnaby, B. C. V5A 156
                              Canada
                              Phone: (604) 291-3332
Type of Problems: Nonlinear multipoint boundary value; mixed order
    ordinary differential equation
Method: Finite element
Documentation: Program listing and [1]
Hardware: IBM 370
Language: FORTRAN
Availability: Contact Professor Russell.

REFERENCE

1 Proc. Working Conference on Codes for BVP in ODE's, Lecture Notes in Com. Science, Springer-Verlag, 1979.

Pile Foundation Analysis/Design Systems

David R. Schelling

Douglas P. Neary

University of Maryland

INTRODUCTION

In late 1978 a project to initiate the development of an integrated, modular bridge design system was initiated through the National Cooperative Highway Research Program (Project HR-12-18) [1]. As planned, this integrated system would encompass current bridge design specifications and allow the engineer a wide range of interaction with the computer in performing his design function.

As part of the first phase of this project, an extensive review of existing bridge pile-group foundation analysis and design programs was conducted. Documentation for existing pile foundation software was solicited from all state and Canadian provincial highway agencies. The responses revealed either that many agencies did not perform their own bridge pile foundation design function or that they used a computer solution based on the very popular P/A ± Mc/I analysis method. In fact, it was found that there is a general reluctance on the part of engineering design personnel to discontinue their use of this approximate analysis technique even in light of the several computer-based solutions now available.

Given herein is a brief presentation of several available methods for the analysis of pile foundations, followed by a review of the nine pile foundation analysis systems identified by this study. Some of the analysis methods presented are incorporated into these pile software systems.

The features and capabilities within each program are presented in tabular format followed by an abstract detailing program availability, methodology, etc. It is felt that this information accurately reflects the present state-of-the-art of bridge pile-group foundation design.

ANALYSIS METHODS

General Flexure Formula

Pile forces are computed by the general equation P/A $\pm$ Mc/I, where the applied loads are usually taken at the centroid of the pile group cap. Consideration is usually given to both applied lateral and transverse moments and to the corresponding moment of inertia of the pile group. Displacements, lateral shears, bending moments, and other design criteria for individual pile members are generally determined by approximation, since the analysis seldom considers pile batter and/or lateral pile-soil interaction. In addition, this method does not directly yield pile torsional forces or allow for variation of pile lengths or sectional properties within a group. This analysis method is particularly unsuitable for pile bents since bending rather than axial stress often governs this design.

2D Planar Analysis

This analysis method generally employs matrix formulations similar to the 3D stiffness procedure. However, foundation loads and the resulting structural displacements and forces are developed only in two-dimensional space. A three-dimensional analysis requires two separate analytical procedures, in which loads and the pile group configuration are given for each in-plane case. As with the 3D stiffness method, consideration is given to pile bending and axial and translation stiffnesses, as well as to pile end fixity. This procedure does not, however, yield pile torsional forces or final cap (and pile) displacements due to applied loads and/or moments in two planes.

Saul's Method

This is a three-dimensional analysis method which employs stiffness coefficients in a matrix formulation to yield final pile forces. These coefficients can be developed in several ways. Analysis options available to the engineer permit a pile to be modeled as a semi-infinite beam on an elastic foundation, as a cantilever fixed at some depth, or as a combination of these. In addition, a pile may have a different bending stiffness about its principal axis, be fixed or hinged at the cap, have any batter and torsional stiffness, and be laterally supported to any degree by the surrounding soil.

Unbalanced Shear

This analysis method is most generally applicable to pile groups having constant pile batter within each row of piles. Analysis of load distribution and pile forces is performed for the lateral and transverse case separately. For each planar case, applied axial loads and moments taken at the footing centroid are distributed by general flexure analysis to each individual pile. Battered piles develop a magnitude of shear which is proportional to their angle of inclination. The sum of the individual pile shears is then compared to any applied horizontal forces to the footing (within the same plane). If the sum of the shears exceeds these applied loads, then the pile group configuration is satisfactory for loading within that plane. This analysis is performed in both the transverse and lateral directions. In addition, the axial stress developed within each pile is usually checked against allowable compressive (and tensile) stresses.

Hrennikoff's Method

This stiffness matrix analysis method idealizes the pile group, which
is composed of vertical and battered piles, as a planar structure with
lateral resistance of individual piles taken into account. Pile stiffness coefficients are developed as a function of each pile's sectional
properties, batter, and location within the group, with piles treated
as infinite beams on an elastic foundation. Piles may be considered
pinned or fixed at the cap. Following the formation of a stiffness
matrix for each pile, the group stiffness matrix is assembled, and the
structure is solved for displacements, forces, and moments in the usual
matrix analysis manner.

Francis's Method

This two-dimensional analysis method takes into account the flexure rigidity of piles and of pile bents. This rigidity is related to the increasing soil stiffness with increasing depth of pile embedment. The soil
stiffness characteristics are given as a function of various soil properties, and result in the determination of a depth at which the pile can be
considered fully fixed. Analysis then proceeds, assuming each pile to be
cantilevered from some depth below the ground surface, and the pile top
to be pinned, fixed, or free as determined by the engineer.

3D Stiffness Method

This matrix analysis method employs the general relationship for all
linear elastic structures, $A = S \times D$, where A is the load of action matrix,
S is the stiffness matrix, and D is the displacement matrix. For a pile
group the stiffness matrix is formulated in the usual manner, taking into
account axial, torsional, translational, and bending stiffnesses of each
pile member, with consideration given to pile end fixity as determined
by the engineer. Member forces and displacements are developed in three
dimensions as the foundation loading dictates. This analysis procedure
yields forces and moments (including torsion) which, when summed with
the applied load, are in static equilibrium. In addition, this method
directly yields the deflections and rotations of the pile cap. Finally,
the 3D stiffness method is appropriate for taking into account lateral
soil-pile interaction and variation of subgrade properties with increasing depth of pile embedment.

Ashenbrenner's Method

This method is an expansion of that developed by Hrennikoff into a three-
dimensional stiffness matrix analysis method. Piles are assumed hinged
at the cap or footing, and development of the group's lateral resistance
uses values for the coefficient of subgrade reaction as given by Terzaghi.

Reese, O'Neil, and Smith

This is a three-dimensional matrix analysis of a batter-pile foundation
which yields the structure in static equilibrium with a system of applied
loads. The structural stiffness matrix is formulated from various stiff-

Table 1 Program Identification--Bridge Pile-Group Foundations

ACRONYM	Developer and/or Source of Program	DESCRIPTION
	State Highway Department of Georgia Office of Systems Development Capitol Square, No. 2 Atlanta, Georgia 30334	THE ANALYSIS AND DESIGN OF PILE FOOTINGS This program will compute critical stresses and loads using the general flexure formula for each pile of a symmetric footing; the design mode determines the required number and arrangement of piles as well as footing reinforcement requirements; application of standard AASHTO group loadings is automatic.
	Hawaii Dept. of Transportation Engineering Computer Services Office 869 Punchbowl Street Honolulu, Hawaii 96813	PILE FOUNDATION ANALYSIS General flexure formula analysis of random or rectangular pile group configurations; pile cap must be rectangular, and piles are assumed to be of equal area and capable of resisting both tension and compression; computes pile axial forces and cap design moments and shears.
PILGR 76.1	State of Maine Dept. of Transportation Augusta, Maine 04333	GROUP PILE ANALYSIS Three-dimensional matrix analysis of an embedded pile group or a pile bent; uses the equivalent cantilever concept for the matrix formulation; battered piles and piles having different section properties are possible; piles may be friction, bearing, or a combination type; analysis is in accordance with 1974 AASHTO specifications.

Table 1   Program Identification--Bridge Pile-Group Foundations   (cont.)

ACRONYM	Developer and/or Source of Program	PROGRAM NAME and DESCRIPTION
PGA 76.01	Maryland State Highway Administration Department of Transportation Bureau of Bridge Design Baltimore, Maryland	PILE GROUP ANALYSIS Stiffness matrix analysis of 3D pile group having any pile configuration; considers piles of varying batter, section properties, or length; friction or bearing piles with a hinged or fixed cap; optional consideration of subgrade intersection; allows specification of structural model, i.e., infinite beam on an elastic foundation, cantilever beam fixed at some depth, or an elevated platform.
P20-100	New Jersey State Department of Trans. Bureau of Bridge Design 1035 Parkway Avenue Trenton, New Jersey 08625	ANALYSIS OF PILE GROUP FOUNDATIONS Modified flexure formula analysis of a pile group; pile batter must be constant within a row; horizontal loads are distributed as a function of pile batter; cap must be rectangular.
P20-204	New Jersey State Department of Trans. Bureau of Bridge Design 1035 Parkway Avenue Trenton, New Jersey 08625	PILE BENT ANALYSIS Pile bent analysis assuming piles fixed top and bottom; computes shears, moments, and pile axial forces; all piles must be of the same length.

Table 1   Program Identification--Bridge Pile-Group Foundations   (cont.)

ACRONYM	Developer and/or Source of Program	DESCRIPTION
BR-00610	Ontario Ministry of Trans. & Communications Computer Systems Branch Downsview, Ontario	PILE GROUP ANALYSIS Two-dimensional planar analysis using the elastic center method. All loads are assumed to be taken by axial pile resistance. Induced bending moments and lateral soil resistance are neglected. Pile configuration includes piles of varying length and batter; group may be freestanding or completely embedded.
	Oregon Department of Transportation Transportation Building Salem, Oregon	PILE CAP ANALYSIS Modified stiffness matrix analysis of a pile cap; computes cap displacements and pile axial forces; does not directly account for lateral pile resistance and other bending effects.
GROUP	Texas Department of Highways and Public Transportation Highway Building Austin, Texas 78701	ANALYSIS OF FOUNDATION WITH WIDELY SPACED BATTER PILES Two-dimensional analysis of pile bent or pile group foundation; pile properties and length and degree of batter may vary; considers a nonlinear soil-pile interaction system as well as nonlinear pile material; uses the finite difference analysis technique.

Table 2   General Program Data

ACRONYM OR NAME	Developer and/or Source	INSTALLATION AID	BUG FIXES	BUG NOTICES	CONDUCTS WORKSHOPS	AID IN PRODUCTION	SPECIAL CHANGES	SELF-CONTAINED	EXAMPLE PROB.	FLOW DIAGRAMS	THEORY	PROPRIETARY	PUBLIC DOMAIN	PRODUCTION PROGRAM
		PROGRAM MAINTENANCE						DOCUMENTATION				STATUS		
Analysis and Design of Pile Footings	State Highway Dept. of Georgia		X	X			X		X		X		X	X
Pile Found. Analysis	Hawaii Dept. of Transportation		X	X					X	X	X		X	X
PILGR 76.1	Maine Dept. of Transportation			X					X	X	X		X	X
PGA 76.01	Maryland State Highway Administration	X		X					X	X	X		X	X
P20-100	New Jersey State Dept. of Transportation								X				X	X
P20-204	New Jersey State DOT								X				X	X
BR00610	Ontario Ministry of Transportation & Communications			X									X	X
Pile Cap Analysis	Oregon Dept. of Transportation	X							X	X	X		X	X
GROUP	Texas Dept. of Transportation	X	X					X	X	X	X		X	X

Table 3   System Data

IDENTIFICATION (ACRONYM OR PROGRAM NAME)	COMPUTER HARDWARE	SOURCE LANGUAGE	INPUT						OUTPUT				PROGRAM CONSTRUCTION		
			FIXED FIELD	FREE FIELD	POL	INTERACTIVE	DIRECT ACCESS DATA BASE	EDIT	TABULAR OUTPUT	MULTILEVEL BY OPTION	DIAGNOSTICS	OUTPUT WIDTH (CHARACTERS)	MODULAR CONSTRUCTION	NO. OF PRIMARY OVERLAYS	NO. OF SUBROUTINES
Anal. and Design of Pile Footings		FORTRAN IV-F	x								x	132	x	1	
Pile Found. Analysis		FORTRAN IV-F	x										x	1	
PILGR.65.1	IBM 1130	FORTRAN	x						x	x	x	90	x	1	
PGA 76.01	B 6700	FORTRAN IV-F	x		x		x		x	x	x	90	x	1	3
P20-100		FORTRAN	x												
P20-204		FORTRAN													
BR00610	IBM 360	FORTRAN IV-F	x				x		x	x	x	90		1	
Pile Cap Analysis		FORTRAN	x						x	x					
GROUP		FORTRAN	x						x	x		90	x		

Table 4   General Pile Group Foundation Program Limitations

PROGRAM NAME OR ACRONYM	NO. OF PILES	NO. OF LOAD CONDITIONS	NO. OF GROUP LOADINGS	NO. OF IN SPACE DEFLECTION POINTS	H-BEAM	I-BEAM	CIRCULAR (SOLID)	CIRCULAR (SHELL)	RECTANGULAR	UNIFORMLY TAPERED	STEEL	CONCRETE: REINFORCED PRESTRESSED	WOOD	COMPOSITE	PILE CAP RECTANGULAR	PILE CAP ROUND	PILE CAP ARBITRARILY SHAPED	SOIL CONTINUOUS MEDIA	SOIL LAYERED	PARTIALLY EMBEDDED PILES (BENTS)	BATTERED PILES (ANY DIRECTION)	TEXAS TOWERS	ANY PILE ARRANGEMENT
Anal. and Design of Pile Footings	17	5	9		×		×	×	×		×		×	×	×			×					
Pile Found. Analysis	200	8	3		×		×	×	×		×		×	×	×			×					×
PILGR 76.1	120	10	∝		×	×	×	×	×		×	×	×	×	×	×	×	×	×	×	×		
PGA 76.01	300	40		10	×	×	×	×	×		×	×	×	×	×	×	×	×		×	×		×
P20-100					×		×	×	×		×		×		×								
P20-204					×		×	×	×		×		×		×								
BR00610					×	×	×	×	×		×	×	×	×	×	×	×	×	×	×	×		×
Pile Cap Analysis	300				×		×	×			×		×		×	×		×	×	×			
GROUP					×	×	×	×	×		×	×	×	×	×	×		×	×	×	×		×

Table 5   General Program Options and Capabilities

PROGRAM NAME OR ACRONYM	PILE END RESTRAINTS: TOP FIXED	TOP PINNED	TOP FREE	BOTTOM FIXED	BOTTOM PINNED	LOADING: VERTICAL	LATERAL (2 DIRECTIONS)	TRANSVERSE MOMENT	TORSIONAL	PILE CAP: ROTATION AND TRANSLATION	PILE CAP: DESIGN MOMENTS AND SHEARS	PILES: AXIAL FORCE	LATERAL SHEARS	TORSIONAL FORCE	BENDING MOMENT	END ROTATIONS	DISPLACEMENTS	BEARING PILES	FRICTION PILES	COMBINATION BEARING/FRICTION	DIFFERENT PILE LENGTHS	DIFFERENT SECTIONAL PROPERTIES
Anal. and Design of Pile Footings	×	×		×		×	×	×			×	×	×					×	×			
Pile Found. Analysis	×	×		×		×	×	×			×	×						×	×			
PILGR 76.1		×		×	×	×	×	×	×	×	×	×	×	×	×	×	×	×	×		×	×
PGA 76.01		×		×		×	×	×	×	×	×	×	×	×	×	×	×	×	×		×	×
P20-100	×			×		×		×				×	×					×	×			
P20-204				×	×	×		×		×		×	×		×							
BR00610						×		×		×	×	×	×		×	×	×	×	×			×
Pile Cap Analysis	×	×								×												
GROUP	×	×		×	×	×		×		×		×	×		×	×	×	×	×		×	×

Table 6 Design/Analysis Data for Pile Group Foundation Programs

PROGRAM NAME OR ACRONYM	CAPABILITIES				METHODS OF ANALYSIS										COMMENTS
	COMPUTES PILE SIZES	GENERATES PILE COORDINATES	PILE REACTIONS/LOAD EQUILIBRIUM	CAP SIZE/REINFORCEMENT DESIGN	GENERAL FLEXURE FORMULA	UNBALANCED SHEAR	3D STIFFNESS METHOD	2D PLANAR ANALYSIS	FRANCIS'S METHOD	ASHENBRENNER'S METHOD	REESE, O'NEIL, AND SMITH	HRENNIKOFF'S METHOD	SAUL'S METHOD	PECK'S METHOD	
Anal. and Des. of Pile Footings		X		X	X										
Pile Found. Anal.															
PILGR 76.1		X	X				X								Design mode is incomplete
PGA 76.01		X	X				X								
P24-100		X				X									
P20-204		X					X								
BR00610	X	X	X				X	X							Uses the elastic center method
Pile Cap Analysis															
GROUP		X	X					X							Considers a nonlinear soil or pile material

ness and response expressions developed for each pile. These expressions consider the nonlinearity of the load deformation relationships for an individual pile member, laterally supported by a varying soil resistance. Resulting pile reactions are consistent with pile-head rotation and translation.

Pile Footing Foundations

Categories: Group pile analysis; stresses; reinforcement
Title: The Analysis and Design of Pile Footings
Author: Glen H. Sikes, State Highway Department of Georgia, Bridge
        Division, No. 2 Capitol Square, Atlanta, Georgia 30334.
Maintenance: Department of Transportation, State of Georgia, Office of
        Systems Development, No. 2 Capitol Square, Atlanta, Georgia 30034.
Date: August 1971
Capability: This program will analyze or design a pile footing including
        number and arrangement of piles, footing size, and required rein-
        forcing steel. Using one of thirteen built-in pile group configura-
        tions, the program will compute critical stresses and loads for
        each pile. Standard AASHTO Group loads or user input load cases
        are available, and the program can handle overstressed piles in
        design. Built-in values for allowable stresses, cost-estimating
        factors, and other constants are available for the user.
Method: Pile reactions are computed by the flexure formula, using both
        the transverse and lateral section modulus of the pile group. Each
        pile is assumed to have an area of unity and the capability of re-
        sisting tension. Footing reinforcement is designed using average
        moments and shears across a section.
Limitations: The minimum and maximum number of piles is four and seven-
        teen respectively, and biaxial symmetry is required. In addition,
        the program considers only H-piles and will not consider batter
        piles or piles having different section moduli about their principal
        axes.
Programming Language: FORTRAN IV-F
Documentation: A user's manual is available which includes program de-
        scription, user instructions, and an example problem
Input: Transverse and longitudinal loads, allowable compressive and ten-
        sile forces, depth of pile embedment, soil unit weight, pier di-
        mensions, number of piles, and the pile spacing
Output: Pile reactions, transverse and longitudinal forces, bond and
        diagonal tension shear, footing dimensions, pile data, actual/
        allowable stresses, reinforcement requirements
Software Operations: Batch
Hardware: Unknown
Usage: This program is currently used by the State of Georgia as part of
        a design system for multiple column piers of highway bridges.
Typical Running Time: Insignificant as described by the author
Availability: Contact the author at the Georgia State Highway Department.

Group Pile Analysis (PILGR 76.1)

Categories: Foundations; bents; pile analysis; matrix methods; structural
        engineering
Title: The Analysis of Pile Group Footings

Authors: W. Verrill, T. Karasopoulos, et al., Maine Department of Trans-
    portation, Augusta, Maine 04333
Maintenance: Authors
Date: May 1976
Capability: This program will analyze both a completely embedded pile
    group and a pile bent with or without a bracing system. The pile
    group may be analyzed as strictly bearing or friction or a
    combination of the two. Piles may be battered in any direction and
    differently within the same row. Section properties for standard
    H and pipe piles are automatically assigned, or the user may input
    properties for any nonstandard pile section. In addition to com-
    puting resulting pile forces for each user input load condition,
    the program will analyze the pile footing for critical moments and
    shears in accordance with the 1974 AASHTO specifications.
Method: A three-dimensional matrix solution is employed which considers
    the soil's lateral resistance and the relative stiffness of the
    soil-pile group system. The concept of the equivalent cantilever
    or a pile's effective length below ground is employed in this dis-
    placement matrix analysis method.
Limitations: A maximum of 6 rows with 20 piles per row is possible.
    A maximum of 10 loads may be input for each solution.
Program Language: PROBLEM ORIENTED LANGUAGE (POL)
Documentation: A user's manual is available which details program
    theory and input and contains sample problems.
Input: Column data, soil properties, pile data, footing geometry,
    allowable loads, load data
Output: Pile coordinates and geometry, footing displacements, pile
    forces (bilateral shear and moment, torsion)
Software Operation: Batch or via remote terminal
Hardware: IBM 1130
Usage: The program is used on a limited basis by the Maine Department
    of Transportation for pile foundation analysis.
Typical Running Time: Unknown
Availability: Contact the authors at the Maine Department of Transporta-
    tion, Augusta, Maine 04333.

Pile Foundation Analysis

Categoreis: Group pile analysis; pile reactions; cap stresses
Title: Pile Foundation Analysis
Author: Unknown
Maintenance: Hawaii Department of Transportation, Engineering Computer
    Services Office, 869 Punchbowl Street, Honolulu, Hawaii 96813
Date: Unknown
Capability: This program analyzes random or rectangular pile group
    configurations with a rectangular cap and pier. AASHTO Group or
    user-specified load types are used.
Method: Pile reactions are computed by the flexure formula with the loads
    applied at the pier centroid. Piles are assumed to be of equal area
    and capable of resisting both tension and compression.
Limitations: The maximum number of piles permitted is 200. The program
    does not consider batter piles or piles with different sectional
    properties. Pile caps and piers must be rectangular.
Programming Language: FORTRAN IV
Documentation: Unavailable
Input: Pier centroid and pile coordinates, pile cap and pier dimensions,

allowable compressive and tensile forces in piles, load data, soil
density, and height of fill
Output: Record of input, pile axial reactions, pile cap moments and
shears, peripheral shear, and unit peripheral shearing stress
Software Operation: Batch
Hardware: Unknown
Usage: Program is currently used by the Hawaiian Department of Trans-
portation for pile foundation design problems.
Typical Running Time: Unknown
Availability: Available from the Hawaiian Department of Transportation,
Engineering Computer Services Office

Pile Group Analysis (PGA 76.01)

Categoreis: Pile group foundations; matrix structural analysis; struc-
tural engineering
Title: The Analysis of Pile Group Foundations
Author: D. R. Schelling, Department of Civil Engineering, University of
Maryland, College Park, Maryland 20742
Maintenance: Maryland State Highway Administration, Bureau of Bridge
Design, Baltimore, Maryland
Date: June 1976
Capability: This program performs the analysis of arbitrarily positioned
battered or plumb piles. The piles may be uniform or of differing
section properties and lengths, be fixed or pinned at the cap, and
be bearing or friction piles which react laterally with the sub-
grade. Loads consist of three force and three moment components
located at the origin of the coordinate system of the pile group.
These loads can automatically be grouped according to the AASHTO
Code or arbitrarily grouped by the user. The program computes all
forces and stresses induced in each pile as well as determining
deflections and checking piles for overloads as given in the code.
Lastly, a plot of the pile layout can be output as an option.
Method: The program uses the direct stiffness matrix analysis method to
compute directly the loads, stresses, and deflections for each pile
of the pile group.
Limitations: The maximum number of piles is 300; a maximum of 40 load
conditions is possible; a maximum of 10 locations for deflection
computations is possible.
Programming Language: FORTRAN IV
Documentation: A complete user's manual is available which details
program methodology and use and contains numerous example problems.
Input: Structural configurations; boundary conditions; pile lengths;
section properties; coordinates; load data; desired output level
Output: All output is in numbered tabular form. It includes an input
echo; pile axial and torsion force, shears, moments, and their
associated stresses; deflections; summary of group load effects.
Software Operation: Batch
Hardware: Burroughs 6700
Usage: The program has been used in production by Maryland State Highway
Engineers.
Availability: Contact the Maryland State Highway Administration.

Pile Group Analysis (BR00610)

Categories: Pile group foundations; pile bents; structural engineering
Title: Pile Group Analysis
Author: Unknown
Maintenance: Ontario Ministry of Transportation and Communications:
    Highway Engineering Division, 1201 Wilson Ave., West Building
    Downsview, Ontario M3M 1J8, Canada
Date: September 1977
Capability: This program performs a two-dimensional analysis of either
    a rigid or a flexible pile group. All loads are input by the
    designer and are assumed to be taken by axial pile resistance.
    Induced bending moments and lateral soil resistance are neglected.
    Pile group may be freestanding or embedded. Program has English
    and metric unit capability.
Method: The program employs the elastic center method to analyze a given
    pile configuration.
Limitations: The maximum number of pile rows is 50; piles are assumed
    to be hinged at top and bottom.
Programming Language: FORTRAN IV
Documentation: Program instructions and sample problems are available
    in a user's manual.
Input: Pile coordinates, section properties, batter, and lengths; load
    data
Output: Input echo; location of elastic center; pile group displace-
    ments; for each group loading: pile axial loads, Euler critical
    load, factor of safety; maximum and minimum pile load summary
Software Operation: Batch
Hardware: IBM 360
Usage: Program has been used on a production basis by Ontario bridge
    engineers.
Typical Running Time: Unknown
Availability: Contact the Ontario Ministry of Transportation and
    Communications.

Pile Group Analysis (P20-100)

Categories: Group pile analysis; foundations; structural engineering
Title: Analysis of Pile Group Foundations
Authors: Unknown
Maintenance: New Jersey State Department of Transportation, Bureau of
    Bridge Design, 1035 Parkway Avenue, Trenton, New Jersey 08625
Date: Unknow
Capability: This program will analyze a pile group subject to
    eccentric loads and applied moments to determine the resulting
    axial load per row of piles. Pile batter is assumed constant within
    a row, but may vary between rows. Resistance of horizontal loads
    is determined per foot of the cap structure and proportioned between
    the resistance of the batter and the horizontal shearing resistance
    of each pile.
Method: Application of the general flexure formula to the pile group
    yields the vertical load component taken by each pile row. The
    horizontal component and the total axial load in each pile row are
    then derived from this as a function of the batter angle. Com-
    putation of the horizontal resistance of the batter is done for the
    entire group on a per foot of pile cap basis and is not attributed

to individual pile members.
Limitations: All piles are assumed to have the same cross section, and
    the maximum number of rows is eight. The pile cap must be a rec-
    tangular shape. Loads and moments may only be applied longitudi-
    nally or toward the direction of the batter. (Resistance of trans-
    verse forces requires another analysis along the transverse axis.)
    Finally, no consideration is given to lateral pile-soil interaction
    or other group effects.
Programming Language: FORTRAN
Documentation: Unknown
Input: Pile spacing and batter; load data
Output: The pile group's center of gravity and moment of inertia;
    the horizontal resistance by batter per foot of footing; the
    horizontal shear per pile; the axial force per row of piling
Software Operation: Batch
Hardware: Unknown
Usage: Unknown
Typical Running Time: Unknown
Availability: Contact the New Jersey State Department of Transportation
    for further information.

Pile Cap Analysis

Categories: Group pile analysis; matrix analysis; structural engineering
Title: Matrix Analysis of Rigid Pile Cap Foundations
Author: Unknown
Maintenance: Oregon Department of Transportation, Transportation Building,
    Salem, Oregon   97310
Date: April 1976
Capability: This program will analyze a pile cap subject to bending
    and axial loads to determine pile cap displacements and the re-
    sulting axial forces developed in each pile. Additional cap
    stiffness coefficients may be input to account for pile stiffness
    effects, lateral soil resistance, and other bending considerations
    as determined by the user.
Method: The program uses input pile geometry and properties to develop
    a stiffness matrix for the pile cap. Additional stiffness co-
    efficients as input by the user are added to the matrix, and the
    resulting equations yield cap displacements for each load case.
    These deflections are then used to determine the axial load in each
    pile. Analysis assumes a rigid pile cap and piles pinned top and
    bottom.
Limitations: The maximum number of piles is 300. Only linear proper-
    ties may be specified, and no account is made for pile bending
    or footing distortions. The program assumes pile properties to be
    uniform but allows cross-sectional areas to vary.
Programming Language: Unknown
Documentation: Documentation is limited, and is available from the
    Oregon Department of Transportation.
Input: Pile elastic modulus and cap loads; pile coordinates and cross-
    sectional area; additional stiffness coefficients
Output: Record of input, footing stiffness matrix, load and displacement
    vectors, pile axial forces
Software Operation: Batch
Hardware: Unknown

Usage: Unknown
Typical Running Time: Unknown
Availability: Program is available from the Oregon Department of Trans-
    portion.

Pile Group Analysis

Categories: Pile group foundations; nonlinear systems; stresses; de-
    flections, structural engineering
Title: Analysis of Foundation with Widely Spaced Batter Piles
Authors: L. C. Reese and K. Awoshika, Center for Highway Research, The
    University of Texas at Austin, Austin, Texas 78701
Maintenance: Texas State Department of Highways and Public Transportation,
    Austin, Texas 78701
Date: February 1971
Capability: This program performs a two-dimensional analysis of a pile
    bent or group pile foundation having piles with variable section pro-
    perties along their axis, different degrees of batter, and differ-
    ent lengths. Program capabilities allow for the specification of
    a nonlinear pile-soil interaction system as well as nonlinear pile
    material.
Method: A finite difference numerical procedure is used which seeks
    equilibrium between the applied loads and the pile reactions in
    a matrix interative procedure.
Limitation: Unknown
Language: FORTRAN
Documentation: An extensive research report detailing program theory,
    development, etc., is available.
Input: Footing geometry, pile and soil properties, load data
Output: Input data, load settlement curves, soil data, displacements
    and reactions of pile members
Software Operation: Batch
Hardware: Unknown
Usage: Unknown
Typical Running Time: Unknown
Availability: Contact the Texas State Department of Highways and Public
    Transportation for information on program status and availability.

REFERENCE

    1 "Development of an Integrated Bridge Design System," NCHRP
Project Statement No. HR 12-18, Transportation Research Board, National
Research Council, Washington, D.C., 1976.

General Purpose Nonlinear Finite Element Programs

T. Y. Chang

J. Padavon

University of Akron

INTRODUCTION

Significant and far-reaching advancements have been made in the past decade in the development and application of nonlinear continuum mechanics theory to the deformation of complex structures via finite element procedures. This has primarily been an outgrowth of two major factors: a better understanding of physical principles and the extensive advances made in both computational mechanics and computer technology.

In recent years, the role of the linear elastic finite element method has expanded from its occasional usage for "postdesign" analyses to a routine design tool. Furthermore, with the increased attention given to the design of structures which must survive extreme loads and environments, the finite element procedure is confronted with a much greater challenge, namely the nonlinear analysis.

The early stage of the development of nonlinear finite element methodology was highly influenced by the technical needs of the aerospace industry wherein nonlinearity is primarily due to large displacements and the stability behavior of thin-walled structures, such as plates and shells [1-4]. In most cases, the material behavior was considered as either linearly elastic or inelastic with small strains. More recently, the stringent safety requirements in the nuclear industry have called for nonlinear analyses of structural components under abnormal loading or elevated temperature conditions. Much research effort has been devoted to the development of inelastic analysis methodology and constitutive relations of high temperature materials undergoing creep, plastic deformations, and fatigue [6-17]. Although nonlinear, most of the work is still limited to small or moderate strain levels. At the current time, much attention has been devoted to the modeling of very large strain plastic deformations typical of the metalworking industries [17]. Other applications of nonlinear finite element analysis include interface problems [18-20], solid-fluid interactions [21],

large deformations of offshore structures [22], tire mechanics problems
[23, 24], and others.
     This survey is basically an overview of the analysis capabilities
of the currently available general purpose nonlinear finite element codes.
Although numerous nonlinear codes have been developed during the past,
only eleven programs are included here based on the information obtained from our survey. Moreover, a discussion is given on the sources
of nonlinearity which may arise in structural problems and on the solution procedures currently employed for static and dynamic analysis. This
will set the stage for summarizing various analysis features of the
general purpose codes that are surveyed in this chapter.

NONLINEAR ANALYSIS FEATURES

Nonlinearities for structural mechanics problems may have a wide range
of meaning, and correspondingly, the nonlinear features that are included
in various finite element codes can be quite different. In spite of the
diverse opinions that may exist, structural nonlinearities can arise
from the following categories, namely:

     1. Geometric nonlinearity
     2. Nonlinear materials
     3. Other sources

     A brief discussion of these sources and the solution procedures for
handling nonlinear problems is given in this section. Additionally, some
comments are made concerning the choice of kinematics and kinetics in
relation to constitutive theories.

Geometric Nonlinearity

This may imply either large displacements, large strains, or both; and
it is probably the most common cause of structural nonlinearity. In
dealing with such nonlinearity, a choice of the reference frame
(Lagrangian or Eulerian) and the corresponding strain (kinematics) and
stress (kinetics) measures must be made in order to describe the deformation process of a structure. Currently, the kinematic and kinetic
aspects of structural modeling employ the following types of measures:

     1. Kinematics [25]
         a. Green's Strain
         b. Almansi Strain
         c. Rate of Deformation
     2. Kinetics [25]
         a. 1st and 2D Piola-Kirchhoff Stress
         b. Cauchy Stress
         c. Stress Rate

Generally for small strain/large rotation problems involving hyper-
elastic materials, the Green and 2nd Piola-Kirchhoff tensors are used
to model the geometric nonlinearities of structural behavior [2, 5, 9].
These measures are usually employed with the total Lagrangian type finite

element mesh wherein all calculations are referred to in the initial
configuration.

An alternative approach to handling geometric nonlinearity is the
so-called updated Lagrangian [15] procedure wherein the finite element
mesh is Lagrangian while the kinematic and kinetic measures are essentially Eulerian [11, 15]. Here, two stages of calculations are employed.
In particular, while the overall fields for a given state of loading
are defined in terms of Cauchy and Almansi measures, the incremental
state is generally obtained through the use of the 2nd Piola-Kirchhoff
and Almansi tensors [11, 15].

The foregoing approaches can be applied to small strain large rotation problems with essentially complete confidence. However for moderate
and large strain situations, some care must be given to choosing the
appropriate kinematic-kinetic measures [8-11, 17]. Recent work in large
strain plasticity [8-10, 17] revealed that the rate of deformation and
the frame indifferent stress rate, e.g., Jaumann rate, are the proper
measures to use.

Nonlinear Materials

Clearly the subject of nonlinear material characterization is so large
that it is impractical even to list all the available material models
that have been proposed by researchers. Typical models that are of
current interest may include

    1. Von Mises plasticity with isotropic or kinematic hardening
[26, 27]
    2. Drucker-Prager plasticity model for soils or rocks [28]
    3. Concrete plasticity models with cracking simulation [29]
    4. Nonlinear creep law [13, 30-32]
    5. Viscoplastic model [31, 32]
    6. Endochronicle theory [33]

With the limitation of small strains and proper programming practice, it is now possible to insert any new material model into most
general purpose nonlinear programs without coding difficulty. However,
for large strain situations caution must be taken to employ the correct
kinematic and kinetic measures as pointed out previously.

Other Sources

While geometric considerations and constitutive characterizations are
the main form of nonlinearity, there are many other sources of nonlinearity. These may include

    1. Nonlinear boundary conditions
        a. Contact of two or more bodies under static or dynamic
            situation [18-20]
        b. Interface problems with sliding and friction [18-20]
        c. Nonconservative pressure or force system [34]
    2. Ductile fracture analysis including crack initiation and
stable crack growth [35-37]

3. Coupled problems
    a. Thermal-mechanical coupling [38,39]
    b. Fluid-solid interactions [21]
    c. Combustion - mechanical

   A nonlinear finite element code may include one or more than one of
the aforementioned analysis features; and the user must be able to identify
the right capability in a code that is being sought.

NONLINEAR SOLUTION PROCEDURE

   In addition to the nonlinear analysis features discussed in the previous
section, solution procedure is another important factor that will dic-
tate the solution dependability and capability of a code. A brief discussion of the various methods that have been used is given in this
section.
   While convergence and solution uniqueness can generally be guaran-
teed for linear simulations, such is not the case for nonlinear situations. In particular, nonlinear problems are generally subject to the
following types of solution difficulties, namely:

1. Potential nonuniqueness due to improved mesh choice
2. Potential solution bifurcations
3. No guarantee on convergence
4. High cost (in comparison to linear analysis)

This applies to both static and dynamic cases; a brief discussion
follows.

Static Solution Procedures

There are many alternatives for the numerical solution of the static non-
linear-discretized modeling equations which arise from finite element
simulations. Such a wide variety inevitably leads to the question of the
"best choice." Unfortunately, from the standpoint of computational effort
and numerical accuracy, the applicability of one method may vary considerably relative to the others, depending on the type of nonlinear problems
to be solved. Hence, for general purpose codes the choice then involves
implementing procedures that have the widest range of applicability. For
this purpose, the load incrementation [15, 16] approach in conjunction
with the Newton-Raphson method [16] is the most widely adopted procedure.
The major differences in the implementation of this approach are whether
a modified or a fully updated Newton-Raphson procedure should be used to
generate the incremental solution. Generally the optimum approach is to
employ the Newton approach together with occasional updates of the
structural stiffness.

Dynamic Solution Procedures

The solution of dynamic problems generally involves the use of numerical
integration schemes, namely, implicit and explicit approaches [40, 41].

Neither is completely effective over the entire range of possible structural response. For instance, from a pseudo-linear point of view, for a
structural dynamic problem whose response is controlled by a small number
of the lower "spectral branches," the implicit approach has been found
to be most effective [41]. In shock/wave propagation problems where the
response involves a profusion of spectral branches but where the lower
branches are somewhat subordinate, the explicit approach has been found
to be best [41]. In light of this, both options should be available.
Since neither approach is completely satisfactory, future work in this
area should concentrate on determining criteria which provide crossover
points between the explicit and implicit method.

PROGRAM SURVEY AND DESCRIPTION

A total of eleven general purpose finite element codes with nonlinear
analysis capabilities have been surveyed. As mentioned earlier, the
actual number of such codes may far exceed those included here. Our
report is merely based on the information gathered from our survey.
    The analysis capabilities of the surveyed programs are summarized
with respect to the following items:

1.	Element Library	(Table 1)
2.	Materials Models	(Table 2)
3.	Procedure Library	(Table 3)
4.	Geometric Nonlinearity	(Table 4)
5.	Loading Types	(Table 4)
6.	User's Features	(Table 5)
7.	Other Software Options	(Table 5)
8.	Operating Systems	(Table 5)

    In addition, a brief description of each program is given in this
section.

ADINA

Category: Nonlinear analysis of structures under static and dynamic
          loads
Author: K. J. Bathe
          Department of Mechanical Engineering
          MIT
          Cambridge, Massachusetts 02139
Date: 1975: revised 1977
Capability: The program is intended for linear and nonlinear, static
          and dynamic analyses of structures. Nonlinearities may be due to
          large displacements and nonlinear material behavior. It contains
          four different types of elements: 3D truss, 3D beam, 2D and 3D
          isoparametric solid elements. Nonlinear material models include
          von Mises plasticity, thermal-elastic-plastic creep, nonlinear
          elastic (Mooney-Rivlin model under plane stress), concrete plastic-
          ity, Drucker-Prager plasticity, and curve description. Heat trans-
          fer analysis is performed by an associated code, ADINAT.

Method: Nonlinear response is calculated by an incremental procedure
together with equilibrium iterations, which corresponds to a modified Newton method. For dynamic analysis, either implicit time
integration (Newmark or Wilson method) or explicit time integration
(central difference method) can be used. The program has an out-
of-core solver of equilibrium equation, and hence large size problems can be handled. The entire structural stiffness matrix is
processed in blocks, and only those elements under the skyline of
the stiffness matrix are stored to provide maximum system capacity
and solution efficiency.
Limitations: Available element types are limited; only for small strains;
material models are element-dependent.
Programming Language: FORTRAN IV
Documentation: Theoretical report [42] and user's manual [43]; user
manual for heat transfer analysis [44]
Operating System: CDC; IBM and UNIVAC (double precision required)
Availability: Program can be used on CDC CYBERNET system; source program
is available from the developer for a fee (negotiable)

ANSYS

Category: General purpose finite element program for linear and nonlinear analyses.
Author: Swanson Analysis Systems, Inc.
        870 Pine View Drive
        Elizabeth, Pa. 15037
Date: 1970: Continuously updated
Capability: Linear and nonlinear, static and dynamic structural analyses,
heat-transfer analyses (steady-state and transient, conduction,
convection, and radiation). Additional analysis features, although
not as extensive as the structural and heat transfer capabilities,
include thermal-fluid flow, coupled thermal-electric, and wave-
motion problems. Nonlinearities considered in the program are due
to large deflections, nonlinear materials, and the effects of interface friction or gap. The program has a wide variety of elements in its library: more than forty element types for structural
analysis and thirteen for heat transfer analysis. The structural
elements include spars, pipes and elbows, beams, 2D and 3D
solids, plane and axisymmetric membranes, plates and shells,
springs and dampers, gap elements, etc. The heat transfer elements
are conducting bars, plates and solids, and convection and radiation links. Nonlinear material models include nonlinear elastic,
von Mises plasticity, high-temperature creep, and creep and
swelling due to irradiation. Loading inputs for both structural
and heat transfer analyses are quite general. Extensive pre- and
postprocessing capabilities such as mesh generation, a graphics
package, data check, and error detection are available.
Method: Static analysis is based on the incremental displacement method.
Dynamic analysis uses implicit numerical integration. Eigenvalue
solution is obtained by the Jacobi eigenvalue extraction method.
The wave-front method is employed to solve the system of
simultaneous linear equations.

Limitations: Only for small-strain nonlinear analyses
Program Language: FORTRAN IV
Documentation: Extensive user's manual [45] and other reports are
    available from the developer.
Operating Systems: CDC, IBM, UNIVAC, Honeywell 6000 Computers, also
    Modcomp and Prime minicomputers
Availability: Program can be used on CDC CYBERNET System; source program
    is available from the developer for a charge.

ASAS

Category: General purpose finite element program
Author: Atkins Research and Development
    Ashley Road
    Epsom, Surrey
    United Kingdom
Date: Nonlinear version will be available in October 1979.
Capability: Initially static nonlinear analyses with creep and plastic-
    ity; utimately dynamic and transient nonlinear analyses will be
    available. Its element library has trusses, beams, 2D and 3D
    solids, thin and thick shells. Material models include nonlinear
    elastic, linear viscoelastic, von Mises plasticity, and high-temp-
    erature creep.
Method: The program is based on the displacement method with Lagrangian
    or updated Lagrangian formulation (depending on the element type).
    Nonlinear static analysis is carried out by both tangent stiffness
    and initial load approaches. Dynamic response is obtained by
    direct integration with the Newmark β-method.
Limitations: Unknown
Program Language: FORTRAN IV
Documentations: User's Manual [46]
Operating Systems: IBM, UNIVAC,and RXDJ Sigma-9
Availability: Available from the developer for a fee

ASKA

Name: Automatic System for Kinematic Analysis
Category: General purpose finite element programs
Author: J. H. Argyris with the ASKA group
    Institut für Statik und Dynamik
    University of Stuttgart
    Stuttgart, Germany
Date: 1972, revised in 1973
Capability: ASKA itself is basically a linear analysis (both static and
    dynamic) program. Quasi-static nonlinear analysis is performed by
    ASKA III-1, which has material nonlinearities under small deforma-
    tions. Material models include von Mises plasticity, Drucker-
    Prager plasticity, parabolic Mohr-Coulomb law, and nonlinear creep.
    Linear buckling analysis is performed by another supporting
    program called ASKA III-2.
Method: ASKA III-1: Right-hand side iteration (initial stress approach,
    appropriately adopted to handle also perfectly plactic material).

ASKA III-2: (a) is performed using simultaneous vector iteration
(b) is performed by the buckling mode superposition technique using
the modes and load scale factors, obtained in (a).
Limitations: Unknown
Program Language: FORTRAN IV
Documentation: Description of ASKA [47]; User's reference manuals [48,49]
Operating Systems: CDC, IBM, UNIVAC, and Honeywell
Availability: Program is available from the developer and the cost varies
depending on the extent of usage.

                                  EPACA

Category: Elastic-plastic-creep finite element analysis program.
Author: Z. Zudan, et al.
        Franklin Institute Research Laboratories
        The Franklin Institute
        Philadelphia, Pa. 19103

        Program is maintained by:
        Oak Ridge National Laboratory
        Oak Ridge, Tennessee 37830
Date: 1972
Capability: Static elastic-plastic-creep, free vibration, dynamic time-
        history, and buckling analyses. The program was written primarily
        for nonlinear analyses of plates and shells. Its element library
        contains bars, shells of revolution, plates, and higher-order
        curved shell elements. Material models include von Mises plastic-
        ity and high-temperature creep with large strains.
Method: Incremental loading with tangent stiffness method; implicit
        integration for dynamic analysis
Limitations: The program has a limited element library and material
        models.
Program Language: FORTRAN IV
Documentation: Theory and user's manual [50, 51]
Operating Systems: IBM, UNIVAC,and DEC-20
Availability: A nonproprietory code, available from the Oak Ridge
        National Laboratory

                                  MARC

Category: A general purpose nonlinear finite element program
Author: MARC Analysis Research Corporation
        260 Sheridan Avenue
        Palo Alto, California 94036
Date: 1970
Capability: MARC is one of the earliest and most complete general pur-
        pose finite element computer programs for conducting nonlinear
        structural and heat transfer analyses. The current version of
        MARC is Revision H, completed in the early part of 1978. The
        program is capable of conducting a wide range of nonlinear analyses,

including large displacements of beams, plates,and shells, nonlinear material behavior, large-strain plasticity, buckling of
thin-walled structures, contact of solids, pipe-whip, and fracture
mechanics calculations.
  The main program of MARC (for stress analysis) has more than
35 element types, ranging from trusses, beams, and isoparametric
solids to more sophisticated plates, shells, and pipe bend elements.
Nonlinear material models include von Mises plasticity, nonlinear
creep law, concrete plasticity with cracking, Drucker-Prager
plasticity, Mooney-Rivlin material, and others. It has extensive
user-oriented features such as mesh generation, and pre- and post-
plotting of finite element grids, stress, or strain contours.
Method: Nonlinear solution is carried out by use of incremental loading
    steps with the tangent modulus approach. Finite strain elasticity
    problems are solved on the basis of Lagrangian formulation in con-
    junction with a hybrid variational principle,whereas large strain
    plasticity is based on an updated Lagrangian. Dynamic analysis is
    performed using the Newmark β-method or Houbolt operator (implicit)
    integration or the central difference (explicit) integration.
Limitations: Unknown
Programming Language: FORTRAN IV
Documentation: MARC user's manuals [52, 53]
Operating Systems: CDC, IBM, UNIVAC, and Prime
Availability: Program can be used on the CDC CYBERNET system or it is
    available from the developer; source program is also available for
    sale from the developer.

NASTRAN (Level 16.0)

Category: General purpose finite element program
Author: National Aeronautics and Space Administration
Date: March 1978
Capability: NASTRAN is one of the earliest general purpose codes for
    conducting structural, fluid-structural, and heat transfer analyses.
    Although the code was primarily written for linear problems, its
    current version now has several nonlinear features. In particular,
    a small strain/moderate rotation option has been added. This op-
    tion is directly available for static problems but must be added
    to the transient rigid format. The constitutive models available
    include von Mises plasticity, as well as a piecewise linear option
    for plastic materials. The conductive heat transfer analysis
    features are extensive as temperature-dependent properties, and
    radiation boundary conditions can be handled. The code is also
    capable of conducting analyses of buckling of thin-walled struc-
    tures, axisymmetric compressible fluid-solid interaction, flutter,
    etc. The extensive user features available include mesh genera-
    tion (cyclic symmetry option, automatic substructuring, etc.), as
    well as   pre- and postgraphics options.
Method: The static nonlinear solution is developed through the use of
    an incremental differential stiffness approach employing a total
    Lagrangian kinematic-kinetic formulation. Dynamic response is ob-
    tained by direct integration via the Newmark β-method. Eigenvalue

extraction is obtained by either the Givens, determinant search,
inverse power, or upper Hessianburg procedures.
Limitations: Kinematic-kinetic representation is limited to small strain/
moderate rotations.
Programming Language: FORTRAN IV
Documentation: Extensive program documents are available. This includes
user, programmer, and theory as well as example problem manuals.
Operating System: CDC, IBM, UNIVAC
Availability: CDC CYBERNET system; source available from COSMIC at the
University of Georgia, or MacNeal-Schwendler

NEPSAP

Category: Nonlinear elastic-plastic structural analysis program
Author: P. Shariki and S. Nagarajan
       Lockheed Missiles & Space Company
       P.O. Box 504
       Sunnyvale, California 94088
Date: 1974
Capability: The program is capable of performing large displacement
elastic-plastic-creep analysis, dynamic modal analysis with initial
stresses, and nonlinear transient dynamic analysis. Its element library contains beam, 2D and 3D isoparametric solids, 3D membrane,
plate, thin and thick shells, and 3D pipes. Material models include von Mises plasticity and high-temperature creep. Incompressible elastic materials and composite material models are also
available.
Method: The program is based on the Lagrangian formulation for large
deformations. The incremental solution approach with either constant stiffness or modified Newton-Raphson method is employed.
Transient dynamic analysis is performed using an implicit integration scheme, in which either Newmark β, Houbolt, or Park method
can be used. The code allows for variable time step size.
Limitations: Limited nonlinear material models with small strains only
Programming Language: FORTRAN IV
Documentation: User's manual [54] and theory [55, 56] are available.
Operating Systems: CDC, IBM, and UNIVAC.
Availability: Program can be purchased from the developer.

LARSTRAN

Cateogry: A general purpose nonlinear finite element program for large-
strain analysis
Author: J. H. Argyris, et al.
       Institut für Statik und Dynamik
       University of Stuttgart
       Stuttgart, Germany
Date: March 1978
Capability: The program, which appears to be an extended version of ASKA,
can perform nonlinear elastic or large-strain inelastic static
analyses and nonlinear elastic dynamic analysis. It has truss,

beam, 2D and 3D solid elements, plates, and shells. Nonlinear
material models include nonlinear elasticity, von Mises plasticity,
and viscoplasticity.
Method: Nonlinear elastic static analysis is based on total Lagrangian
formulation,whereas nonlinear large-strain inelastic analysis is
based on updated Lagrangian formulation. Both analyses are carried
out by an incremental approach with Newton-Raphson or modified Newton-Raphson iterations. Nonlinear elastic dynamic analysis is performed by use of the third-order Hermitian or Newmark method for
direct integrations.
Limitations: For 64K computer central memory, problem size is limited
to static analysis with up to 800 degrees of freedom and dynamic
analysis with up to 2500 degrees of freedom. Mixed element types
are not acceptable.
Programming Language: FORTRAN IV
Documentation: User's manual [57]; theory [58, 59]
Availability: Source program is available for purchase (subject to
negotiation). Binary codes are normally free of charge for edu-
cational or nonprofit organizations.

NONSAP

Category: A nonlinear structural analysis program
Author: K. J. Bathe, E. L. Wilson,and R. H. Iding
Department of Civil Engineering
University of California
Berkeley, California   97420
Date: 1974
Capability: The program can perform linear and nonlinear, static, and
dynamic analyses of structures. It has 3D truss, and 2D and 3D
isoparametric solid elements in its library. Nonlinear material
models include von Mises plasticity with linear isotropic hard-
ening, Drucker-Prager plasticity, variable tangent moduli, curve-
description nonlinear material, and the Mooney-Rivlin law for plane
stress. Most of the nonlinear material models are available only
for 2D elements.
Method: Same as ADINA
Limitations: Element library and material models are limited. Other
limitations can be found in Ref. [60].
Programming Language: FORTRAN IV
Documentation: User's manual [61]
Operating Systems: CDC
Availability: The program is nonproprietory and available from:
NISEE/Computer Applications
Davis Hall
University of California
Berkeley, California 94720
Cost: $300

In addition, two extended versions of NONSAP, namely NFAP [62] and
AGGIE I [63], are also nonproprietary. They are available from:

T. Y. Chang - NFAP
Department of Civil Engineering
The University of Akron
Akron, Ohio 44325

W. E. Haisler - AGGIE I
Aerospace Engineering Department
Texas A & M University
College Station, Texas 77843

PAFEC 75

Category: A general purpose program for automatic finite element calcu-
    lations
Author: PAFEC Ltd.
    PAFEC House
    40, Broadgate
    Beeston
    Nottingham, England
Date: 1975
Capability: It is primarily a linear analysis program with some nonlin-
    ear capabilities including creep, plasticity, buckling, and large-
    displacement analyses. The program has an extensive element li-
    brary including truss, beam, 2D and 3D solids, plate, shell,
    semi-Loof shell, spring, temperature, and fracture mechanics elements.
    Only two nonlinear material models, namely von Mises plasticity and
    high-temperature creep, are available. The code has an elaborate
    interactive graphics capability and many user's features which are
    attractive to the structural analyst.
Method: Nonlinear analysis is conducted by incremental loading with the
    initial strain/initial stress method. The program employs a wave-
    frontal method for solving large systems of linear equations. Tran-
    sient dynamic analysis is performed by the Newmark β-method of
    direct integration.
Limitations: Nonlinear capability is rather limited.
Programming Language: FORTRAN IV
Documentation: Fairly complete program documents are available; theory
    [64], data preparation [65], and user guide [66].
Operating Systems: CDC, IBM, UNIVAC, Burroughs, DEC 10, Prime 400
Availability: Source program is available from the developer at cost:
    Fortran subroutines - $12,000
    Annual maintenance fee - $3,000 plus travel
    A discount of 75% is available for academic institutions.

GUIDELINES FOR CODE SELECTION

Numerous nonlinear finite element codes are in existence, and they
can be obtained either free (nonproprietary) or by purchasing them from
the developers. The analysis capability of one code may vary considerably from that of the others, and often it is difficult to identify the
right software to meet a specific need. If a code is to be used as a
long-term in-house capability, several important factors must be taken

into consideration:

1. Analysis capabilities and range of application — In addition to
the analysis capabilities outlined by the developers, it is imperative for
the user to realize the limitations or the range of application of a code.
Such limitations may be inherited from the mathematical principles and
numerical procedures adopted by the code.
2. Transportability — Although most of the finite element codes
are written in FORTRAN language, a software developed on one computer
system may not be entirely compatible with another system due to differences in factors such as the precision of the machine (e.g., CDC vs. IBM),
I/O facilities, etc. Additional manpower and coding effort may be necessary to implement a program on the user's system.
3. Maintainability — If a nonlinear code is not maintained, it will
become outdated rapidly due to the advances in computational methods,
programming technology, and computer hardware. Before its acquisition,
one must determine whether the code will be maintained by the developer
or by the user's organization. Maintenance of a code by personnel other
than the developer is expensive as well as time-consuming, and the organization must provide full commitment for such an undertaking.
4. Availability of user-oriented features — For nonlinear analysis
it is very desirable to have user's features such as mesh generation,
plot of input geometry, and error checks, in order to minimize input mis-
takes. After an analysis is completed, postprocessing graphics are extremely useful for handling large volumes of results.

Once a code is acquired and implemented onto the user's computer system,
verification and qualification [67] by benchmark problem runs are necessary in order to establish a functional status for the code.

ACKNOWLEDGMENT

The authors wish to express their sincere thanks to the program developers
for providing useful information and answering the survey letters.

REFERENCES

1 Proc. 1st and 2nd Conf. Matrix Methods in Struct. Mech., Wright-
Patterson Air Force Base, Ohio AFFDL-TR-68-150, 1967-1978.
2 Martin, H. C., "On the Derivation of Stiffness Matrices for the
Analysis of Large Deflection and Stability Problem," Proc. 1st Conf. on
Matrix Methods in Structural Mechanics., AAFDL-TR-66-80, 1966.
3 Martin, H. C., "Finite Elements and the Analysis of Geometrical-
ly Nonlinear Problems," Recent Advances in Matrix Meth. in Struct. Mech.,
and Design, ed. R. H. Gallagher et al., Univ. of Alabama Press, 1971.
4 Gallagner, R. H., "Finite Element Analysis of Geometrically Non-
Linear Problems," Theory and Practice in Finite Element Str. Anal.
Univ. Tokyo Press, 1973.
5 Hibbitt, H. D., Marcal, P. V., and Rice, J. R., "A Finite Element
Formulation for Problems of Large Strain and Large Displacement," Intern.
J. of Solids and Structures, Vol. 6, 1970, pp. 1069-86.

6   Hofmeister, L. D., Greenbaum, G. A., and Evansen, D. A., "Large Strain Elasto-Plastic Finite Element Analysis," AIAA Journal, Vol. 9, 1971, pp. 1248.

7   Yanada, Y., Takatsuka, K. and Iwata, K., "Nonlinear Analysis by Finite Element Method and Some Expository Examples, " Theory and Practice in Finite Element Struc. Anal., Univ. Tokyo Press, 1973, pp.125.

8   Osias, J. R. and Swedlow, J. L., "Finite Elasto-Plastic Deformation - I: Theory and Numerical Examples," Int. J. Solids and Structures, Vol. 10, 1974, pp. 321-39.

9   McMeeking, R. M. and Rice, J. R., "Finite Element Formulation for Problems of Large Elastic-Plastic Reformation," Int. J. Solids and Structures, Vol. 11, 1974, pp. 601-9.

10   Nemat-Nasser, S., "Continuum Bases for Consistent Numerical Formulations of Finite Strains in Elastic and Inelastic Structures," Finite Element Analysis of Transient Nonlinear Structural Behavior, ed. T. Belytschko et al., ASME, Vol. AMD-14, 1975, p. 85.

11   Belytschko, T., "Nonlinear Analysis - Descriptions and Numerical Stability," Computer Programs in Shock and Vibration, ed. W. Pilkey and B. Pilkey, Shock and Vibration Information Center, Washington, D.C., 1975, pp. 537.

12   Oden, T. J., Finite Elements of Nonlinear Continua, McGraw-Hill, New York, 1972.

13   Cyr, N. A., and Teter, R. D., "Finite Element Elastic Plastic Creep Analysis of Two Dimensional Continuum with Temperature Dependent Material Properties," Comp. Struct., Vol. 3, 1973, pp. 849-63.

14   Bathe, K. J., Ramm, E., and Wilson, E. L., "Finite Element Formulation for Large Deformation Dynamic Analysis," Int. J. Num. Meth. Engrg. Vol. 9, 1975, pp. 353-86.

15   Zienkiewicz, O. C., and Cormean, I. C., "Visco-plasticity, Plasticity and Creep in Elastic Solids - a Unified Numerical Solution Approach," Int. J. Num. Meth. Engr., Vol. 8, 1974, pp. 821-45.

16   Zienkiewicz, O.C., The Finite Element Method, McGraw-Hill, London, 1977.

17   Lee, E. H., Mallett, R. L., and Yang, W. H., "Stress and Deformation Analysis of the Metal Extrusion Process," Computer Meth. Appl. Mech. and Engrg., Vol. 10, 1977, pg. 339.

18   Chan, S. K., and Tuba, I. S., "A Finite Element Method for Contact Problems of Solid Bodies," Int. J. Mech. Sci., Vol. 13, 1971, pp. 615-39.

19   Hughes, T. J. R., Taylor, R. L., Sackman, J. L., Curnier, A., and Kamoknukulchai, W., "Finite Element Method for a Class of Contact-Impact Problems," Comp. Meth. Appl. Mech. Engrg, Vol. 8, 1976 pp. 249-76.

20   Fredrickson, B., "Finite Element Solution of Surface Nonlinearities in Structural Mechanics with Special Emphasis to Contact and Fracture Mechanic Problems," Computers and Structures, Vol. 6, 1976, pp. 281-90.

21   Belytschko, T., and Geers, T. L., eds., Computational Methods for Fluid-Structure Interaction Problems, ASME AMD-Vol. 20, 1977.

22   Proc. of 8th Annual Offshore Technology Conference, Vols. 1, 2, and 3, May 3-6, 1976, Houston, Texas.

23   Patel, H. P., Turner, J. L. and Walter, J. D., "Radial Tire Cord Rubber Composites," Rubber Chemistry and Technology, Vol. 44, 1976, pg. 1095.

24 Padovan, J., "Finite Element Modeling of Rolling Tires," <u>Proc. of the Symposium on Applications of Computer Methods in Engrg</u>. Vol. 2, 1977, pg. 1115.
25 Malvern, L. E., <u>Introduction to the Mechanics of a Continuous Medium</u>, Prentice-Hall, Englewood Cliffs, N.J., 1969.
26 Fung, Y. C., <u>Foundations of Solids Mechanics,</u> Prentice-Hall, Englewood Cliffs, N.J., 1965.
27 Yamada, Y., Yishimura, N., and Sakurai, T., "Plastic Stress-Strain Matrix and its Application for the Solution of Elastic-Plastic Problems by the Finite Element Method," <u>Int. J. Mech. Sci.</u>,Vol. 10, 1968 pp. 343.
28 Zienkiewicz, O. C., Humpheson, C., and Lewis, R. W., "Associated and Nonassociated Visco-plasticity and Plasticity in Soil Mechanics," <u>Geotechnique</u>, Vol. 25, 1975, pg. 671.
29 McGeorge, R., and Swec, L. F., "Refined Cracked Concrete Analysis of Concrete Containment Structures Subject to Loadings," <u>Nuclear Engrg. Des.</u>, Vol. 29,1974, pp. 58-70.
30 Finnie, I., and Heller, W. R., <u>Creep of Engineering Materials</u>, McGraw-Hill, New York, 1959.
31 Zienkiewicz, O. C.,and Cormean, I. C., "Visco-plasticity, Plasticity and Creep in Elastic Solids - A Unified Numerical Solution Approach," <u>Int. J. Num. Method Engrg.</u>, Vol. 8,1974, pp. 821-45.
32 Hughes, T. J. R., and Taylor, R. L., "Unconditionally Stable Algorithms for Quasi Static Elasto/visco-plastic Finite Element Analysis," <u>Computers & Structures</u>, Vol. 8, 1978, pg. 169.
33 Valanis, K. C., "A Theory of Visoplasticity Without a Yield Surface, Part I, General Theory, Part II, Application to Mechanical Behavior of Metals," <u>Archive of Mechanics</u>, Vol. 23, 1971, p. 517.
34 Nemat-Nasser, S., <u>On Elastic Stability Under Nonconservative Loads,</u> Solid Mechanics Division, University of Waterloo, Waterloo, Ontario May 1972.
35 Paris, P. C.,et al., "The Theory of Instability of the Tearing Mode of Elastic-Plastic Crack Growth," NUREG-0311, Nuclear Regulatory Commission, Washington, D.C., 1977.
36 "EPRI Ductile Fracture Research Review Document," Special Report EPRI NP-701-SR, Electric Power Research Institute, Palo Alto, Cal.,1978.
37 Rice, J.R., "Elastic-Plastic Fracture Mechanics", <u>The Mechanics of Fracture</u>, AMD - ASME, Vol. 19, 1976.
38 Oden, J. T., <u>Finite Elements of Nonlinear Continua</u>, McGraw-Hill, New York, 1972.
39 Nickell, R. E., and Sackmann, S. "Approximate Solutions in Linear Coupled Thermoelasticity," <u>J. Appl. Mech.</u>, Vol. 35, 1968, pp. 255-66.
40 Hughes, T. J. R., and Liu, W. K., "Implicit-Explicit Finite Elements in Transient Analysis," <u>J. Appl. Mech.</u>, Vol. 45, 1978, pp. 371-74.
41 Felippa, C. A.,and Park, K. C., "Direct Time Integration Methods in Nonlinear Structural Dynamics," presented at FENOMECH, University of Stuttgart,1978.
42 Bathe, K. J., "ADINA - A Finite Element Program for Automatic Dynamic Incremental Nonlinear Analysis," Report 82448-1, Acoustics and Vibration Lab., Mechanical Engineering Department, M.I.T., September 1975, (revised May 1977).
43 Bathe, K. J., "Static and Dynamic Geometric and Material Nonlinear Analysis Using ADINA," Report 82448-2, Acoustics and Vibration Lab.,

Mechanical Engineering, M.I.T., May 1976, (**revised** May 1977)..

44 Bathe, K. J., "ADINAT - A Finite Element Program for Automatic Dynamic Incremental Nonlinear Analysis of Temperatures," Report 82448-5 Acoustics and Vibration Lab., Mechanical Engineering Department, M.I.T., May 1977.

45 Swanson, J. A., "ANSYS - Engineering Analysis System User's Manual," Swanson Analysis Systems, Inc., Elizabeth, Pa.

46 "ASAS - User's Manual," Atkins Research and Development, Epsom, Surrey, England.

47 Schrem, E., "A Short Description of ASKA," ASKA UM 215, University of Stuttgart, Germany, 1975.

48 "ASKA Part III - 1 - Material Nonlinearities, User's Reference Manual," ASKA UM 207, University of Stuttgart, Stuttgart, Germany, 1972.

49 "ASKA Part III - 2 - Linear Buckling, User's Reference Manual," ASKA UM 209, University of Stuttgart, Stuttgart, Germany, 1973.

50 Zudan, Z., et al., "Theory and User's Manual for EPACA," Report F-C-3038, Franklin Institute Research Laboratories, Philadelphia, Pa.

51 Zudan, Z., et al., "Elastic-Plastic Creep Analysis of High Temperature Nuclear Reactor Components," Nuclear Engineering and Design, Vol. 28, No. 3, September 1974, pp. 414-45.

52 "MARC-CDC-Nonlinear Finite Element Analysis Program," A User's Information Manual, published by Control Data Corp., Minneapolis, MN.

53 "Structural Analysis with MARC - Background Papers", MARC Analysis Research Corporation, Palo Alto, California.

54 "User's Manual for NEPSAP," Report No. D556019, Lockheed Missiles and Space Company, Sunnyvale, California, August 1977.

55 "Theoretical Manual for NEPSAP," Report No. D556041, Lockheed Missiles and Space Company, Sunnyvale, California, October 1976.

56 Sharifi, P., and Yates, D. N., "Nonlinear Thermo-Elastic-Plastic and Creep Analysis by the Finite Element Method," AIAA Journal, Vol. 12, No. 9, September 1974, pp. 1210-15.

57 "LARSTRAN User's Manual," University of Stuttgart, Stuttgart, Germany, March 1978.

58 Argyris, J. H., and Kleiber, M., "Incremental Formulation in Nonlinear Mechanics and Large Strain Elasto-Plasticity-Natural Approach, Part 1," Comp. Meths. Appl. Mech. Eng., Vol. 11, 1977, pp. 215-47.

59 Argyris, J. H., Doltsinis, J. St., and Kleiber, M., "Incremental Formulation in Nonlinear Mechanics and Large Strain Elasto-Plasticity-Natural Approach, Part 2," Comp. Meths. Appl. Mech. Eng., Vol. 14, 1978, pp. 259-94.

60 Chang, T. Y., Prachuktam, S., and Reich, M., "Assessment of a Nonlinear Structural Analysis Finite Element Program (NONSAP) for Inelastic Analysis," Paper presented at the ASME Energy Technology Conference, Houston, Texas, September 18-22, 1977, also ASME Paper 77-PVP-10.

61 Bathe, K. J., Wilson, E. L., and Iding, R. H., "NONSAP - A Structural Analysis Program for Static and Dynamic Response of Nonlinear Systems," SESM Report No. 74-3, Department of Civil Engineering, University of California, Berkeley, 1974.

62 Chang, T. Y., and Prachuktam, S., "NFAP - A Nonlinear Finite Element Analysis Program," Report No. 76-3, Department of Civil Engineering, The University of Akron, October 1976.

63 Haisler, W. E., "Status Report of AGGIE I Computer Program," Technical Report No. 3275-78-2, Aerospace Engineering Department, Texas A & M University, April 1978.

    64 "PAFEC 75 Theory, Results," PAFEC Ltd., Beeston, Nottingham, December 1975.
    65 "PAFEC 75 Data Preparation," PAFEC Ltd., Beeston, Nottingham, December 1975.
    66 "PIG User Guide," PAFEC Ltd., Beeston, Nottingham, December 1975.
    67 Berman, I., ed., <u>Engineering Computer Software: Verification, Qualification, Certification</u>, ASME publication, 1971.

Table 1 Element Library

Element Type	ADINA	ANSYS	ASAS	ASKA-III	EPACA	LARSTRAN	MARC	NASTRAN	NEPSAP	NONSAP	PAFEC-75
Truss	X	X	X	X		X	X	X	X	X	X
Beam	X	X	X	X		X	X	X	X		X
2D Solid	X	X	X	X		X	X	X	X	X	X
3D Solid	X	X	X	X		X	X	X	X	X	X
Plate		X		X	X	X	X	X	X		X
Thin Shell		X	X	X	X	X	X	X	X		X
Thick Shell			X		X	X	X		X		X
Boundary Element		X					X				X

Table 2 Material Library

Material Models	ADINA	ANSYS	ASAS	ASKA-III	EPACA	LARSTRAN	MARC	NASTRAN	NEPSAP	NONSAP	PAFEC-75
Linear Elastic Isotropic	X	X	X	X	X	X	X	X	X	X	X
Linear Elastic Anisotropic	X	X	X	X		X	X	X	X	X	X
Nonlinear Elastic	X	X	X	X		X	X	X		X	
Linear Viscoelastic			X				X	X			
Metal Plasticity	X	X	X	X	X	X	X	X	X	X	X
High-Temperature Creep	X	X	X	X	X		X		X		X
Viscoelastic						X	X				
Large Strain Plasticity						X	X				

NONLINEAR FINITE ELEMENTS

Table 3   Procedure Library

Procedures	ADINA	ANSYS	ASAS	AKSA-III	EPACA	LARSTRAN	MARC	NASTRAN	NEPSAP	NONSAP	PAFEC-75
Static Analysis	X	X	X	X	X	X	X	X	X	X	X
Transient Dynamic Analysis	X	X	X		X	X	X	X	X	X	X
Mode Frequency	X	X	X				X	X	X	X	X
Determination of Buckling Load		X	X	X	X		X	X	X		
Post-Buckling Analysis		X	X				X	X	X		
Linear Elastic Fracture Mechanics			X				X				X
Nonlinear Contact Problems		X	X	X			X				
Heat Transfer Analysis	X	X					X	X			X

Table 4   Geometric Nonlinearity and Loading

	Description	ADINA	ANSYS	ASAS	ASKA	EPACA	LARSTRAN	MARC	NASTRAN	NEPSAP	NONSAP	PAFEC-75
Geometric Nonlinearity	Large Displacement	X	X	X	X	X	X	X	X	X	X	X
	Large Strain	X	X			X	X	X		X		
	Buckling Formulation	X		X	X	X		X	X	X		X
Loading Types	Concentrated Force	X	X	X	X	X	X	X	X	X	X	X
	Pressure Load	X	X	X	X	X	X	X	X	X		X
	Deformation Dependent Pressure		X			X		X		X		X
	Initial Stress Strain	X	X	X	X	X	X	X	X		X	
	Thermal Load	X	X	X	X	X		X	X	X		X
	Body Load	X	X	X	X	X		X	X	X		X
	Prescribed Displacement	X	X	X	X	X	X	X	X	X		X

Table 5 Additional Items

	Description	ADINA	ANSYS	ASAS	ASKA	EPACA	LARSTRAN	MARC	NASTRAN	NEPSAP	NONSAP	PAFEC-75
User's Features	Automatic Mesh Generation	X	X	X		X		X	X	X	X	X
	Automatic Load Adjustment		X	X		X		X				X
	Plot Routines		X	X	X	X		X	X	X		X
	Interactive Graphics		X	X	X		X	X		X		X
	Free Format Input		X		X			X		X		X
Other Software Options	Restart Capability	X	X	X	X	X	X	X	X	X	X	X
	Nodal Numbering Optimization		X	X				X		X		X
	Substructuring		X	X	X				X			X
Operating System	CDC	X	X		X		X	X	X	X	X	X
	IBM	X	X	X	X	X	X	X	X	X	X	X
	UNIVAC	X	X	X	X	X	X	X	X	X		X
	Honeywell		X		X							
	Prime		X					X				X
	DEC					X						X

Rotor Dynamics

Coda H. T. Pan

Shaker Research Corporation

INTRODUCTION

In the normal operation of a rotating machine, the axis of rotation of
its vital component is required to be constrained in the close proximity
of a reference point and to be maintained parallel to a fixed direction in
its housing. Ideally, the rotor would be a rigid body; and, except for
the rotational motion, the other five degrees of freedom would be totally
restrained. In a real situation, various parts of the rotor may depart
from their respective ideal locations/orientations due to the lack of
total rigidity of the rotor body and due to unavoidable displacements in
the bearing components. Very often, compliance and inertia can interact
to cause large amplitude dynamic motions. Other times, certain dynamic
peculiarities in one or more components of the rotor system can lead to
self-excited instability. The purpose of performing rotor dynamic
analysis is to predict the departures from the ideal locations/orienta-
tions of various parts of the rotor under a dynamic environment.
    A total rotor system can be logically divided into three subsystems:
the structural subsystem; the restraining subsystem, and the forcing
subsystem. A thorough analysis of the rotor motion must deal with each
of these three subsystems. The structural subsystem is the deformable
rotating body. The system of forces which cause deformation of the
rotor structure include internal forces which represent the interactions
with the restraining subsystem and those imposed forces which constitute
the forcing subsystem. Conceptual separation of these subsystems allows
free body treatments of the rotor structure and the restraining machine
elements. Subsequent synthesis of the structural and restraining subsystems yields the dynamic characteristics of the rotor system and permits
computation of its response due to the action of a particular forcing
subsystem.   These ideas are schematically illustrated in Fig. 1. Although the overall organization of a particular computer code does not
have to reflect the division of the three subsystems in a formal sense,
the substance of the underlying ideas cannot be violated.

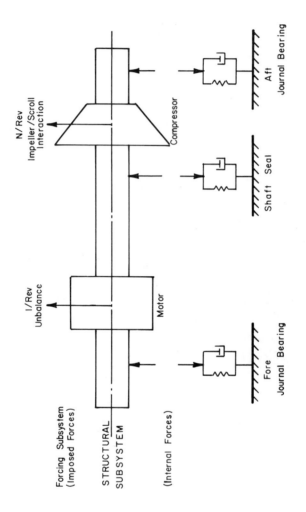

Fig. 1   Schematic of a rotor system

Prior to describing currently available software for rotor dynamic analysis, a generic discussion of the fundamental issues concerning each of the subsystems and their mutual interactions will be given in sufficient detail to guide the reader in the selection of the computer code which would best suit his particular needs.

NOMENCLATURE

$[B]_b$ = bearing damping coefficients, a square matrix
$[B]_b^p$ = pedestal damping coefficients, a square matrix
$[B_{xx}]_b^p$ = translational bearing stiffness coefficients, a square matrix $(F \cdot T/L)$
$[B_{\theta\theta}]_b$ = angular bearing stiffness coefficients, a square matrix $(F \cdot L \cdot T)$
c = dynamic damping coefficient of rotor system
div = divergence operator in the bearing surface (L^{-1})
$\{\Delta f\}$ = perturbation force, a column vector
$\{\Delta f\}_b$ = bearing reaction force, a column vector
$\{\Delta f\}_p$ = pedestal reaction force, a column vector
$\{\Delta f\}_{ex}$ = external forcing function, a column vector
$grad$ = gradient operator in the bearing surface (L^{-1})
H = lubricant film thickness (1)
k = dynamic stiffness coefficient of rotor system
$[K]_b$ = bearing stiffness coefficients, a square matrix
$[K]_b^p$ = pedestal stiffness coefficients, a square matrix
$[K_{xx}]_b^p$ = translational bearing stiffness coefficients, a square matrix (F/L)
$[K_{\theta\theta}]_b$ = angular bearing stiffness coefficients, a square matrix $(F \cdot L)$
$[M]_p$ = pedestal mass coefficients, a square matrix
P = lubricant film pressure (F/L^2)
$[R]$ = response coefficients, a square matrix
s = $\lambda + i\nu$, complex rate coefficient (T^{-1})
t = time (T)
$\vec{V}$ = mean surface velocity vector (F/T)
$\{\Delta x\}$ = generalized rotor displacement, a column vector
$\{\Delta x\}_b$ = bearing displacement, a column vector
$\{\Delta x\}_p$ = pedestal displacement, a column vector
$[Z]_b$ = bearing impedance coefficients, a square matrix
$[Z]_b^p$ = pedestal impedance coefficients, a square matrix
$[Z]_{ex}^p$ = impedance of rotor system viewed externally, a square matrix
λ_n = growth rate of nth natural transient mode (T^{-1})
μ = lubricant viscosity $(F \cdot T/L^2)$
ν = circular frequency of vibration (T^{-1})
ν_n = natural frequency of vibration for the nth mode (T^{-1})

The rotor structure is subject to interactions with other components of the rotor system. Torsional interactions appear as torques about the rotational axis. Flexural interactions may be in the form of either a transverse force or a transverse moment contained in either of two transverse planes. At any axial location, there may be up to five degrees of freedom for external actions to be applied to the rotor structure. They are:

    1. Torsional moment, e.g., gear mesh torque, impeller torque
    2. Transverse force in a plane normal to the rotor platform, e.g., journal bearing reactions
    3. Transverse moment in a plane normal to the rotor platform, e.g., reaction moment of a duplex bearing
    4. Transverse force in a plane parallel to the rotor platform
    5. Moment in a plane parallel to the rotor platform

If there are N stations at which the rotor structure can experience imposed or internal actions (the illustration in Fig. 1 shows five such stations), the total dynamic rank of the rotor structure is 5 x N irrespective of the details of modelling. At each station, corresponding to the five action types, there is a displacement subset with the five elements: the torsional angular displacement; the transverse normal lineal displacement; the transverse normal angular displacement; the transverse parallel lineal displacement; and the transverse parallel angular displacement. The structural analysis would result in the dynamic perturbation equation

$$[R]\{\Delta f\} = \{\Delta x\} \tag{1}$$

$[R]$ is symmetrical and is positive-definite.
    Disregarding any pathological condition, such as a loose joint, which cannot be tolerated in practice, the rotor structure is a linear, conservative (sub) system as described by Eq. (1). While undamped natural vibrations at discrete frequencies are possible, any self-excited instability and/or nonlinear phenomena of the rotor system would be caused by factors external to a well-engineered rotor structure.

RESTRAINING SUBSYSTEM

Linear Perturbation Bearing Coefficients

The restraining subsystem serves to maintain the nominal location of the rotor axis. Its principal components are the journal bearings. Departure of the rotor axis from its nominal location is resisted by bearing forces which may depend on

    1. Displacement of the rotor axis from its nominal location in the bearing plane
    2. Rate of motion of the rotor axis
    3. Rotational speed of the shaft

For rotor dynamic analyses, the bearing reactions due to deviations from
the static equilibrium condition are of interest. Most of the time, a
linear representation of the dynamic bearing characteristics is sufficient.
The perturbation bearing reaction vector may not be colinear with either
the displacement vector or the velocity vector.   Furthermore, depending
on the bearing type, the reaction may be in the form of a transverse moment
instead of or in addition to a transverse force.   Thus, the bearing reaction is characterized by the equation

$$\{\Delta f\}_b = -[Z]_b (\{\Delta x\}_b - \{\Delta x\}_p) \tag{2}$$

$\{\Delta f\}_b$ is of rank four; the elements of it are the two transverse reaction
forces and the two transverse reaction moments. $\{\Delta x\}_b$ and $\{\Delta x\}_p$ are also
of rank four.   They are respectively the generalized transverse displacement vectors of the rotor axis at the bearing plane and of the bearing
pedestal;   each consists of the two transverse lineal displacement
components and the two transverse angular displacement components. $[Z]_b$
is the dynamic perturbation impedance matrix of the bearing and can
usually be separated into a constant part and a rate dependent part:

$$[Z]_b = [K]_b + [B]_b \frac{d}{dt} \tag{3}$$

$[K]_b$ is called the stiffness matrix, while $[B]_b$, which is peculiar to fluid
film bearings, is called the damping matrix. Thus it is a common practice
to illustrate the restraining effects of a journal bearing by a spring-
dashpot arrangement as shown in Fig. 1. This terminology, unfortunately,
is very misleading because it does not correctly represent the separation
of conservative and dissipative effects. In the most general case $[K]_b$
and $[B]_b$ each would consist of sixteen coefficients. However, they are
usually sparsely filled matrices and can be approximately represented as

$$[K]_b = \begin{bmatrix} [K_{xx}] & [\,0\,] \\ [\,0\,] & [K_{\theta\theta}] \end{bmatrix}_b ; \quad [B]_b = \begin{bmatrix} [B_{xx}] & [\,0\,] \\ [\,0\,] & [B_{\theta\theta}] \end{bmatrix}_b \tag{4}$$

The nonvanishing partitions are 2 x 2 matrices. In fact, most of the time
$[K_{\theta\theta}]$ and $[B_{\theta\theta}]$ can both be neglected.

Pedestal Compliance and Inertia

The bearing reaction is transmitted to the foundation or platform through
the moderation of its compliance and inertia.   Analogous to Eqs. (2) and
(3), the pedestal effect can be expressed as

$$\{\Delta f\}_p = -[Z]_p \{\Delta x\}_p \tag{5}$$

$$[Z]_p = [K]_p + [B]_p \frac{d}{dt} + [M]_p \frac{d^2}{dt^2} \tag{6}$$

$[M]_p$ can include the mass of those bearing parts which would move with the pedestal.

The dynamic compliance of the housing of a gas turbine aircraft engine can be regarded as a form of pedestal compliance. However, it may not be possible to isolate its inertia effects in the form of a lumped mass matrix $[M]_p$.

Simple Harmonic Analysis

The linearized dynamic perturbation problem can be examined in terms of the simple harmonic motion. It is common practice to use the complex notation $\exp\{i\nu t\}$ to represent the simple harmonic time dependence of the circular frequency ν. The time derivative operation, d/dt, is thus equivalent to the phase shift operation, $i\nu$. Eqs. (3) and (6) are accordingly reduced to

$$[Z]_b = [K]_b + i\nu[B]_b \tag{7}$$

$$[Z]_p = [K]_p - \nu^2[M]_p + i\nu[B]_p \tag{8}$$

With the derivative operation replaced by an algebraic operation, Eqs. (7) and (8) can then be formally inverted, so that for a simple harmonic motion, Eqs. (2) and (3) can be combined as

$$\{\Delta f\}_b = -\left[[Z]_b^{-1} + [Z]_p^{-1}\right]^{-1}\{\Delta x\}_b \tag{9}$$

which describes the overall restraining action observed at the bearing location.

Fluid Film Bearing Analysis

The fluid film bearing film pressure can be determined from the lubrication theory, which is commonly described by the incompressible, laminar, isoviscous Reynolds equation:

$$\text{div}\left\{-\frac{H^3}{12\mu} \text{ grad } P + \frac{\vec{V}}{2}\right\} + \frac{\partial H}{\partial t} = 0 \tag{10}$$

The film thickness function, H, is directly related to the instantaneous journal position.

Given a specific bearing geometry, the film thickness function H is known. In principle, P can be solved according to Eq. (10), then subsequently integrated over the bearing surface area to describe the bearing reaction in the form of Eqs. (2) and (3). It is clear that only when the small perturbation concept is introduced can $[K]_b$ and $[B]_b$

be regarded as invariants. It is due to the peculiar behavior of fluid film journal bearings that $[K]_b$ and $[B]_b$ have nonvanishing off-diagonal terms. It is due to these off-diagonal terms that one cannot directly associate nonconservative effects with $[B]_b$. In fact, a form of self-excited instability can be attributed to the off-diagonal terms in $[K]_b$.

Numerical procedures of the finite difference or the finite element variety can be applied to solve Eq. (10). Although direct dynamic simulation of Eq. (1) together with structural analysis is conceptually possible, the prevailing trend in current practice is to take advantage of the small perturbation concepts and to compute the linear bearing coefficients once and for all. Dimensionless data banks for commonly used bearing configurations can be stored in files and can be retrieved subsequently in an automated data system.

Uncertainty in the accuracy of such data banks may be due to several sources.

   1. Limitations in the theoretical model for the lubricant film pressure exist in the following areas.
       a. Temperature distribution in the lubricant film can be estimated only approximately. Unfortunately, the viscosity of most lubricants is strongly dependent on temperature.
       b. Nonlaminar fluid flow phenomena and inertia effects are amenable to theoretical treatment only in rather crude ways.
       c. The possible existence of a gaseous regime in the unloaded portion is generally known. However, a precise description of the physical parameters which govern the location of the interphase boundary under combined static and dynamic loads is not known.
   2. Precise knowledge of the nominal bearing gap in a real operating environment is seldom available. Contributing to this difficulty:
       a. Stack up tolerance in the bearing gap is usually appreciable.
       b. Stress and temperature induced distortions add to the uncertainty.
It should be noted that the scaling law of lubrication theory indicates that the dynamic perturbation coefficients of a fluid film bearing are inversely proportional to the third power of the mean bearing gap.
   3. Inherent inaccuracy in the numerical procedure, which was employed to compile the data bank.
   4. The amplitude of motion of the rotor axis in the bearing may be sufficiently large so that the concept of small dynamic perturbations may be grossly violated.

The concept of utilizing a stored data bank in the prediction of the dynamic behavior of the rotor system can be extended to include large amplitude motions. This is because the lubrication theory suggests the possibility of solving for the instantaneous bearing reaction vector uniquely in terms of the instantaneous location of the rotor axis and its kinematic vector in the bearing plane. One should be aware that the limitations in the theoretical model apply equally to both the small perturbation solution and the finite amplitude solution of the governing equation.

Rolling Element Bearing Analysis

The relationship between the transmitted force and the displacement of the rotor axis relative to the bearing housing, in the case of a rolling element bearing, is largely an elasticity effect. The predominant elastic deformation, which contributes to the relative displacement of the rotor axis, is at the Hertzian contacts between the rolling elements and the inner and outer races. Although the solid surfaces are actually separated by a thin lubricant film, the thickness of this lubricant film varies very little with the load in comparison to the variation of a Hertzian contact with load. Thus, it is quite adequate to disregard the condition of lubrication insofar as the bearing reaction to the rotor axis displacement is concerned. The Hertzian contact has a highly nonlinear behavior between load and displacement. This is reflected in the overall behavior of $[K]_b$ of a rolling element bearing in that

      1. $[K]_b$ is very sensitive to the level of preload.
      2. $[K]_b$ in the presence of a radial static load may not be isotropic. The principal axis of $[K]_b$ coincides with the static load direction.
      3. For high-speed rolling element bearings, the centrifugal force on the rolling elements intensifies the outer contacts but relieves the inner contacts. Consequently, the elements of $[K]_b$ are speed dependent.

In terms of a coordinate system which coincides with the principal axis of $[K]_b$, off-diagonal terms are negligible. $[B]_b$ can usually be neglected entirely for rolling element bearings. Thus, as a major component in the restraining subsystem, rolling element bearings can be regarded as conservative devices.

      Within the rolling element bearing itself, there exists the possibility of some anomalous dynamic phenomena; the most notable ones are known as contact skidding and retainer instability. Computer codes for studying these specialty problems are not included in the present survey.

Other Restraining Reactions

Other machine elements may also restrain the motion of the rotor axis in a manner similar to the action of a journal bearing. Their effects can be included in a rotor dynamic analysis so long as their equivalent bearing impedance matrices can be estimated. Among these, the most common ones are shaft seals, magnetic gaps, and leakage-sensitive fluid machinery stages. See Ref. [1].

Nonlinear Effects

In the event that a relatively large motion of the rotor axis should develop, nonlinear effects are most likely to be encountered in the restraining subsystem. The possibility of analyzing rotor motion with nonlinear effects is thus dependent on the ability to characterize the nonlinear behavior of the restraining components themselves.

STRUCTURAL SUBSYSTEM

From the standpoint of rotor dynamics, elasticity of the rotor comes
into the picture mainly in torsional and flexural motions. Although
torsional motion does not directly cause a deflection of the rotor
axis, the dynamic torque associated with torsional vibration is
necessarily related to a tangential force at a gear mesh which can
cause lateral or flexural vibrations. The latter thus becomes the agent
for torsional vibrations to assume a nontrivial role in rotor dynamics.
Furthermore, torsional vibrations of excessive amplitude can cause
damage in gearing.
     An important approximation in the structural part of rotor dynamic
analysis is the slender bar treatments of both the torsional and the
flexural problems. Although the cross section of a real rotor is likely
to have extended transverse dimensions, an adequate approach is to model
it as a shaft with numerous attached wheels or discs. The shaft cross
section may be stepped at discrete axial locations. Torsional and flexural compliances are due to the shaft segments, while rigid body inertias
are assigned to the attached wheels.   Such an approach was first used by
Holzer to compute torsional vibrations; a similar treatment for rotor
flexure was pioneered by Prohl. The Holzer-Prohl modelling technique
has been retained throughout the years. See Refs. [2-9].
     In a contemporary computer code, the torsional problem can be treated
as a piecewise distributed system interspersed with concentrated polar
moments of inertia for disc-like bodies which are attached to the rotor
shaft. The required computational procedure is quite straightforward.
     For the flexure problem, the rotor structure is treated as a shaft
(of more-or-less slender proportions) with attached disc-like appendages.
Cross-sectional variations of the shaft are approximated by piecewise
uniform shaft segments. In the original Prohl treatment, each shaft segment is modelled in terms of lumped half-masses at either end of a flexure spring. In some contemporary computer codes, a distributed mass
treatment is employed. A disc-like appendage is modelled in terms of
a lumped mass, transverse inertia, and polar inertia.
     Shear deformation and rotary inertias of the shaft segment can be
included as refinements of the flexure analysis. Although shear deformation is generally regarded as being of as much importance as the rotary
inertias in calculating the higher-mode flexural vibration of a slender
rod, the rotary inertias can be the more important features if the rotor
system consists of a stubby structure on relatively compliant bearings.
     Natural flexure boundary conditions are equally divided between
the ends of the shaft. They are reconciled through recursive computation
through the successive shaft segments. Implementation of this type of
computation procedure is commonly done by the Matrix Transfer Method.
The computation starts from one end with unspecified parameters, which,
through successive matrix transfers, become linearly related to the
boundary conditions known at the other end and can thus be determined
by an inversion computation. Straightforward application of the Matrix
Transfer Method can encounter "loss of numerical accuracy" in the
flexural calculation. Use of multiple precision word structure in
the computer code would postpone its occurrence. More recently, it has
been shown that use of the Riccati Matrix Transfer Method can eliminate
this difficulty altogether.

The only generally applicable method available to study nonlinear problems is the dynamic simulation of the entire rotor system in the time domain using step-by-step numerical integration to display the history of the motion. As a problem-solving engineering tool, the usefulness of the dynamic simulation method is restricted by the following factors.

    1. Both computation and display of results require large-scale use of computer time.
    2. Lack of full knowledge of the nonlinear characteristics of the pertinent components precludes total credibility in the simulation results.
    3. The time step for integration must be small enough to resolve the details of high-frequency oscillation components. Thus a correspondingly large number of integration steps must be used even if the details of the high-frequency oscillation are of little consequence.
    4. There are no absolute criteria to assure accuracy in simulation computations.

An alternative approach for treating nonlinear problems is to improvise ad hoc means for studying specific issues. The most notable nonlinear phenomena in the dynamics of rotor systems include:

    1. The existence and the stability of a limit cycle
    2. The extent of harmonic distortions
    3. The possibility of secondary parametric instabilities

FORCING SUBSYSTEM

The forcing subsystem includes all effects which appear as a source of excitation but do not have an amplitude dependence on the motion of the rotor axis. To be specifically excluded are:

    1. Internal forces which are directly proportional to the rotor motion
    2. Parametric excitations which originate from nonlinear effects in the restraining subsystem

Dynamic problems associated with these two processes were already covered by linear and nonlinear aspects of the restraining subsystem.
    The most prominent examples of the forcing subsystem are:

    1. Mass unbalance
    2. Frame fixed momentum exchange with the working fluid
    3. Nonstationary impulsive action from the working fluid
    4. Seismic type acceleration of the platform.

The general features of each of these mechanisms are separately discussed below.

Mass Unbalance

Mass distribution of an ideal rotor structure would be rotationally symmetrical about the rotor axis. Deviation from this ideal mass distribution appears as a centrifugal force which is <u>proportional</u> to the square of the rotational speed and is a <u>revolving vector </u>in synchronism with shaft rotation.

Mass unbalance may be a residual effect of manufacturing tolerances or it may be an anomalous condition developed in the operational environment. Examples of the latter include a mass shift caused by momentary loosening of shrink-fit parts, or the loss of a blade or bucket from a turbine or compressor wheel.

The unbalance condition may exist in various magnitudes along the rotor axis and may be contained in different radial planes.

Frame Fixed Fluid Impulses

If asymmetry exists in the fluid passageway in the stationary housing, the tangential force acting on each blade or bucket passage would be oscillatory. The predominant component of this type of excitation is at the blade passing frequency and appears as a fixed planar force. Struts in the inlet and exhaust housings and the partial admission nozzle box are typical sources of this excitation mechanism.

Nonstationary Fluid Impulses

When an axial flow compressor is operating near its stall limit, incipience of stall would first appear as local blockage of blade passages. The pattern of flow blockage tends to "slip" relative to either the stationary blades or the rotor blades at the same rate. If the stall pattern is not evenly distributed around the flow annulus, a residual lateral force would appear to the rotor. Such a force would be revolving at approximately one-half of the rotor speed.

Seismic Acceleration

Seismic acceleration does not have a distinct frequency, but may have a broad band distribution. The predominant direction of the seismic acceleration depends on whether the platform is directly anchored to the ground or is attached to the floor of an upper level.

A similar circumstance exists for airborne equipment during take-off and at landing.

Generalizing from these specific examples, one may characterize the forcing subsystem in terms of:

1. Dependence of amplitude on speed
2. Frequency of oscillation
3. Axial location
4. Platform fixed or revolving
5. Axial distribution of relative orientation or phase.

PROBLEM CLASSIFICATION

In dynamic analysis of a rotor system, three questions may be raised in succession.

1. What is the character of its natural modes? Are they damped, self-sustaining, or self-amplifying?

2. If none of the natural modes are self-amplifying, how do they respond to potential excitation mechanisms?

3. If a natural mode either is self-amplifying or may be driven to a large amplitude, what are the consequences if there are nonlinear effects?

The first question is often asked in two parts. First, if one neglects nonconservative effects, what are the undamped natural frequencies? Answers to this part allow one to explore the nonconservative natural modes more thoroughly. The latter usually requires a more extensive effort.

The second question centers around whether or not the more sensitive natural modes may encounter resonant excitation of some kind. Characterization of the relevant forcing subsystem is important for this step. Since the natural frequency cannot be precisely determined due to uncertainties in rotor structure modelling as well as in bearing impedance data, one should allow the frequency of excitation to cover a suitable range around the nominal value, typically about $\pm$ 10%.

The linear response and stability analysis would yield results that, when compared with the linear characteristics of the restraining subsystem, would indicate whether or not nonlinear phenomena deserve attention. Very often, an engineering fix to reduce the amplitude or response is necessary, and with such a fix, one can be satisfied with the results of the linear analysis.

CHARACTERISTIC SOLUTIONS OF THE ROTOR SYSTEM

Determination of the natural modes of a rotor system is an important step in a rotor dynamic analysis. If the free body diagram of Fig. 1 is resolved so that

$$\{\Delta f\} = \{\Delta f\}_{ex} + \{\Delta f\}_b \qquad (11)$$

where $\{\Delta f\}_{ex}$ is the system of external forcing effects and $\{\Delta f\}_b$ is the internal force effects of the total restraining subsystems, then combining with Eq. (9), one can write

$$\{\Delta f\}_{ex} = [Z]_{ex} \ \{\Delta x\} \qquad (12)$$

$$[Z]_{ex} = \left[[Z]_b^{-1} + [Z]_p^{-1} \right]^{-1} + [R]^{-1} \qquad (13)$$

$[Z]_{ex}$ is the impedance of the rotor system as viewed "externally." In writing the above expressions, it is understood that the ranks of $\{\Delta f\}_{ex}$, $\{\Delta f\}_b$, $[Z]_b$, $[Z]_p$, and $[R]$ have been reconciled. The properties of $[Z]_{ex}$ determine the behaviors of the natural modes of the rotor system.

Conservative System

If the restraining subsystem is conservative, then self-sustaining simple harmonic motions exist at discrete frequencies ν_n such that

$$|Z(\nu_n)|_{ex} = 0 \qquad (14)$$

At each ν_n a natural mode shape can be described by $\{\Delta x_n\}$, which can be found by solving

$$[Z(\nu_n)]_{ex} \{\Delta x_n\} = \{0\} \tag{15}$$

with the largest element of $\{\Delta x_n\}$ set to unity. All other elements of $\{\Delta x_n\}$ are real and ν_n represents an undamped resonant condition. Its coincidence with potential excitation mechanisms should be avoided.

Nonconservative System

The natural modes of a nonconservative system are not self-sustaining. They can be treated with two alternative points of view.

In the absence of a driving force, amplitude growth (or decay) or a free natural mode can occur simultaneously with oscillations of the natural frequency. The mode shape examined at congruent instants of successive oscillations would be similar in spite of the amplitude change. This is the point of view of a transient analysis. A free natural mode can be nonundulating; then a rate constant (without a corresponding natural frequency) alone characterizes the nature of time dependence.

On the other hand, one can also consider a simple harmonic motion sustained by external forcing. The principal mode shape would yield a force vector which is similar to the displacement vector. At the steady-state natural frequency, the phase angle between the force and displacement vectors would be precisely 90 degrees, and the principal mode thus becomes a steady-state natural mode.

Both approaches would yield valid results regarding the state of stability of the rotor system. The free natural mode analysis characterizes the system in terms of a rate constant while the steady-state natural mode analysis invokes the concept of energy dissipation.

Free Natural Modes

In the absence of external forcing, the homogeneous equation

$$[Z]_{ex} \{\Delta x\} = \{0\} \tag{16}$$

allows a time dependence in the form of $\exp\{st\}$, where

$$s = \lambda + i\nu \tag{17}$$

is a complex rate coefficient, which takes on the discrete roots of

$$\left|Z(\lambda_n + i\nu_n)\right|_{ex} = 0 \tag{18}$$

The simultaneous vanishing of both the real and the imaginary parts of the above determinant allows (λ_n, ν_n) to be calculated, after which the nonconservative mode shape can be found by satisfying the homogeneous equation

$$[Z(\lambda_n + i\nu_n)]_{ex} \{\Delta x_n\} = \{0\} \qquad (19)$$

λ_n indicates the growth rate of $\{\Delta x_n\}$ with time. For a damped system, λ_n must be negative. A positive value of λ_n indicates instability.

If λ_n is not zero, then the transient natural mode is an oscillation with a varying amplitude. In this case, the elements of $\{\Delta x_n\}$ may have imaginary parts, indicating a spatially varying phase shift. ν_n is the free natural frequency while $2\pi\lambda_n/\nu_n$ is the log-growth factor. The amplitude of the natural transient changes by a factor of $\exp\{2\pi\lambda_n/\nu_n\}$ for every period of the natural oscillation.

Steady-State Natural Modes

If a simple harmonic time dependence, $\exp\{i\nu t\}$, is imposed, Eq. (12) can be diagonalized to become

$$\{\Delta f\}_{ex} = [Z(\nu)]_{ex} \{\Delta x\}$$

$$= (k+i\nu c)[I] \{\Delta x\} \qquad (20)$$

Since this is also a homogeneous system, the characteristic determinant must vanish:

$$\left| [Z(\nu)]_{ex} - (k+i\nu c) [I] \right| = 0 \qquad (21)$$

For a given ν, a set of (k,c) can be determined to satisfy the simultaneous vanishing of both real and imaginary parts of the above determinant. The condition

$$k (\nu_n) = 0 \qquad (22)$$

establishes the steady-state natural frequency. The steady-state natural mode shape is determined by the homogeneous equation

$$\left[[Z(\nu_n)]_{ex} - i\nu_n c(\nu_n)[I] \right] \{\Delta x_n\} = \{0\} \qquad (23)$$

The steady-state natural mode is "self-similar" but not self-sustaining. It can be driven by a similar forcing function which would lead the oscillation by a quadrant if $c(\nu_n)>0$ and lag the oscillation by a quadrant if $c(\nu_n)<0$. In fact, the steady-state motion of the rotor would be sustained by receiving energy from the forcing function for $c<0$ and by transferring energy to the forcing function if $c<0$. Thus, c is proportional to the energy dissipation rate, and $c<0$ is the condition for instability. According to the behavior of Eq. (21), as $\nu \to \nu_n$, $c(\nu_n)$ can be expressed in the dimensionless form of a critical damping ratio (for the nth mode).

METHODS FOR SOLVING CHARACTERISTIC PROBLEMS

Since the natural modes of a rotor system are potentially synonymous to the conditions of large amplitude vibrations, their determination is often the most important step in rotor dynamic analysis. The mathematical problem for the determination of the natural modes is called the characteristic problem, and information concerning the natural modes includes the characteristic value and the characteristic vector. A variety of computational procedures is available to solve the characteristic problems. The major categories of these computational procedures are described below.

Classical Method

A classical method for a lumped parameter representation of the rotor system exists, by which the characteristic values are sought as the roots of a characteristic polynomial equation. The order of the polynomial equation equals the total degrees of freedom of the lumped parameter representation. If the system is conservative, the characteristic value, expressed in terms of an exponential rate constant, is always imaginary. In this case, the procedure can be devised to yield the characteristic values in successively higher numerical values. If the rotor system involves fluid film journal bearings, the characteristic values may have both real and imaginary parts, and generally the characteristic values are ordered according to their absolute magnitude. In the latter situation, one is required to find the complete set of characteristic values and vectors and, if desirable, to rearrange them in the desired order. One should note that since the lumped parameter model inherently loses accuracy for the higher modes, a common rule is to accept the lowest one-third (in frequency) of the entire set as satisfactory results for engineering purposes [10-12].

Power Iterative Method

The power iterative method is a procedure by which the characteristic value and the characteristic vector are found by continuous iteration of a homogeneous set of equations. This method was originally devised to solve the problem with a lumped parameter representation. It can also be adapted to treat a general rotor system using a distributed model and the steady-state harmonic response approach.

Natural Boundary Condition

The natural boundary conditions of a rotor structure can be utilized to determine the unknown characteristic value iteratively. This technique was similar to the methods of Holzer, Myklestad, and Prohl for conservative structures. It has been recently adapted by Lund to treat a general rotor system.   This approach can be extended to consider external excitations at any axial location of the rotor axis. Iterative methods do not automatically find the characteristic values according to a desired order but may be devised to search for all characteristic solutions within an assigned frequency domain.

PROGRAM SUMMARIES

Overview

During the preparation of the present review, a set of survey questionnaires was sent to organizations which are known to be active in the development of rotor-dynamics softwares to request the latest data for their
softwares which can be assessed by the potential user public. Eight replies
were received; among these, six organizations furnished the requested data;
the other two indicated no change from the review of 1975. Acronyms for
identification of the organization and for referencing the applicable computer programs, which can be made available by these six organizations, are
given in Table 1. The results of this survey, containing a summary of
information furnished by the six organizations,are shown in Tables 2, 3,
and 4. Program abstracts are listed first for those programs identified in
Table 1, then also for the programs of those three organizations that indicated no change since 1975. Replies to the survey indicate that most of the
organizations are constantly adding new programs and updating current programs. The programs identified by this review represent the official catalog which has been released to the public at the preparation of this
article. Finally, organizations which were identified in the 1975 review
with operational programs but which did not respond to the present survey
are listed in Table 5 together with the names and brief descriptions of
their programs.

Program Abstracts - Group I
New or Updated Programs

ROTDYN

Categories: Time-history response, stability analysis, complex eigenvalues
Descriptive Program Title: Nonsynchronous Flexible Rotor Dynamics Program
Author: M. M. Reddi
Maintenance: Franklin Research Center
            A Division of The Franklin Institute
Dates: First release 1972, most recent update 1977
Capability: This program determines stability and orbit response of flex-
    ible rotor bearing systems. The response computation yields the time
    history for each degree of freedom of the assembly. Stress, forces,
    and moments at bearings are generated for user-specified locations.
    For each shaft speed the stability analysis yields the rigid body and
    bending criticals, their growth or damping factors, and for each of the
    criticals, the displacement and velocity mode shapes. Shaft is
    represented by finite elements based on beam theory with shear factors.
    Sectional and inertial properties are internally generated for axis-
    symmetric, hollow or solid elements of revolution. Axial taper of the
    shaft within each element is also taken into account. Bearings are
    represented by stiffness and damping coefficients. Foundations are
    represented by stiffness and damping coefficients. Foundation inertial
    properties are included in the analysis. Damping in shaft and founda-
    tion materials is allowed. Response calculations are made for both
    unbalance and external loads.
Method: For stability analysis, the dynamical equations are converted to an
    eigenvalue problem by assuming small excursions from the equilibrium
    configuration. In this process, noninertial degrees of freedom are
    eliminated from the system by a theoretically consistent procedure.

Table 1   Acronyms of Organizations and Programs

ORGANIZATION	ACRONYM	PROGRAM
FRANKLIN RESEARCH CENTER	FRC	IDENTIFICATION ROTDYN TORVIB HYJURN GENROL REBAP
MECHANICAL TECHNOLOGY INCORPORATED	MTI	ALL COMPUTER PROGRAMS AVAILABLE FROM MTI ARE IDENTIFIED BY A CADENSE PROGRAM NUMBER. THE FOLLOWING ARE RELATED TO ROTOR-DYNAMICS ANALYSIS: 20 21 21A 22 23 24 25 30 31 32
NATIONAL AERONAUTICS AND SPACE ADMINISTRATION LEWIS RESEARCH CENTER	LEWIS	EPHB
SHAKER RESEARCH CORPORATION	SRC	RSVP BEARDATA BALL ROLLER TAPER SPIRAL
THE STRUCTURAL MEMBERS USERS GROUP	SMUG	DAMPEDROTOR SHAFT TWIST
TRUMPLER ASSOCIATES, INC.	TAI	LATCRIT

Table 2   Summary of Problem Capabilities of Rotor Dynamics Programs

		ORGANIZATION				
		FRC	MTI	SRC	SMUG	TAI
FLEXURE PROBLEMS	**SYNCHRONOUS PROBLEMS**					
	Critical Speeds	ROTDYN	20	RSVP	SHAFT	LATCRIT
	Damped Unbalance Response	ROTDYN	21	RSVP	SHAFT	LATCRIT
	NON-SYNCHRONOUS PROBLEMS					
	Undamped Resonances	ROTDYN		RSVP	SHAFT	
	Damped Response	ROTDYN	21A	RSVP	SHAFT	
	Stability Analysis	ROTDYN	25	RSVP	DAMPED ROTOR	
	TRANSIENTS					
	Response Orbits	ROTDYN				LATCRIT
	Acceleration Through Critical Speeds	ROTDYN				
TORSION PROBLEMS	UNDAMPED RESONANCES	TORVIB	22	RSVP	TWIST	
	TRANSIENTS	TORVIB	24			
	DAMPING EFFECTS	TORVIB	23			

Table 3 Summary of Features of Rotor Dynamics Programs

				FRC	MTI	SRC	SMUG	TAI
FLEXURE PROBLEMS	ELASTICITY		FLEXURE	ROTDYN	20,21,21A,25	RSVP	DAMPEDROTOR, SHAFT	LATCRIT
			SHEAR	ROTDYN	20,21,21A,25		DAMPEDROTOR, SHAFT	
	INERTIA		LUMPED MASS	ROTDYN	20,21,21A,25	RSVP	DAMPEDROTOR, SHAFT	LATCRIT
			DISTRIBUTED MASS		20,21,21A	RSVP	SHAFT	
			LUMPED ROTARY	ROTDYN	20,21,21A,25	RSVP	DAMPEDROTOR, SHAFT	
			LUMPED POLAR	ROTDYN	20,21,21A,25	RSVP	DAMPEDROTOR, SHAFT	
			DISTRIBUTED ROTARY		20,21,21A		SHAFT	
			DISTRIBUTED POLAR		20,21,21A		SHAFT	
	DISCRETIZATION		LUMPED PARAMETER	ROTDYN	25		DAMPEDROTOR	LATCRIT
			FUNCTIONAL FINITE ELEMENT	ROTDYN				
			PIECEWISE EXACT		20,21,21A	RSVP	SHAFT	
	SUPPORTS		LINEAL SPRING				SHAFT	LATCRIT
			LINEAL DAMPER				SHAFT	
			ISOTROPIC SPRING		20		DAMPEDROTOR	
			ISOTROPIC DAMPER				DAMPEDROTOR	
			STATIC FOUNDATION COMPLIANCE	ROTDYN	20,21,21A,25	RSVP	SHAFT	LATCRIT
			LUMPED FOUNDATION INERTIA	ROTDYN	25	RSVP	SHAFT	LATCRIT
			DISTRIBUTED FOUNDATION INERTIA			RSVP	SHAFT	
			FOUNDATION DAMPING	ROTDYN	25	RSVP	SHAFT	LATCRIT
			ROLLING ELEMENT BEARING	ROTDYN		RSVP		
			FLUID FILM BEARINGS	ROTDYN	21,21A,25	RSVP	DAMPEDROTOR SHAFT	LATCRIT
	STRUCTURAL ANALYSIS		TRANSFER MATRIX		20,21,21A,25	RSVP	SHAFT	LATCRIT
			RICCATI TRANSFER MATRIX				DAMPEDROTOR	
			BANDED MATRIX	ROTDYN				
			IMPEDANCE MATCHING			RSVP		
	LINEAR ANALYSIS		FREQUENCY RESPONSE		21,21A	RSVP	SHAFT	LATCRIT
			REAL EIGENVALUE		20	RSVP	DAMPEDROTOR SHAFT	LATCRIT
			NATURAL COMPLEX EIGENVALUE	ROTDYN	25		DAMPEDROTOR	
			PHASE SHIFT COMPLEX EIGENVALUE			RSVP		
			TRANSIENT	ROTDYN				
	NONLINEAR ANALYSIS		TRANSIENT					LATCRIT
			AMPLITUDE EFFECT					LATCRIT
			LIMIT CYCLE					LATCRIT
TORSION PROBLEMS	ELASTICITY		UNDAMPED	TORV	22,23,24	RSVP	TWIST	
			DAMPED	TORV	23,24			
	INERTIA		LUMPED	TORV	22,23,24	RSVP	TWIST	
			DISTRIBUTED		22,23	RSVP		
	DISCRETIZATION		LUMPED PARAMETER	TORV	24			
			PIECEWISE EXACT		22,23	RSVP	TWIST	
	EXTERNAL CONSTRAINTS		ELASTIC	TORV	22,23,24		TWIST	
			DAMPED	TORV	23,24			
	BRANCHES			TORV	22,23,24			
	FREQUENCY RESPONSE		RESONANCES		22		TWIST	
			RESPONSE		23	RSVP		
	TRANSIENT			TORV	24			
	BACKLASH			TORV	24			

Table 4 Summary of Bearing Data Programs

		FRC	LEWIS	MTI	SRC	TAI
ROLLING ELEMENT	Ball Bearing	REBAP GENROL			BALL	*
	Cylindrical Roller	{			CYLINDER	
	Tapered Roller				TAPER	
INCOMPRESSIBLE FLUID FILM	**CONFIGURATION**					
	Plain Journal	HYJURN		30	BEARDATA	
	Partial Arc	HYJURN		30	BEARDATA	
	Axial Groove	HYJURN		31	BEARDATA	
	Lobed	HYJURN		30	BEARDATA	
	Pressure Dam	HYJURN				
	Pocket Journal	HYJURN				
	Tilting-Shoe	TILPAD		32	BEARDATA	
	PROGRAM FUNCTION					
	Custom Solution	HYJURN TILPAD		30		
	Data Bank System			31,32	BEARDATA	
GAS BRG.	Externally Pressurized		EPHB			
	Spiral Grooved		EPHB		SPIRAL	

*TAI can furnish data on a variety of fluid film bearings upon request.

Table 5 Programs Listed in 1975 Reviews

Person or Organization	Program Name	Program Capability
Dr. Melbourne F. Giberson 212 Welsh Pool Road Lionville, Pa. 19353	Time-Transient Nonsynchronous Rotor Response	Time domain step-by-step integration of the history of motion of a flexible rotor bearing system
Prof. E. J. Gunter Dept. of Mechanical and Aerospace Engineering University of Virginia Charlottesville, Va. 22901	MFIN4	Damped natural frequency and stability analysis
	CRITSPD	Undamped speeds, amplification factor
	JBRGCOEF	Bearing coefficients calculated by the short-bearing π-film approximation
	LJBFEM	Long journal bearing analysis with leakage correction
	FJBFEMI	Finite length journal bearing analysis
	BRGCML2	Fixed geometry fluid film bearings of various configuration
Cosmic Information Services Barrows Hall University of Georgia Athens, Georgia 36061	CSPRJT	Critical speeds
CDC - Kronos	CRITSPEED	Critical speeds

The eigenvalue problem is then solved for complex roots by the QR-2 algorithm. See Ref. [10]. For each root of interest, the mode shape is computed by solving the resulting matrix equation by Gaussian elimination.

Response of the rotor-foundation system is computed by forward integration in time. An unconditionally stable algorithm due to Newmark is used for this purpose.

Limitations and Restrictions: Bearing stiffness and damping coefficients must be constant. Uses linear theory.

Programming Language: FORTRAN IV

Documentation: User's manual and program documentation manual are available.

Input: Number of stations, shaft elements, discs, bearings, shaft materials, and time steps. Material properties of shaft elements (moduli of elasticity and shear, hysteresis factor, and weight density). Shaft element geometry (solid, hollow, rectangular, tapered, length, diameters). Disc locations and inertia properties. Unbalance locations, magnitudes and phase angles. External force, locations and time varying magnitudes. Bearing stiffness and damping matrices. Bearing pad and resilient mount mass inertia (multiple matrix — degree of freedom allowed at each bearing)

Output: Stability analysis (for each speed) — critical frequencies, growth or damping factors, displacement mode shapes, velocity mode shapes, stability and critical speed diagram.

Orbit analysis:
Orbital amplitudes at each mass station.
Transmitted bearing force
Shaft moments and stresses

Software Operation: Either batch or time-sharing

Hardware: CDC, UNIVAC 1100-1108, IBM 360-370, PRIME 300, DEC 20

Usage: About ten users

Typical Running Time: Varies with problem

Availability: Can be purchased or leased from:
Franklin Research Center
Division of Franklin Institute
The Benjamin Franklin Parkway
Philadelphia, Pennsylvania 19103
Attn: Richard Colsher

HYJURN

Category: Hydrodynamic journal, incompressible fluid film bearing, static and dynamic characteristics

Descriptive Program Title: Hydrodynamic Journal Bearing

Author: Richard Colsher

Dates: First release 1970. Most recent update 1977.

Capability: Numerical solution of the lubrication equation to obtain performance characteristics of journal bearings of various configurations are found. Boundary pressure levels may be designated by the user. Film turbulence effects are considered. The rotation axis may be misaligned. Configuration capability includes plain journal, partial arc, oil ring, axial grooves, lobes, tapered land, and pressure dam. Cavitation boundary is fixed by the Gumbel criterion; user can specify the vapor pressure for cavitation.

Method: A finite difference algorithm with variable grid spacing is used
to achieve high accuracy. Dynamic stiffness and damping coefficients
are established by a perturbation calculation upon the equilibrium
solution.
Limitations and Restrictions: Isoviscous lubricant, no film inertia,
linearized dynamic coefficients, flow transition condition not considered
Program Language: FORTRAN IV
Documentation: User's and technical manuals are available.
Input: Geometry, eccentricity or load, density and viscosity of lubricant,
rotational speed, internal and boundary pressures, vapor pressure for
cavitation
Output: Load or position, attitude angle, inlet and side leakage flows,
power loss, minimum clearance, equilibrium moment components, optional
output of pressure and gap distribution, spring and damping matrix
coefficients, critical mass for instability
Software Operation: Batch or time-sharing
Hardware: CDC, UNIVAC 1108, IBM 360-370, PRIME 300, DEC 20
Usage: About ten users
Typical Running Time: 60 seconds CPU on UNIVAC 1108
Availability: Can be purchased or leased from:
Franklin Research Center
Division of Franklin Institute
The Benjamin Franklin Parkway
Philadelphia, Pennsylvania 19103
Attn: Richard Colsher

TILPAD

Category: Tilting-pad journal bearing, incompressible fluid film bearing,
partial-arc bearing pad, static and dynamic characteristics
Descriptive Program Title: Hydrodynamic Tilting-Pad Journal Bearing,
Incompressible Lubricant
Author: Richard Colsher
Maintenance: Franklin Research Center
Dates: First release 1970; most recent update 1976
Capability: Calculation of the "assembled" bearing characteristics from
single pad data. Single pad data are generated by HYDJRL or may be
optionally furnished by the user. Pivot location is user specified.
Method: Steady-state condition is determined iteratively to satisfy the
condition of null pitching moment about the pivot. Dynamic perturba-
tion coefficients are determined with a consistent pitching perturbation such that the perturbed pitching moment remains zero. See HYDJRL
for the calculation of single pad data.
Limitations and Restrictions: Pad inertia is neglected. Pitching frequency
is assumed to be synchronous. Roll and yaw motions are not considered.
See also HYDJRL.
Programming Language: FORTRAN IV
Documentation: User's manual and program documentation manual are available.
Input: Geometry of the bearing system, input data for single pad calculation (optional, see HYDJRL), single pad data (optimal), pivot locations, load or journal position

Output: Nondimensional single-pad performance: load capacity; power
    loss; minimum film thickness; side leakage; inlet flow; cross-
    couple spring and damping coefficients.
        Dimensional full bearing performance: performance determined
    as a function of given eccentricities or given loads; load or
    position; viscous power loss; minimum film thickness; side leakage;
    inlet flow; complete cross-coupled, spring and damping coefficient
    including pad motions and equivalent spring and damping coefficients
    excluding pad motions.
Software Operation: Either batch or time-sharing
Hardware: CDC, UNIVAC 1100-1108, IBM 360-370, PRIME 300, DEC 20
Usage: About ten users
Typical Running Time: 10-20 seconds CPU on UNIVAC 1108 per case
Availability: Can be purchased or leased from
    Franklin Research Center
    A Division of Franklin Institute
    The Benjamin Franklin Parkway
    Philadelphia, Pennsylvania 19103
    Attn: Richard Colsher

REBAP

Category: Rolling element bearing, ball bearing, roller bearing
Descriptive Program Title: Rolling Element Bearing Analysis Program
Author: John H. Rumbarger
Maintenance: Franklin Research Center
Dates: First release 1970; most recent update 1978
Capability: This program can be used to determine load-life performance
    characteristics of a single bearing or a system of bearings with the
    "3 degrees of freedom" analysis. It determines B_{10} life of system
    as well as each bearing in the system, establishes spring rates,
    computes load and stress for maximum and minimum loaded element, and
    can be used to optimize bearing design. It predicts bearing response
    to clearance, preload, and spring mounting.
Method: The solution is a Newton-Raphson iteration scheme on the load
    equilibrium equations as constructed from bearing deflection theory.
    Life calculations are done in accord with AFBMA standards.
Limitations and Restrictions: Body forces are neglected.
Programming Lanuage: FORTRAN IV
Documentation: User's manual and program documentation manual are avail-
    able.
Input: Number of bearings in system, applied loads or displacements,
    speed of rotation, bearing type, internal geometry, special features
    (preload, etc.)
Output: System B_{10} life, bearing reactions and displacements, bearing
    spring rates, load and stress for maximum and minimum loaded element,
    bearing friction torque
Software Operation: Either batch or time-sharing
Hardware: CDC, UNIVAC 1100-1108, IBM 360-370, PRIME 300, DEC 20
Usage: About ten users
Typical Running Time: 40 seconds CPU on UNIVAC 1108
Availability: Can be purchased or leased from:
    Franklin Research Center
    A Division of Franklin Institute
    The Benjamin Franklin Parkway

Philadelphia, Pennsylvania 19103
Attn: Richard Colsher

GENROL

Category: Rolling element bearing, ball bearing, roller bearing
Descriptive Program Title: General Rolling Element Bearing Analysis
    Program
Author: John H. Rumbarger
Maintenance: Franklin Research Center
Dates: First release 1970; most recent update 1978
Capability: This program will determine load-life performance charac-
    teristics of a single bearing or a system of bearings with exact
    analysis of internal element to element load and stress, determine
    B_{10} life of system as well as each bearing in the system, establishes
    spring rates, and predict bearing response to preload and structural
    deformations. It can be used to optimize bearing design. Bearing can
    be modelled with reduced number of elements.
Method: The solution is a Newton-Raphson iteration scheme on the load
    equilibrium equations as constructed from the theory of A. B. Jones
    and A. Palmgren. Life calculations can be carried out by AFBMA
    standard methods or by the Lundberg and Palmgren method.
Limitations and Restrictions: Centrifugal forces are neglected.
Programming Language: FORTRAN IV
Documentation: User's manual and program documentation manual are avail-
    able.
Input: Number of bearings in system, applied loads or displacements,
    speed of rotation, bearing type, all internal geometry information,
    material characteristics, special mounting features (preload, etc.)
Output: System B_{10} life, bearing reactions and displacements, bearing
    spring rates, internal element load and stress, contact area size
    and geometry
Software Operation: Either batch or time-sharing
Hardware: CDC, UNIVAC 1100-1108, IBM 360-370, PRIME 300, DEC 20
Usage: About ten users
Typical Running Time: 40 seconds CPU on UNIVAC 1108
Availability: Can be purchased or leased from:
    Franklin Research Center
    A Division of Franklin Institute
    The Benjamin Franklin Parkway
    Philadelphia, Pennsylvania 19103
    Attn: Richard Colsher

TORVIB

Category: Natural frequencies, transient response, torsional vibration
Descriptive Program Title: Torsional Vibration Analysis
Author: Richard Coloher
Maintenance: Franklin Research Center
                A Division of the Franklin Institute
Dates: First released 1974 ; most recent update 1979
Capability: This program can be used to determine natural frequencies and
    transient response of undamped and damped torsional systems. The sys-
    tem may consist of up to fifteen branches with multiple masses on each

shaft. Coupling compliance can be treated. External constraints may
have both elastic and dissipative components. Dynamic stresses are
computed. For transient studies, system excitation may include exciting torques as functions of time which are independently assigned to
a number of locations. Motor parameters may be used to compute motor
torque as a function of speed. Gear blacklash can be included.
Method: The method treats the system as a series of masses connected by
shafts. For a multishaft system, the actual system is replaced by
a dynamically equivalent system in which all shafts and masses rotate
with the same angular velocity.
   Using D'Alembert's principle, the equilibrium equations are
written for each station of the system. The number of equations is
equal to the number of degrees of freedom in the entire rotating
assembly.
   For stability calculations, the set of equations is transformed
into the standard form of an eigenvalue problem. The problem is then
solved by the QR-2 algorithm [10]. The solution yields the natural
frequencies and the mode shapes of the system.
   For response calculations, a time transient (forward integration
in time) analysis is conducted using a Newmark numerical approach.
Initial conditions are set and shaft twists and torques are computed
at each time interval.
Limitations and Restrictions: Coupling with flexure motion is not allowed.
Programming Language: FORTRAN IV
Documentation: User's manual and program documentation manual are avail-
able.
Input: Geometry and inertia properties of rotating system, rotating speeds
of multi-shaft system, material, and external dampings, flexible
supports, excitation characterization (torques, frequencies, phase
angles and locations)
Output: Natural frequencies, growth factors, mode shapes, vibratory
amplitudes at transient and steady state, dynamic stresses
Software Operation: Either batch or time-sharing
Hardware: CDC, UNIVAC 1100-1108, IBM 360-370, PRIME 300, DEC 20
Usage: About 10 users
Typical Running Time: 30 seconds CPU on UNIVAC 1108
Availability: Can be purchased or leased from:·
   Franklin Research Center
   Division of Franklin Institute
   The Benjamin Franklin Parkway
   Philadelphia, Pennsylvania 19103
   Attn: Richard Colsher

CAD 20

Category: Critical speeds of rotors
Descriptive Program Title: Lateral Critical Speeds of Flexible Rotors
Author: J. W. Lund
Maintenance: Mechanical Technology Incorporated
Dates: First release 1970, most recent update 1979
Capability: This program computes the lateral critical speeds of single
or coupled rotors with flexible bearing supports. The rotor is
modelled as a series of shaft segments with distributed mass inter-
spersed with concentrated inertia elements. The bearings are repre-
sented by a spring constant between rotor and pedestal, which may

then be considered as elastically mounted. Isotropic, linear bearing characteristics are assumed. Up to 100 stations can be handled. Useful quantities such as the total rotor weight and moments of inertia, together with center of gravity position and static bearing loads are provided in the program output.

Method: The analysis is an extension of the Prohl method for calculating critical speeds. The shaft is treated as a distributed mass to which concentrated masses (wheels, thrust runners, etc.) may be added. The effects of shear deflection and gyroscopic moments can be specified along the rotor system.

Limitations and Restrictions: Bearing anisotropy is neglected.

Programming Language: FORTRAN IV

Documentation: User's manual

Input: Rotor dimensions, concentrated inertia values, material properties, bearing stiffness, speed range of interest

Output: Input data reprinted, also critical speeds, normalized vibration amplitude at each rotor station, mode shape printer plots

Software Operation: An option is available to access the program via batch or time-sharing mode.

Hardware: CDC, Honeywell, IBM

Usage: Extensively used

Typical Running Time: 0.4 seconds CPU per critical speed on CDC 6600

Availability: Can be leased from:
Mechanical Technology Incorporated
968 Albany-Shaker Road
Latham, New York 12110
Attn: Paul Babson (Availability)
      Doug Hatch/Emily Koch (Maintenance)
Also available from commercial networks; Cybernet, GE Mark III, and United Computing Services.

CAD 21

Category: Unbalance response of a flexible rotor
Descriptive Program Title: Unbalance Response of a Flexible Rotor
Author: J. W. Lund
Maintenance: Mechanical Technology Incorporated
Capability: This program computes the elliptical whirl response of a flexible, elastically mounted rotor to a given unbalance excitation. It scans incrementally a specified speed range and computes the absolute amplitude of vibration (unbalance response) for each rotor station at each speed increment. The rotor mountings are considered as elastic bearings described by their stiffness and damping coefficients. Bearing pedestals may be treated as rigid or elastic. The rotor is described in terms of lengths and radii of discrete sections. Concentrated inertias may be placed on the rotor and described by their masses and moments of inertia. For the case of a rigid pedestal, the program output includes the force transmitted to the bearing housing. For a flexible pedestal, the program provides the pedestal motion and the force transmitted to the foundation. The pedestal is represented by a model having two translational degrees of freedom.
Method: The program employs an extension of the Prohl critical speed method [4], which is described by Lund and Orcutt in Ref. [13]. Prohl's method is modified to account for elastic rotor mountings and for the influence of distributed shaft mass.

Limitations and Restrictions: Constant bearing coefficients are assumed.
Programming Language: FORTRAN IV
Documentation: User's manual
Input: Rotor dimensions, material properties, concentrated inertia values, speed ranges of interest, bearing stiffness and damping coefficients at each speed increment, unbalance values.
Output: All input data are reprinted, as well as major and minor axes of rotor orbit at each station, phase angle of rotor amplitude, forces transmitted to bearings and pedestals. There is a printed summary output option for selected stations.
Software Operation: An option is available to access the program via batch or time-sharing mode.
Hardware: CDC, Honeywell, IBM
Usage: Extensively used
Typical Running Time: 2 to 4 speeds per second on CDC 6600
Availability: Can be leased from:
    Mechanical Technology Incorporated
    968 Albany-Shaker Road
    Latham, New York 12110
    Attn: Paul Babson (Availability)
          Doug Hatch/Emily Koch (Maintenance)
Also available from commercial networks - Cybernet, GE Mark III, and United Computing Services.

CAD 21A

Category: Response of flexible rotors to nonsynchronous sinusoidal excitation
Descriptive Program Title: Response of Flexible Rotors to Nonsynchronous Sinusoidal Excitation
Author: J. W. Lund
Maintenance: Mechanical Technology Incorporated
Dates: First release 1976, most recent update 1978
Capability: This program computes the elliptical whirl response of a flexible elastically mounted rotor to a given force excitation, either synchronous or asynchronous. It scans incrementally a specified speed range and computes the absolute amplitude of vibration (forced response) for each rotor station at each speed increment. The rotor mountings are considered as elastic bearings described by their stiffness and damping coefficients. Bearing pedestals may be treated as rigid or elastic. The rotor is described in terms of lengths and radii of discrete sections. Concentrated inertias may be placed on the rotor and described by their mass and moments of inertia. For the case of a rigid pedestal, the program output includes the force transmitted to the bearing housing. For a flexible pedestal, the program provides the pedestal motion and the force transmitted to the foundation. The pedestal is represented by a model having two translational degrees of freedom.
Method: The program employs an extension of the Prohl critical speed method [4] which is described by Lund and Orcutt in Ref [13]. Prohl's method is modified to account for elastic rotor mountings and for the influence of distributed shaft mass.
Limitations and Restrictions: Constant bearing coefficients are assumed.
Programming Language: FORTRAN IV

Documentation: User's manual
Input: Rotor dimensions, material properties, concentrated inertia values,
        speed ranges of interest, bearing stiffness and damping coefficients
        at each speed increment, unbalance and/or force values, excitation
        frequencies
Output: All input data, major and minor axes of rotor orbit at each
        station, phase angle of rotor amplitude, forces transmitted to bear-
        ings and pedestals
Software Operation: An option is available to access the program via batch
        or time-sharing mode.
Hardware: CDC
Usage: Extensively used
Typical Running Time: 2 to 4 speeds per second on CDC 6600
Availability: Can be leased from
        Mechanical Technology Incorporated
        968 Albany-Shaker Road
        Latham, New York 12110
        Attn: Paul Babson (Availability)
               Doug Hatch/Emily Koch (Maintenance)
        Also available from commercial networks - Cybernet, GE Mark III,and
        United Computing Services

                              CAD 22

Category: Torsional critical speeds, natural frequencies, real eigenvalues
Descriptive Program Title: Torsional Critical Speeds of a Geared System
Author: J. W. Lund
Maintenance: Mechanical Technology Incorporated
Dates: First release 1970, most recent update 1978
Capability: This program calculates the critical frequencies of a torsional
        system. The system may include branches, gears, epicyclic gears, and
        elastic torsional connection to ground. At each critical frequency,
        the program evaluates the normalized mode shape and corresponding torque
        distribution.
Method: The program employs the Holzer method extended to account more
        accurately for continuously distributed shaft sections. Effective root
        finding methods are employed to calculate all critical frequencies with-
        in specified ranges.
Limitations and Restrictions: Coupling with flexural motion is neglected.
Programming Language: FORTRAN IV
Documentation: User's manual
Input: Rotor geometry, rotor material properties, additional concentrated
        inertias, single reduction gear dimensions, epicyclic gear train
        dimensions, frequency ranges to be searched
Output: Holzer end torque as a function of frequency, critical frequencies,
        mode shape at each critical, torque distribution at each critical
Software Operation: An option is available to access the program via batch
        or time-sharing mode
Hardware: CDC, Honeywell
Usage: Used extensively
Typical Running Time: Four critical speeds per second CPU on CDC Cybernet
Availability: Can be leased from:
        Mechanical Technology Incorporated
        968 Albany-Shaker Road
        Latham, New York 12110

Attn: Paul Babson (Availability)
       Doug Hatch/Emily Koch (Maintenance)
Also available from commercial networks - Cybernet, Honeywell and
United Computing Services

CAD 23

Category: Damped torsional response, sinusoidal excitation
Descriptive Program Title: Damped Torsional Response of a Geared System
Author: J. W. Lund
Maintenance: Mechanical Technology Incorporated
Dates: First release 1970, most recent update 1978.
Capability: This program computes the damped torsional response of a system
    to excitation in the form of either torques, or angular displacements
    (gear errors). The system may include branches, single reduction gears,
    and constraints to ground with both stiffness and damping. The gears
    may be rigidly or elastically mounted. The system amplitudes, torque
    distribution,and gear tooth meshing forces are calculated by the program,
    and for elastically mounted gears the transmitted forces and gear tooth
    displacements are evaluated.
Method: A Holzer-type method is used, extended to account more accurately
    for continuously distributed shaft sections.
Limitations and Restrictions: Coupling with flexural motion is neglected.
Program Language: FORTRAN IV
Documentation: User's manual
Input: Rotor geometry, rotor material properties, additional concentrated
    inertias, single reduction gear dimensions, epicyclic gear train
    dimensions, frequency values of interest, gear error amplitudes,
    exciting torque amplitudes
Output: Rotor station amplitudes at each frequency, system torque distri-
    bution, gear tooth forces, gear shaft bearing forces (for elastically
    mounted gears), axial and lateral tooth forces and displacements (for
    elastically mounted gears).
Software Operation: An option is available to access the program via batch
    or time-sharing mode.
Hardware: CDC
Usage: Used extensively
Typical Running Time: Four response speeds per second CPU on CDC Cybernet
Availability: Can be leased from:
    Mechanical Technology Incorporated
    968 Albany-Shaker Road
    Latham, New York 12110
    Attn: Paul Babson (Availability)
           Doug Hatch/Emily Koch (Maintenance)
    Also available from commercial network - CDC Cybernet

CAD 24

Category: Torsional transient, time-history
Descriptive Program Title: Transient Torsional Response of a Geared
    System
Authors: A. Smalley and A. Artiles
Maintenance: Mechanical Technology Incorporated

Dates: First release 1973, most recent update 1978
Capability: This program computes the transient torsional response of a
    system to specified input at one or more stations of the system. Such
    topics as drive train start-up, rolling mill shock, or any situation
    with intermittent torsional loading, such as from synchronous motors,
    may be simulated. The system may include branches, subbranches and
    gears. Backlash may be specified at any point. The program takes
    account of both stiffness and damping in each elastic member, and also
    allows for stiffness and damping between any station and ground. Both
    nonlinear stiffness and damping elements, such as found in Holset
    couplings, may be specified at any point. Motor torques may be
    specified by tabular functions of motor speed. Both steady state and
    oscillatory torque components may be included. The user may specify
    either the number of timesteps, the amount of real time, or a
    designated maximum motor speed to control the length of the run. An
    option to print out only maximum and minimum torque summary and time
    of occurrence at each station is included for use when detailed print-
    out at all time steps is not desired.
Method: The system of dynamic equations is solved by either a fourth order
    Runge-Kutta or the Newmark beta method to give angular displacements.
    System torques are calculated from the displacements.
Limitations and Restrictions: Coupling with flexural motion is neglected.
Programming Language: FORTRAN IV
Documentation: User's manual
Input: The input may be a torque history, a velocity history, or a motor
    torque table, including initial displacements or velocities. An
    alternative input is the specification of: steady and alternating
    torque-speed relationships for a synchronous motor: stiffness and
    damping; backlash, polar moments of inertia, and pitch radii of gears;
    initial displacements and velocities.
Output: Station displacements and velocities as a function of time; system
    torques as a function of time and a separate Mechanical Technology Inc.
    general purpose plot program which uses Calcomp software are also avail-
    able.
Software Operation: An option is available to access the program via batch
    or time-sharing mode.
Hardware: CDC, IBM
Usage: Used extensively
Typical Running Time: Approximately 30 seconds CPU per run on CDC Cybernet
Availability: Can be leased from:
    Mechanical Technology Incorporated
    968 Albany-Shaker Road
    Latham, New York 12110
    Attn: Paul Babson (Availability)
        Doug Hatch/Emily Koch (Maintenance)
    Also available on CDC commercial network

CAD 25

Category: Stability, complex eigenvalue
Descriptive Program Title: Dynamic Stability of a Flexible Rotor
Author: J. W. Lund
Maintenance: Mechanical Technology Incorporated
Dates: First release 1971, most recent update 1978

Capability: This program computes the damped natural frequencies of a
   rotor bearing system. For each natural frequency the magnitude and
   sign of the effective system damping is calculated. Based on this result the dynamic stability of the rotor-bearing system may be assessed.
   The rotor is described in terms of lengths and radii of discrete
   sections. Concentrated inertias may be placed on the rotor and
   described by their mass and moments of inertia. Fluid film bearings
   are described by linear stiffness and damping values. Passive aero-
   dynamic excitation may be accounted for and is represented by
   linearized coefficients based on the torque per stage, vane efficiency,
   and the wheel to stator clearance-to-vane height ratio. Internal
   material damping, and damping in shrink fits and friction joints may
   also be accounted for and are specified in terms of an associated
   logarithmic decrement. The program uses very efficient root searching
   techniques based on a generalized Newton-Raphson method.
Method: An extension of the Prohl critical speed method is employed to
   determine the complex eigenvalues of the system dynamic matrix. The
   imaginary part is the natural frequency and the real part is the amplitude growth exponent.
Limitations and Restrictions: Constant bearing coefficients are assumed.
Programming Language: FORTRAN IV
Documentation: User's manual
Input: Rotor dimensions, material properties, concentrated inertia values,
   frequency ranges of interest, table of nondimensional bearing stiffness
   and damping coefficients, bearing dimensions, operating speed(s) of
   interest
Output: All input data, damped natural frequencies, logarithmic decrement
   (indicator of system damping) for each mode, rotor major and minor
   mode shapes at frequency, phase angle of rotor amplitude
Software Operation: An option is available to access the program via batch
   or time-sharing mode.
Hardware: CDC, Honeywell
Usage: Used extensively
Typical Running Time: 1 to 2 seconds CPU on CDC Cybernet for a damp natural
   frequency.
Availability: Can be leased from:
   Mechanical Technology Incorporated
   968 Albany-Shaker Road
   Latham, New York 12110
   Attn: Paul Babson (Availability)
        Doug Hatch/Emily Koch (Maintenance)
   Also available from commercial networks - CDC Cybernet, GE Mark III,
   United Computing Service

CAD 30

Category: Hydrodynamic journal, incompressible fluid film bearing, static
   and dynamic characteristics
Descriptive Program Title: Performance of Liquid Lubricated Journal Bearings
Author: J. W. Lund
Maintenance: Mechanical Technology Incorporated
Dates: First release 1970, most recent update 1979
Capability: This program computes the normalized film forces, flow rates,
   friction factor, and stiffness and damping coefficients for multiple-
   pad (with or without preloading) and single and liquid lubricated
   journal bearings. The single arc data are suitable for assembly into

tilting pad bearing data. The program accounts for cavitation of the lubricant, and is applicable to both laminar and turbulent lubricant regimes. The program allows specification of journal location relative to the pads, or is capable of iteratively determining the correct journal attitude angle for a specified load direction. The critical mass for bearing stability is also calculated.

Method: A finite difference solution of the two-dimensional incompressible lubrication equation is used to calculate the bearing pressure distribution for a particular journal location. If the load direction is specified relative to the bearing pads, the program initially assumes a journal location and integrates the corresponding pressure distribution to yield bearing film force components and the direction of their resultant. The journal location is then iteratively adjusted until the bearing forces act vertically within a specified convergence limit, at which stage the stiffness and damping coefficients are calculated by dynamic perturbation of the pressures. See Ref. [14].

Limitations and Restrictions: Constant lubricant viscosity, linear dynamic coefficients, no inertia effects, linearized turbulent film theory, and flow transition conditions are not considered.

Programming Language: FORTRAN IV

Documentation: User's manual

Input: Bearing L/D ratio, Reynolds number (if turbulent), bearing pad geometry

Output: Bearing film forces, bearing eccentricity ratio, friction, flow-rate, attitude angle, stiffness coefficients, damping coefficients, critical journal mass coefficients

Software Operation: An option is available to access the program via batch or time-sharing mode.

Hardware: CDC, Honeywell, IBM

Usage: Extensively used internally; public use is increasing, the main users are manufacturers.

Typical Running Time: A table of 15 points takes 40 seconds CPU on CDC Cybernet.

Availability: Can be leased from:
Mechanical Technology Incorporated
968 Albany-Shaker Road
Latham, New York 12110
Attn: Paul Babson (Availability)
        Doug Hatch/Emily Koch (Maintenance)
Also available from commercial networks - GE Mark III

CAD 31

Category: Hydrodynamic journal, incompressible lubricant, axial grooves, static and dynamic characteristics

Descriptive Program Title: Design of Liquid Lubricated Axial Groove Journal Bearings

Author: Technical staff of Mechanical Technology Incorporated

Maintenance: Mechanical Technology Incorporated

Dates: First release 1970, most recent update 1976

Capability: This program calculates dimensional static and dynamic performance data for liquid lubricated, axial-groove, journal bearings. It will, at the user's option, perform a heat balance based upon power loss, lubricant flow, and lubricant characteristics, to yield an effective mean operating viscosity and corresponding performance data.

Method: The program operates on basic dimensionless pad data to generate
    dimensional bearing data. Dimensionless data are obtained from
    Cadense Program No. CAD-30. The basic pad data consist of dimension-
    less performance parameter values for a single bearing pad at a series
    of discrete values of journal eccentricity ratio. Dimensional design
    and performance data are calculated by the program for specified bear-
    ing size, operating speed, applied load, and lubricant properties using
    interpolation to establish continuously varying performance quantities
    in terms of the discrete basic data points. The heat balance is per-
    formed assuming all heat is carried away by the lubricant (a conserva-
    tive assumption). The user is free to specify the fraction of overall
    temperature rise to be applied in determining the effective mean
    operating viscosity.
Limitations and Restrictions: Constant lubricant viscosity, linear dynamic
    coefficients, no inertia effects, linearized turbulent film theory,
    flow transition conditions not considered.
Programming Language: FORTRAN IV
Documentation: User's manual
Input: Bearing geometry, lubricant characteristics, speeds of interest,
    applied loads of interest, dimensionless bearing data
Output: Bearing eccentricity ratio, lubricant flow, power loss, stiffness
    and damping values, bearing temperature rise
Software Operation: An option is available to access the program via batch
    or time-sharing mode.
Hardware: CDC, Honeywell, IBM
Usage: Used extensively
Typical Running Time: Two seconds CPU per bearing on CDC Cybernet
Availability: Can be leased from:
    Mechanical Technology Incorporated
    968 Albany-Shaker Road
    Latham, New York 12110
    Attn: Paul Babson (Availability)
           Doug Hatch/Emily Koch (Maintenance)
    Also available from commercial networks - CDC, Honeywell

                                CAD 32

Category: Tilting pad journal, static and dynamic characteristics
Descriptive Program Title: Design of Liquid Lubricated Tilting Pad
    Journal Bearings
Author: Technical staff of Mechanical Technology Incorporated
Maintenance: Mechanical Technology Incorporated
Dates: First release 1970, most recent update 1976.
Capability: This program calculates dimensional static and dynamic per-
    formance data for liquid lubricated tilting pad journal bearings. It
    performs a heat balance based upon power loss, lubricant flow, and
    lubricant characteristics to yield an effective mean operating
    viscosity and corresponding performance data.
Method: The program operates on basic dimensionless pad data to generate
    dimensional bearing data. Dimensionless data are obtained from Cadense
    Program No. CAD-30. The heat balance is performed assuming all heat
    is carried away by the lubricant (a conservative assumption). The
    user is free to specify the fraction of overall temperature rise to be
    applied in determining the effective mean operating viscosity. The

basic pad data consists of dimensionless performance parameter
values for a single bearing pad at a series of discrete values of
journal eccentricity ratio. The program initially assembles the
single pad data to yield dimensionless performance parameters
for a journal bearing with a specified number of pads, which
may be preloaded or nominally concentric with the journal. The
assembled bearing data is calculated and stored by the program for a
range of discrete bearing eccentricity ratios. Dimensional performance
data are then calculated by the program for specified bearing size,
operating speed, applied load, and lubricant properties, using interpolation to establish continuously varying performance quantities in
terms of the discrete assembled data points.
Limitations and Restrictions: Constant lubricant viscosity; linear dynamic
    coefficients; no inertial effects; linearized turbulent film theory;
    flow transition conditions not considered; pad inertia is neglected.
Programming Language: FORTRAN IV
Documentation: User's manual
Input: Bearing geometry, lubricant characteristics, speeds of interest,
    applied loads of interest, dimensionless bearing data
Output: Bearing eccentricity ratio, lubricant flow, power loss, stiffness
    and damping values, bearing temperature rise
Software Operation: An option is available to access the program via batch
    or time-sharing mode.
Hardware: CDC, Honeywell, IBM
Usage: Used extensively
Typical Running Time: Five seconds CPU per bearing on CDC Cybernet
Availability: Can be leased from:
    Mechanical Technology Incorporated
    968 Albany-Shaker Road
    Latham, New York 12110
    Attn: Paul Babson (Availability)
         Doug Hatch/Emily Koch (Maintenance)
    Also available from commercial networks - CDC, Honeywell, and United
    Computing Services.

EPHB

Category: Gas lubricated journal bearing, external pressurization, herring-
    bone grooves, stability analysis
Descriptive Program Title: Externally Pressurized, Herringbone Grooved,
    Gas Lubricated, Journal Bearing Analysis
Author: D. P. Fleming
Date: Operational since 1970
Capability: This program determines static and dynamic characteristics of
    gas lubricated journal bearings with either external pressurization or
    herringbone grooves or both. Small eccentricity radial and tangential
    forces are computed as functions of whirl frequency ratio. Stability
    is determined in terms of the critical mass parameter.
Method: The axially symmetric solution is solved iteratively; then eccen-
    tricity effects are determined by a perturbation calculation.
    Restriction characterization is formulated by the line—source approxi-
    mation. Herringbone grooving effects are treated according to the
    narrow groove approximation.
Limitations and Restrictions: Small eccentricity, translational motion
    only, edge effects, and local compressibility are neglected in the
    grooved region.

Programming Language: FORTRAN IV
Documentation: NASA TND-5780, 1970
Input: Geometrical and kinematic parameters required of gas bearing
    designs
Output: Static, small eccentricity force components (load capacity and
    attitude angle), critical mass parameter, and frequency ratio for the
    stability threshold
Software Operation: Batch
Hardware: IBM 360
Usage: Used to compile comprehensive dynamic data in TND-5780
Typical Running Time: 20 CPU seconds on IBM 360
Availability: Contact:
    NASA - Lewis Research Center
    Shaft and Rotor Dynamics Section
    Cleveland, Ohio 44135
    Attn: Dr. D. P. Fleming

RSVP

Category: Flexible rotor, critical speeds, unbalance response, asynchro-
    nous resonances, damped asynchronous response, stability analysis,
    real and complex eigenvalues
Descriptive Program Title: Rotor Structure Vibration Program for Flexural
    and Torsional Motions
Author: C. H. T. Pan
Maintenance: Shaker Research Corporation
    Northway 10 Executive Park
    Ballston Lake, N. Y. 12019
    Attn: Ms. J. A. Bartlett
Date: To be released in November 1979
Capability: This is an all-purpose program for the linear analysis of
    flexible rotors. A single rotor model setup is used for all analysis
    types. Through input control, the program is commanded to execute
    either one of six options: torsional response; critical speeds;
    damped unbalance response; asynchronous resonances; damped asynchro-
    nous response; and stability analysis. Flexural constraints of either
    displacement or angular type are used to account for fluid film bear-
    ings and turbo-excitations. Asynchronous excitation may be specified
    in either space fixed or rotating point of view. Damped critical
    speed or damped natural frequency may be searched in a user-specified
    range for the determination of "peak" damped response. The complex
    eigenvalue problem can be solved with the constraint of synchronous
    frequencies. Damped response and mode shapes are given in elliptical
    orbit parameters. Stability analysis is performed with the point of
    view of a phase-shift natural mode, and the state of stability is in-
    dicated by the critical damping ratio. Frequency dependent constraint
    coefficients may be used to account for foundation compliance effects.
    Structure impedance can be accessed for assembly into a larger system,
    e.g., a multi-shaft rotor system.
Method: Standard transfer method is used to assemble the dynamic system
    matrix of the rotor structure. Impedance matching is used to assign
    constraint effects. Distributed inertia is included in both torsional
    and flexural problems. Real eigenvalue problems are solved with the
    aid of spline interpolation. Complex eigenvalue problems are solved
    with Newton-Raphson iteration in the user-specified frequency range.

Limitations and Restrictions: Torsional analysis does not treat damping.
    Analysis treats each shaft, one at a time, for multi-shaft systems.
Programming Language: FORTRAN IV
Documentation: User's and technical manuals are available [15].
Input: Rotor geometry, material properties, constraint coefficients, speed-
    frequency range, problem specification, excitation force as applicable
Output: Undamped and damped natural frequenices, response and mode shapes,
    stability indicator (critical damping ratio), rotor structure imped-
    ance matrices
Software Operation: The program operates in the batch mode. An interactive
    preprocessor for input preparation and access to fluid-film bearing
    data bank is available.
Hardware: CDC 6600, Prime 350
Usage: No user statistics available
Typical Running Time: Varies with problem
Availability: Basic program available at a nominal cost. Contact:
    USAF/APL
    Wright-Patterson Air Force Base, Ohio 45433
    Attn: John Schrand
    or
    Shaker Research Corporation
    Northway 10 Executive Park
    Ballston Lake, N. Y. 12019
    Attn: Ms. J. A. Bartlett
    For inquiries on preprocessor and custom installation, contact
    Shaker Research Corporation only.

BEARDATA

Category: Fluid film journal bearings, static and dynamic characteristics,
    data bank
Descriptive Program Title: Full Range Retrieval System for Static and
    Dynamic Characteristics of Fluid Film Journal Bearings
Author: C. H. T. Pan
Maintenance: Shaker Research Corporation
            Northway 10 Executive Park
            Ballston Lake, N. Y. 12019
            Attn: Dr. A. I. Krauter
Date: To be released in November 1979
Capability: To perform interpolation or asymptotic extrapolation on
    established data bank of specific types of fluid film journal bear-
    ings. The inverse of Sommerfeld number is used as the input param-
    eter for accessing the data bank and to perform the necessary inter-
    polation-extrapolation operations. Full range smoothness has been
    verified for all installed data banks. Each data file contains
    records of eccentricity ratio, attitude angle, friction, "total" and
    "end leakage" flows, and the eight perturbation stiffness/damping
    coefficients. Present catalog of the data system contains plain
    journal, axial-groove bearings, lobed bearings, partial arc bearings,
    and tilting-shoe bearings. These files can be accessed through the
    use of the preprocessor for the rotor dynamics program RSVP.
Method: Empirical approximate formulas of the rational fraction type are
    constructed from the data bank with near-field and far-field trends
    directly extracted from the data bank. The semi-infinite range of
    the input parameter is uniquely mapped onto a finite range (from zero
    to unity) of an interpolation variable. Deviation between data points

and the approximate empirical formulas are used to establish a set of
spline interpolation coefficients. The retrieval file contains the
coefficients of the rational fraction functions and the interpolation
spline polynomials.
Limitations and Restrictions: The data file is formated for isoviscous
journal bearing solutions. Misalignment effects are neglected.
Dynamic coefficents are for small perturbation from the static equilibrium position. Nonlaminar effects are neglected.
Programming Language: FORTRAN IV
Documentation: User's and technical manuals are available [16].
Input: Selection of bearing configuration. For dimensional data geometri-
cal data, lubricant viscosity,and journal speed are required. For
dimensionless data the user specifies the desired range of the load
parameter (inverse of Sommerfeld number)
Output: Design conditions, dynamic perturbations coefficients in either
dimensionless or dimensional form
Software Operation: Both interactive and batch mode versions are available.
Hardware: CDC 6600, Prime 350
Usage: No user statistics available
Typical Running Time: 8 CPU seconds on Prime 350
Availability: Present data file and retrieval program are available at a
nominal cost. Contact:
USAF - APL
Wright-Patterson Air Force Base, Ohio
Attn: John Schrand
or
Shaker Research Corporation
Northway 10 Executive Park
Ballston Lake, N. Y. 12019
Attn: Ms. J. A. Bartlett
For custom installation of new data, contact Shaker Research
Corporation only.

BALL, CYLINDER, TAPER

Category: Stiffness coefficients, rolling element bearings, centrifugal
force effects
Descriptive Program Title: Dynamic Stiffness Coefficients of Rolling Element
Bearings
Authors: A. B. Jones and John M. McGrew
Maintenance: Shaker Research Corporation
Date: 1979
Capability: Calculation of stiffness coefficients of rolling element bearings with allowance for centrifugal force of the rolling elements. Each
of the three bearing types, the ball bearing, the cylindrical roller
bearing, and the tapered roller bearing, is treated individually in a
separate computer program.
Method: The equilibrium condition, including body forces of the rolling
elements,is first determined iteratively, then displacement perturbation is performed to determine various stiffness coefficients. In
lieu of a detailed analysis of the interelemental tangential traction, the user selects either inner or outer race control (no sliding).
Limitations and Restrictions: These programs are not concerned with the
elastohydrodynamic film and do not deal with routine design parameters.
They are mainly intended for calculating stiffness coefficients for use
in rotor dynamics analysis.

Programming Language: FORTRAN IV
Documentation: User's and technical manuals are available [17,18,19].
Input: Geometrical parameters as applicable to each bearing type, speed,
     material properties, preload as applicable, and static load
Output: Radial, axial, and angular stiffness coefficients
Software Operation: Batch mode
Hardware: CDC 6600, Univac 1108, IBM, Prime 350
Usage: No user statistics available
Typical Running Time: 80 CPU seconds on Prime 350
Availability: Available at a nominal cost, contact:
     USAF/APL
     Wright-Patterson Air Force Base, Ohio
     Attn: John Schrand
     or
     Shaker Research Corporation
     Northway 10 Executive Park
     Ballston Lake, N. Y. 12019
     Attn: Ms. J. A. Bartlett

SPIRAL

Category: Gas lubricated journal bearing, spin bearing, antiwhirl bear-
     ing, cylindrical journal, Whipple thrust bearing, spool bearing,
     conical bearing, spherical bearing, static compliance, dynamic com-
     pliance, rigid rotor response, stability analysis.
Descriptive Program Title: Small Displacement Perturbation Analysis of
     Spiral-Grooved, Self-Acting, Gas Lubricated Bearing Systems
Author: C. H. T. Pan
Date: Operational since 1977
Capability: This is a general purpose computer program to perform a com-
     prehensive design analysis of the spiral-groove type of self-acting
     bearings. Static and dynamic perturbation load coefficients are
     calculated for various bearing configurations. The bearing envelope may
     be any combination of cylindrical, radial, conical, and spherical
     surfaces. Coverage of grooving is user specified on each surface.
     Axially symmetrical gap distortions can be emulated for each surface.
     Boundary conditions are user selected to assign pressurization or
     mass storage effects or simple continuities. The user may designate
     the lubricant to be either an isoviscous liquid or an isothermal per-
     fect gas. The Burgdorfer slip correction for rarefication is used.
     Rigid rotor frequency response and/or stability analysis can be
     activated by input control.
Method: The computer code is based on the locally imcompressible, narrow-
     groove theory. See Ref. [20]. Radial and angular displacement prob-
     lems are linearized by perturbation analysis.
Limitations and Restrictions: Small radial and angular displacements,
     cavitation and nonlaminar effects are neglected in the incompressible
     calculations. Theoretical limitations of the narrow-groove analysis
     pertaining to edge effects and local compressibility also apply.
Programming Language: FORTRAN IV
Documentation: User's manual available.
Input: Geometrical details of the surface configuration, grooving param-
     eters, rotational speeds, viscosity coefficient, selection of
     gaseous or liquid lubricant, ambient pressure and molecular mean free
     path of gas if applicable, boundary conditions, problem specification,

inertia properties of rotor, frequency range of interest, optional
  description of surface distortions
Output: Axially symmetric distribution of pressure, flow rates, pressure
  ripples, static and dynamic bearing reaction forces and moments,
  static and dynamic responses, critical mass for instability
Software Operation: Batch
Hardware: CDC, Univac 1108, Honeywell, Prime 350
Usage: Used extensively in several design improvement studies.
Typical Running Time: Varies with problem
Availability: Can be purchased from:
  Shaker Research Corporation
  Northway 10 Executive Park
  Ballston Lake, N. Y. 12019
  Attn: Ms. J. A. Bartlett

DAMPEDROTOR

Category: Damped critical speeds and whirl stability, complex eigenvalues
Authors: G. Horner and W. D. Pilkey
Maintenance: The Structural Members Users Group
Date: Program first available in 1975, most recent update 1979
Capability: This program determines the complex eigenvalue and eigenvector
  of a damped rotating shaft. The complex eigenvalue gives the stability
  of the rotor-bearing system and the damped natural frequency. A
  special feature of this program allows adjacent rotor sections to be
  connected by a rotary spring and/or a linear spring.
Method: The rotor is modeled as a series of lumped masses with gyroscopic
  moments and massless beam elements. The program uses a new method of
  analysis called the Riccati Transfer Matrix Method. A Newton-Raphson
  iteration is used in determining the complex eigenvalue [5].
Limitations and Restrictions: This program uses linear theory and
  isotropic bearings.
Programming Language: FORTRAN
Documentation: Complete user and technical documentation available
Input: Rotor geometry and bearing coefficients
Output: Damped natural frequency, the "Q" or quality factor, and the
  damped mode shape. Mode shape plotting is included.
Software Operation: Batch or time-sharing with interactive pre- and
  postprocessors.
Hardware: CDC, IBM, UNIVAC, and others. Also various mini- and micro-
  processors.
Usage: Extensive usage on commercial networks and in-house computers.
  Considerable live job usage.
Typical Running Time: About twice as fast as most standard transfer
  matrix programs.
Availability: Program can be used on the United Computing Systems com-
  mercial network or can be purchased at a nominal cost from -
  The Structural Members Users Group
  P. O. Box 3958 University Station
  Charlottesville, VA 22903

SHAFT

Category: Unbalanced response and critical speeds of rotors

Authors: P. Y. Chang and W. D. Pilkey
Maintenance: The Structural Members Users Group
Date: Program first made available in 1971, most recent update made in 1979
Capability: The program SHAFT calculates the unbalanced response and critical speeds of a shaft with no cross-coupling coefficients in the bearings. The critical speeds are found for a rotor with no damping in the bearings. For unbalanced response, the deflection, shape, bending moment, and shear force are calculated with damping in the bearings. The shaft can be formed of lumped or continuous mass segments with foundations, any boundary conditions, and any distribution of unbalanced masses. The user can include any or all of bending, shear deformation, and rotary inertia effects.
    Bearing systems can include springs, dampers, and a pedestal mass.
Method: The transfer matrix method is used [5].
Limitations and Restrictions: No bearing cross-coupling coefficients
Programming Language: FORTRAN
Documentation: Complete user and technical documentation available
Input: The bearing coefficients and rotor properties for each segment are input. An interactive preprocessor is available.
Output: For unbalanced response, the deflection, slope, bending moment, and shear force are printed at each station and each speed. The critical speeds are printed with the corresponding mode shapes.
Software Operations: Batch or time-sharing with interactive pre- and postprocessors.
Hardware: CDC, IBM, UNIVAC, and others. Also various mini- and microprocessors.
Usage: Extensive usage on commercial networks and in-house computers. Considerable live job usage.
Typical Running Time: Standard transfer matrix speed.
Availability: Program can be used on the United Computing Systems commercial network or can be purchased at a nominal cost from:
    The Structural Members Users Group
    P. O. Box 3958 University Station
    Charlottesville, VA 22903

TWIST

Category: Static and dynamic response and frequencies, and mode shapes of torsional bars and systems
Authors: P. Y. Chang and W. D. Pilkey
Maintenance: The Structural Members Users Group
Date: Program made available in 1971, most recent update 1979
Capability: For static and steady state torsional loads it calculates the angle of twist and the twisting moment of a shaft. It also computes the natural frequencies and mode shapes of torsional vibration. The torsion system can be a bar formed of uniform segments with any loading, gears, branches, foundations, and boundary conditions.
Method: The transfer matrix method is used [5].
Limitations and Restrictions: No damping
Programming Language: FORTRAN
Documentation: Complete user and technical documentation available
Input: Geometric and material properties of the torsional system

Output: Static response variables, natural frequencies, and mode shapes
Software Operation: Batch or time-sharing with interactive pre- and post-
     processors
Hardware: CDC, IBM, UNIVAC, and others. Also various mini- and micro-
     processors.
Usage: Extensive usage on commercial networks and in-house computers,
     considerable live job usage
Typical Running Time: Standard transfer matrix speed.
Availability: Program can be used on the United Computing Systems com-
     mercial network or can be purchased at a nominal cost from:
     The Structural Members Users Group
     P. O. Box 3958 University Station
     Charlottesville, VA 22903

                               LATCRIT

Category: Critical speeds, unbalance response
Descriptive Program Title: Lateral Dynamic Response for Synchronous
     Precessing Turborotors
Author: Paul R. Trumpler
Maintenance: Trumpler Associates Inc.
Dates: First available 1965, most recent update 1978
Capability: This program calculates critical speeds and unbalance response.
     Foundation compliance and damping can be treated. Bearing models
     for a variety of fluid film bearings are available. Outputs are
     graphical and tabular.
Method: The standard transfer matrix method is used. A complete descrip-
     tion of the solution method is given in Ref. [21].
Software Operation: Batch
Hardware: IBM 370/68
Typical Running Time: Four minutes plus plotting
Availability: Rental is 100% of direct computer center billing. Contact:
     Trumpler Associates Inc.
     449 Woodcrest Road
     Wayne, Pennsylvania 19087

                      Program Abstracts - Group II
                   Active Programs Updated Before 1976

             COMPUTERIZED MECHANICAL DESIGN ANALYSIS (BEST I)

Capability: The steady-state response, critical speeds and corresponding
     mode shapes of a rotor are determined. The rotor may have asynchro-
     nous motion where the whirl and spin frequencies are different.
     Foundations of bearings are represented by isotropic springs.
Method: The rotor is represented as a lumped mass system and the effects
     of shear and gyroscopic moments are included. The transfer matrix
     method is used for the analysis.
Limitations and Restrictions: A rotor may be represented by no more than
     20 spans and 25 lumped masses per span. No damping may be input, so
     that the critical speeds are for an undamped rotor. Bearings must be
     modeled as a simple linear spring.
Input: Span properties, spring values, frequency interval for critical
     speed search, and loading are required input. No preprocessor is
     available.

Output: Boundary condition equations, critical speed analysis and mode
         shapes, kinetic and potential energy of each span, and mode shape
         plots are output.
Language: FORTRAN
Hardware: Remote Batch
Developer: Structural Dynamics Research Corp.
           5729 Dragon Way
           Cincinnati, Ohio 45227
Availability: Through developer or several commercial systems

SPIN

Description: This program does static and dynamic in-plane bending anal-
         ysis of beams and rotating shafts on elastic foundations yielding
         deflection, slope, bending moment, shear, and bending stress. It
         finds response to static or harmonic loads and calculates natural
         frequencies and mode shapes, including critical speeds of rotating
         shafts. Whirling effects are included. Plotted results of deflec-
         tion, slope, moment, shear, and stress for static or dynamic loads
         can be generated on incremental plotters or storage tube terminals.
Source: Structural Dynamics Research Corporation, Cincinnati, Ohio.

TORSIONAL ANALYSIS OF SHAFT SYSTEMS (TASS)

Description: The TASS computer program calculates the torsional critical
         frequencies and the forced dynamic response in torsion of undamped
         shaft systems. The static deflection pattern can also be found by
         forcing the shaft at 0.0 rpm. This program uses a distributed mass
         approach. TASS can analyze any single branched gear train system
         with any number of gear trains. Each gear train is specified by
         giving the torsional stiffness of the gears and the gear ratio. Ex-
         ternal forces, lumped inertias,and torsional springs to ground can
         also be included in the analysis.
Language: FORTRAN IV
Availability: Structural Dynamics Research Corporation, Cincinnati, Ohio

LATERAL VIBRATION (LAVIB)

Capability: The steady-state response and natural frequencies of a general
         shafting system modeled as a series of stations are calculated. A
         shafting station consists of a massless beam, a lumped mass, springs
         to ground, and a forcing function.
Method: The Holzer-Myklestad-Prohl method is used to calculate natural
         frequencies, and modal analysis is used to calculate the lateral
         vibration response of the shafting system to synchronous and non-
         synchronous shaft speed forcing phenomena. Modal damping is used to
         model dissipative forces.
Hardware: UNIVAC 1108
Developer: Dr. Ronald L. Eshleman
Availability: Can be purchased from:
         The Vibration Institute
         5401 Katrine
         Downers Grove, Illinois 60515
         Attn: Dr. Ronald L. Eshleman, Director

TORSIONAL AND LONGITUDINAL NATURAL FREQUENCIES (TORLONG)

Capability: The torsional and longitudinal natural frequencies of a
     general branched shafting system modeled as a series of stations are
     calculated. A shafting station consists of a section of distributed
     parameter modeled shaft, a lumped inertia, and springs to ground.
Method: The Holzer-Myklestad-Prohl method is used to calculate natural
     frequencies.
Hardware: UNIVAC 1108
Developer: Dr. Ronald L. Eshleman
Availability: Can be purchased from:
     The Vibration Institute
     5401 Katrine
     Downers Grove, Illinois 60515
     Attn: Dr. Ronald L. Eshleman, Director

GENERAL REMARKS

Since the 1975 review of rotor dynamics computer programs, industrial use
of such engineering tools has steadily increased.

Present trends indicate widespread acceptance of linear analysis of
the flexural vibrations and recognition of the importance of stability
analysis for rotor systems vulnerable to fluid film and turbo-flow excitation effects. Softwares based on this approach have undergone considerable consolidation. The updated versions are generally more convenient
to use.

A welcome development is the possibility for the user to acquire fluid
film bearing characteristics in the form of data banks. As fluid film bearings are gaining acceptance in a variety of industrial machinery, availability of experimental verification of computed dynamic bearing characteristics will be most beneficial to the user community.

For machines required to operate above several critical speeds, the
Riccati matrix-type stabilization scheme is essential for the successful
computation of the critical frequencies and the mode shapes of the higher
modes. Although this feature is not presently included in all the programs
abstracted above, it is expected that this capability will soon be incorporated into most of the extensively used programs.

A new capability is the computation of the steady-state natural modes
of a nonconservative rotor system (via the phase-shift complex eigenvalue
analysis); this will undoubtedly have an impact on the development of in-
place balancing procedure for flexible rotors.

Presently, all known programs treat torsional and flexural vibrations
as independent motions. However, recent technical literature suggests
that new softwares to treat the coupled problem will soon be made available.

Time-history calculation of the start-up transient of torsional
motion appears to have become a practical engineering tool. Time-history
calculation of flexural motion, in the light of increased acceptance of
linearzied dynamic analyses, is relegated to the treatment of specialty
problems; however, as computational cost continues to reduce and more
effective graphical display peripherals become available, its use is expected to increase. In particular, diagnosis of parametric vibrations is
likely to require time-history type computations.

Two programs for the dynamic analysis of gas bearings are included in this review; with the anticipated increase of development activities related to energy-conserving machinery, interest in the large-scale application of gas bearings will probably revive. No information regarding gas bearings was returned from the Franklin Research Center and Mechanical Technology Incorporated; however, both organizations are known to have furnished softwares in this area in the past.

ACKNOWLEDGMENTS

The writer wishes to thank all of those who contributed information for this chapter.

REFERENCES

1 Alford, J. S., "Protecting Turbomachinery from Self-Excited Rotor Whirl," Journal of Engineering for Power, Trans. ASME, Series A, Vol. 87, Oct. 1965, pp. 333-44.

2 Holzer, H., Die Berechnung der Dreschwingungen, Springer-Verlag Ohg, Berlin, 1921; republished by J. W. Edwards, Publisher Inc., Ann Arbor, Michigan.

3 Myklestad, N. O., "A New Method of Calculating Natural Modes of Uncoupled Bending Vibration of Airplane Wings and Other Types of Beams," Journal of the Aeronautical Sciences, April 1944, pp. 153-62.

4 Prohl, M. A., "A General Method for Calculating Critical Speeds of Flexible Rotors," Journal of Applied Mechanics, Vol. 12, Trans. ASME, Vol. 67, 1945, pp. 142-48.

5 Pilkey, W. D., and Chang, P. Y., Modern Formulas for Statics and Dynamics, McGraw Hill, New York, 1978.

6 Horner, G., and Pilkey, W. D., "The Riccati Transfer Matrix Method," ASME Paper No. 77-DET-32.

7 Newmark, N. M., "A Method of Computation for Structural Dynamics," Proceedings of the American Society of Civil Engineers, Vol. 85, No. EM3, 1959, pp. 67-94.

8 Krieg, R. D., "Unconditional Stability in Numerical Time Integration Methods," Journal of Applied Mechanics, June 1973, pp. 417-21.

9 Park, K. C., "Evaluation of Integration Operators with Application to Nonlinear Transient Response Analysis," presented at ASME Symposium on Finite Element Analysis of Transient Nonlinear Structural Behavior, Houston, Texas, 5 Dec. 1975.

10 Wilkinson, J. H., The Algebraic Eigenvalue Problem, Oxford University Press, London, 1965.

11 Bathe, K. J., and Wilson, E. L., "Solution Methods for Eigenvalue Problems in Structural Mechanics," Intl. J. Num. Meth. Engr., Vol. 6, 1973, pp. 213-26.

12 Gupta, K. K., "Recent Advances in Numerical Analysis of Structural Eigenvalue Problems," Theory and Practice in Finite Element Structural Analysis, ed. J. T. Oden and University of Tokyo, Japan, 1973, pp. 249-71.

13 Lund, J. W., and Orcutt, F. K., "Calculations and Experiments on the Unbalance Response of a Flexible Rotor," Journal of Engineering for Industry, Trans. ASME, Series B, Vol. 89, No. 4, Nov. 1967, pp. 789-96.

14 Lund, J. W., "Stability and Damped Critical Speeds of a Flexible Rotor in Fluid-Film Bearings," Journal of Engineering for Industry, Trans. ASME, Series B, Vol. 96, No. 2, May 1974, pp. 509-17.

PROGRAM SURVEY

15 Pan, C. H. T., Wu, E. R., and Krauter, A. I., "Rotor-Bearing
Dynamics Technology Design Guide - Part I: Flexible Rotor Dynamics,"
AFAPL-TR-78-6, Part I, Technical Report prepared for USAF under Contract
F33615-76-C-2038. Also issued as Shaker Research Corporation Technical
Report 78-TR-27.

16 Pan, C. H. T., "Rotor-Bearing Dyhamics Technology Design Guide -
Part VIII: A Full Range Retrieval System for Static and Dynamic Performance Characteristics of Fluid Film Bearings," AFAPL-TR-78-6, Part VIII,
prepared for USAF under Contract F33615-76-C-2038.

17 Jones, A. B., and McGrew, J. M., "Rotor-Bearing Dynamics Technology Design Guide - Part II: Ball Bearings," AFAPL-TR-78-6, Part II,
prepared for USAF under Contract F33615-76-C-2038.

18 Jones, A. B., and McGrew, J. M., "Rotor-Bearing Dynamics Technology Design Guide - Part IV: Cylindrical Roller Bearings," AFAPL-TR-78-
6, Part IV, prepared for USAF under Contract F33615-76-C-2038.

19 Jones, A. B., and McGrew, J. M., "Rotor-Bearing Dynamics Technology Design Guide - Part III: Tapered Roller Bearings," AFAPL-TR-78-6,
Part III, prepared for USAF under Contract F33615-76-C-2038.

20 Vohr, J. H., and Pan, C. H. T., "Design Data: Gas-Lubricated
Spin-Axis Bearings for Gyroscopes," Mechanical Technology Incorporated
Technical Report MRI-68-TR-29, June 1978.

21 Tang, T. M., and Trumpler, P. R., "Dynamics of Synchronous-Pre-
cessing Turborotors with Particular Reference to Balancing, Part I:
Theoretical Foundations," Trans. ASME, Journal of Applied Mechanics,
Vol. 31, Series E, 1964, pp. 115-122.

Subroutines for Stiff Differential Equation Systems

Dennis C. Krinke

Boeing-Wichita

Ronald L. Huston

University of Cincinnati

INTRODUCTION

The modelling of the dynamics of a structural system almost always leads to a system of differential equations which need to be solved numerically. Since the state-of-the-art of numerical integration and computer hardware and software has been steadily improving, researchers have increasingly been using so-called canned or off-the-shelf computer integration routines to solve the equations. The purpose of this chapter is to make a comparative evaluation of a number of commonly available computer integration routines ("solvers") as they are applied with "stiff" differential equation systems.

The interest in stiff systems stems from the fact that the governing differential equations of structural systems are frequently stiff. A differential equation system is said to be stiff if: (1) it has widely separated eigenvalues or time constants [1-7], or (2) if its solution has diverging exponential terms with zero coefficients for a particular set of initial conditions [6-10]. These two kinds of stiffness will be called "Type 1 stiffness" and "Type 2 stiffness" here.

The chapter is divided into four parts. The first of these is a tabulation and summary of the specific computer subroutines which are tested and compared. This is followed by a description of the test differential equation systems used to compare the subroutines. The results, conclusions, and recommendations are presented in the final two parts.

SUMMARY OF COMPUTER SUBROUTINES TESTED

Six solver subroutines, DRKGS, DHPCG, DVOGER(ADAMS), DVOGER(GEAR), DREBS, and RK45, were tested and compared regarding their accuracy and efficiency in solving stiff differential equation systems. The subroutines employ a variety of numerical procedures. Also, their ease of use and their input/output requirements vary considerably. However, they are representative of the type of solvers currently available on the large computer systems at most institutions, laboratories, and corporations.

The following paragraphs provide a summary of the features of the solvers:

Solver DRKGS

Category: Integrator of systems of ordinary differential equations
Method Employed: Fourth order Runge-Kutta as modified by Gill [11]
Source: IBM Scientific Subroutine Package [11].
Date: 1966
Language: Fortran IV
Integration Focus: Interval oriented
Error Estimation: Local error is estimated by comparing the solution in
     two steps to the solution in one step.
Maximum/Minimum Step size: The maximum step size is the initial step size.
     The minimum step size is 2^{-10} of the maximum step size.
Input/Output: The user must supply a derivative evaluating subroutine
     and a output subroutine. DRKGS is identical in format to DHPCG.
Hardware Used: Amdahl 470
Software: Batch processing

Solver DHPCG

Category: Integrator of systems of ordinary differential equations
Method Employed: Hamming Predictor-Corrector with a fourth-order
     Runge-Kutta for starting values [11]
Source: IBM Scientific Subroutine Package [11].
Date: 1966
Language: Fortran IV
Integration Focus: Interval oriented
Error Estimation: Local error is estimated by comparing the solution in
     two steps to the solution in one step
Maximum/Minimum Step size: The maximum step size is the initial step size.
     The minimum step size is 2^{-10} of the maximum step size.
Input/Output: The user must supply a derivative evaluating subroutine
     and an output subroutine; DHPCG is identical in format to DRKGS.
Hardware Used: Amdahl 470
Software: Batch processing

Solver DVOGER(Adams)

Category: Integrator of systems of ordinary differential equations
Method Employed: Adams Predictor-Corrector
Source: International Mathematical and Statistical Libraries Reference
     Manual [12, 13, 14].
Date: 1975
Language: Fortran IV
Integration Focus: Step oriented
Error Estimation: The user has the option of specifying either absolute
     or relative (step) error control.
Maximum/Minimum Step size: Separate specification of minimum, initial,
     and maximum step size is permitted.
Input/Output: DVOGER(Adams) is identical in format to DVOGER(Gear) al-
     though the gradient of the derivative evaluating functions is not
     required.

Hardware Used: Amdahl/470
Software: Batch processing

Solver DVOGER(Gear)

Category: Integrator of systems of ordinary differential equations
Method Employed: Gear Predictor-Corrector (written for stiff systems)
Source: International Mathematical and Statistical Libraries Reference
   Manual, Refs. [12,13,14]
Date: 1975
Language: Fortran IV
Integration Focus: Step oriented
Error Estimation: The user has the option of specifying either absolute
   or relative (step) error control
Maximum/Minimum Step size: Separate specification of minimum, initial,
   and maximum step size is permitted
Input/Output: In addition to the derivative evaluating functions, the
   user is asked to supply the gradient of these functions. If the
   gradient is unavailable, an option for its numerical computation
   can be selected. DVOGER(Gear) is identical in format to DVOGER
   (Adams) and DREBS.
Hardware Used: Amdahl 470
Software: Batch processing

Solver DREBS

Category: Integrator of systems of ordinary differential equations
Method Employed: Modification of Bulirsch-Stoer ALGOL routine
Source: International Mathematical and Statistical Libraries Reference
   Manual, Refs. [12,13,14]
Date: 1977
Language: Fortran IV
Integration Focus: Step oriented
Error Estimation: The user has the option of specifying either absolute
   or relative (step) error control
Maximum/Minimum Step size: Separate specification of minimum and initial
   step size is permitted. Maximum step size is not user specified.
Input/Output: DREBS is identical in format to DVOGER(Adams) and DVOGER
   (Gear) although the gradient of the derivative evaluating functions
   is not required.
Hardware Used: Amdahl 470
Software: Batch processing

Solver RK45

Category: Integration of systems of ordinary differential equations
Method Employed: Fourth- and sixth-order Runge-Kutta
Source: Reference [15]
Date: 1978
Language: Fortran IV
Integration Focus: Step oriented
Error Estimation: Absolute. No local error estimate is made.
Maximum/Minimum Step size: Constant step size

Input/Output: A derivative evaluating subroutine is required. Output
    specifications are user determined.
Hardware Used: Amdahl 470
Software: Batch processing

TEST DIFFERENTIAL EQUATIONS

Two differential equation systems are used to compare the solvers. They
represent respectively each of the stiffness types defined in the
introduction. Both systems are relatively simple,and the exact analytical solution of each is known.

System 1

The first system, which has Type 1 stiffness, is presented in Refs.
[3,6,7]. It is a pair of coupled equations which may be written in the
form:

$$\dot{y} = A y \qquad (1)$$

where y is a column array and A is the 2x2 matrix:

$$A = \begin{bmatrix} -a & b \\ b & -a \end{bmatrix} \qquad (2)$$

If the initial value of y is:

$$y(0) = \begin{bmatrix} 0 \\ 2 \end{bmatrix} \qquad (3)$$

then the analytical solution of Eq. (1) is

$$y(t) = \begin{bmatrix} e^{-\alpha_1 t} & - & e^{-\alpha_2 t} \\ e^{-\alpha_1 t} & + & e^{-\alpha_2 t} \end{bmatrix} \qquad (4)$$

where α_1 and α_2 are the eigenvalues of A and are given by:

$$\alpha_1 = a - b, \quad \alpha_2 = a + b \qquad (5)$$

If α_1 and α_2 have widely separated values, the system is stiff. Hence,
to measure the effect of stiffness upon the solver efficiency, the values
of α_1 and α_2 were varied as shown in Table 1.

Table 1   System 1 Parameters

α_1	α_2	a	b	Period of Integration
1	2	1.5	0.5	5
1	5	3.0	0.5	5
1	10	5.5	4.5	5
1	20	10.5	9.5	5
1	50	25.5	24.5	5
1	100	50.5	49.5	5
1	200	100.5	99.5	5
1	500	200.5	249.5	5
1	1000	500.5	449.5	5

System 2

The second system, which has Type 2 stiffness, is presented in Refs. [6,7]. It is a model of a central force elliptical orbit. The eccentricity of the ellipse is varied from moderately elliptical to highly elliptical, or "cigar-shaped," to produce a change in the system stiffness.

The governing equations for this system are:

$$\ddot{r} = r\dot{\theta}^2 - GM/r^2 \tag{6}$$

and

$$\ddot{\theta} = -2\dot{r}\dot{\theta}/r \tag{7}$$

where G and M are physical constants. The initial conditions (taken at the apogee) are:

$$r(0) = a(1 + e), \quad \dot{r}(0) = 0 \tag{8}$$

and

$$\theta(0) = -\pi, \quad \dot{\theta}(0) = 2\pi b/Ta(1 + e)^2 \tag{9}$$

where a and b are the major and minor semi-axes of the ellipse, e is the eccentricity, and T is the orbit period. T and e are given by:

$$T = [4\pi^2 a^3/GM]^{\frac{1}{2}} \tag{10}$$

and

$$e = [1 - (b/a)^2]^{\frac{1}{2}} \tag{11}$$

The solution is periodic in that $r(0) = r(T)$ and $\theta(T) = \pi$.

This system is employed to test the solvers using the parameters given in Table 2. Figure 1 illustrates the solution for a/b = 2.

Table 2   System 2 Parameters

a	a/b	T
5	2	1
5	5	1
5	10	1
5	20	1
5	50	1
5	100	1

RESULTS AND SOLVER SUBROUTINE COMPARISONS

Test and Comparison Procedure

The solver subroutines were tested in their ability to solve both of the above differential equation systems. In all of the tests, the number of derivative evaluating subroutine calls (that is, "right-hand-side" function evaluations), the CPU time of integration, and the maximum error were measured. (The solver DVOGER was used with both Adam's and Gear's methods. When it was used with Gear's method, the option of numerically evaluating the gradient of the derivative functions was used.)

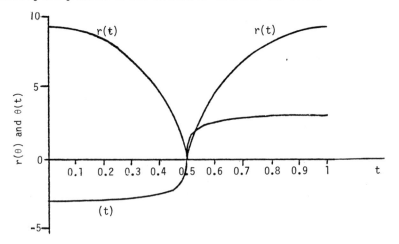

Fig. 1   System 2 Solution for a/b = 2

All of the solvers, except RK45, require that an error tolerance be given. Hence, each integration was performed with a tolerance of 10^{-3}, 10^{-4}, 10^{-5}, and 10^{-6}. This was also extended to 10^{-8} for system 2. RK45 was executed with a range of step sizes, which produced similar

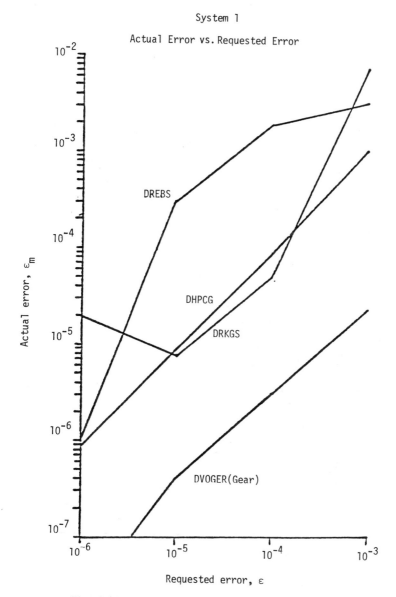

Fig. 2   Actual error vs. requested error - System 1

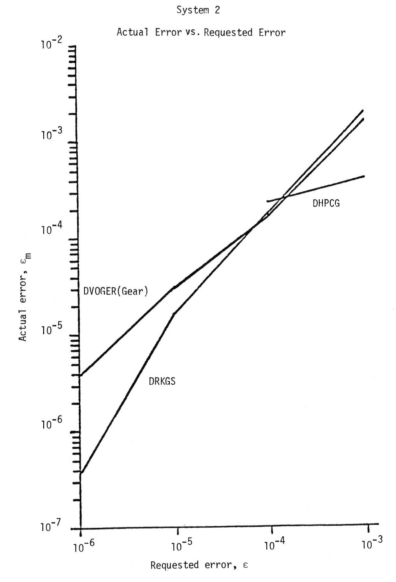

Fig. 3   Actual error vs. requested error - System 2

accuracy. For those solvers requiring a minimum step size, 10-15 of the interval value was used. This corresponds to approximately 140 units of roundoff. Finally, all of the tests were executed in double precision.

Results

Since accuracy and efficiency are the primary concerns of solver routine users, it is helpful to discuss each separately. Moreover, since efficiency is easiest to compare at a specified accuracy, accuracy is considered first.

Accuracy

The documentation of DRKGS and DHPCG states that the maximum global error ε_m (that is, the absolute value of the difference between the computer solution and the analytical solution) should be of the same magnitude as the specified error tolerance ε. Hence, as an accuracy measure, ε_m and ε are compared for the two test systems for a number of solvers. The results are shown in Figs. 2 and 3. It is seen that the actual error can be significantly different than the specified error tolerance of the solvers.

To measure the effect of stiffness upon accuracy, the ratio of the actual error to the specified or requested solver error, $\varepsilon_m/\varepsilon$, is compared with stiffness, as defined in Tables 1 and 2. These results are shown in Figs. 4 and 5. It is seen that almost without exception the error ratio increases with stiffness. The exceptions are DVOGER (Gear) and DHPCG with Type 1 stiffness. DRKGS appears to be the most consistent solver for Type 2 stiffness.

Efficiency

For large structural dynamic systems the major expense in CPU time and run time is the evaluation of the derivative functions. Hence, a measure of solver efficiency is the number of times it needs to evaluate the derivative functions to maintain a given accuracy. Generally, there is a hyperbolic relation between the number of derivative evaluation calls N and the maximum absolute error ε_m. On a log-log scale this relation is nearly linear. A typical graph is shown in Fig. 6 for DRKGS and System 2.

To examine the effect of stiffness upon efficiency, the solvers were tested and compared at a maximum absolute error ε_m of 10^{-5} for each test system for the stiffnesses of Tables 1 and 2. The results are shown in Figs. 7 and 8. They show that for Type 1 stiffness DVOGER(Gear) is relatively unaffected by the stiffness whereas the other solvers require significantly more integration effort as the stiffness increases. For Type 2 stiffness, there is not as much difference between the solvers, but again the DVOGER subroutine appears to be the most effective. (DHPCG, DREBS, and RK45 did not maintain the 10^{-5} accuracy for the full range of stiffnesses of Table 2.)

Finally, the CPU times were compared. A portion of the CPU time is "overhead," that is, time spent in the solver itself rather than in evaluating the derivative functions. Hence the overhead CPU time per derivative evaluation was measured for the various solvers. A comparative listing is presented in Table 3.

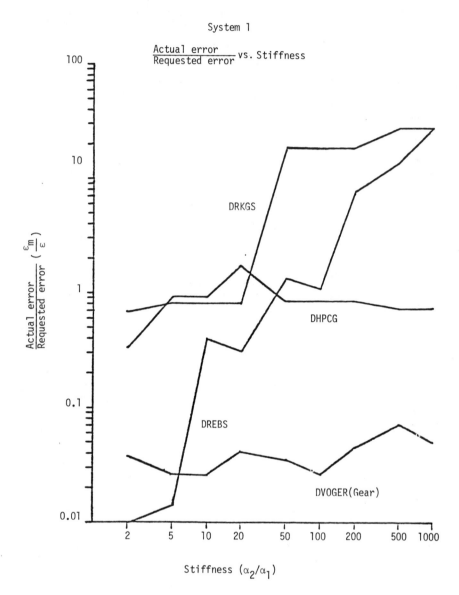

Fig. 4 Accuracy vs. stiffness - System 1

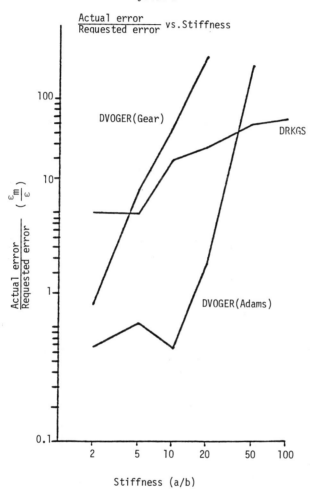

Fig. 5 Accuracy vs. **stiffness** - System 5

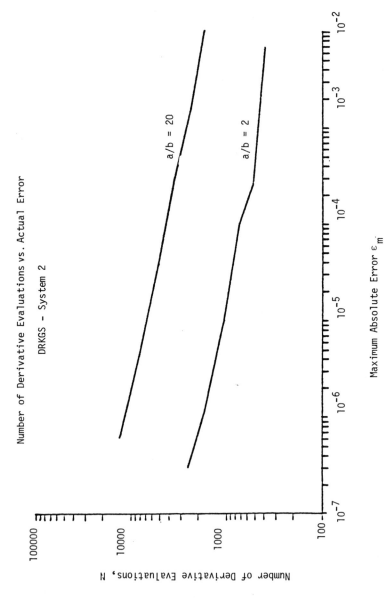

Number of Derivative Evaluations vs. Actual Error

DRKGS – System 2

Fig. 6 Effort vs. accuracy – System 2 – DRKGS

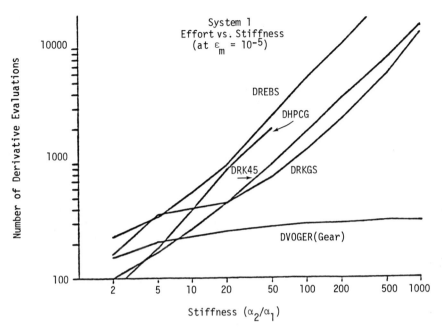

Fig. 7 Effort vs. stiffness - System 1

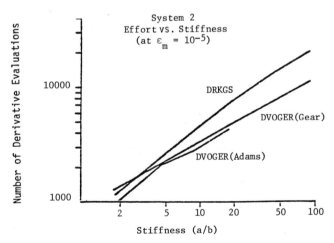

Fig. 8 Effort vs. stiffness - System 2

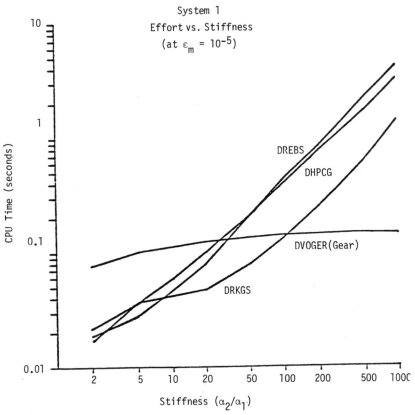

Fig. 9 CPU time vs. stiffness - System 1

Table 3   CPU Overhead Time per Derivative Evaluation

SOLVER	CPU TIME PER DERIVATIVE SUBROUTINE CALL (μ-SEC)
DREBS	80
DRK45	103
DRKGS	106
KHPCG	220
DVOGER(ADAMS)	400
DVOGER(GEAR)	500

The CPU time was also measured as a function of the stiffness for System 1. Fig. 9 shows the comparative results for the various solvers. Here again, as in Fig. 7, DVOGER(Gear) is the least affected by the stiffness.

CONCLUSIONS AND RECOMMENDATIONS

The results presented in the foregoing figures will hopefully help the reader and solver user draw his or her own conclusions. However, a few brief remarks and observations might also be helpful. First, if a differential equation system has Type 1 stiffness and if the derivative evaluations are lengthy, a subroutine using Gear's method (such as DVOGER) should be used. Gear's method was written especially for stiff systems, and it can be strikingly more efficient than the other integration routines. For systems with Type 2 stiffness, the results are not as clear, but the DVOGER routines and DRKGS appear to be the most effective.

Regarding ease of use, the automatic step size capability of DVOGER, DRKGS, DHPCG, and DREBS is very convenient. Also, placing the output requirements into a single subroutine as in DRKGS and DHPCG gives a modular property to the coding and simplifies their use. However, the limit on interval bisections used to maintain accuracy as in DRKGS and DHPCG is a disadvantage, particularly if double precision accuracy is desired.

Finally, it appears that minor adjustments and modifications in of the solvers could significantly enhance their utility. Hopefully, these and more substantial improvements will be made in future versions of these and other comparable integrating routines.

ACKNOWLEDGMENT

Support for the preparation of these results has been partially provided by the Office of Naval Research under Contract N00014-76C-0139 and by the National Science Foundation. This support is gratefully acknowledged.

REFERENCES

1   Lapidus, L., and Schiesser, W. E., Numerical Methods for Differential Systems, Academic Press, New York, 1976.
2   Willoughby, R. A., Stiff Differential Systems, Plenum Press, New York, 1974.
3   Lapidus, L., and Seinfeld, J. H., Numerical Solution of Ordinary Differential Equations, Academic Press, New York, 1977.
4   Shampine, L. R., and Gordon, M. K., Computer Solution of Ordinary Differential Equations: The Initial Value Problem, W. H. Freeman, San Francisco, 1975.
5   Forsythe, G. E., Malcolm, M. A., and Moler, C. B., Computer Methods for Mathematical Computations, Prentice-Hall, Englewood Cliffs, N. J., 1977.
6   Krinke, D. C., and Huston, R. L., "Critical Evaluation of Computer Subroutines for Solving Stiff Differential Equations," University of Cincinnati Report ONR-UC-ES-101578-8 under ONR Contract N00014-76-C-0139, 1978.
7   Krinke, D. C., and Huston, R. L., "An Evaluation of Computer Subroutines in Solving Stiff Differential Equations," Second International Conference on Computational Methods in Mechanics, Austin, Texas, March 1979.
8   Hornbeck, R. W., Numerical Methods, Quantum Publishers, N.Y., 1975.
9   Gerald, C. F., Applied Numerical Analysis, Addison-Wesley Publishing Co., Reading, Massachusetts, 1978.
10   Acton, F. S., Numerical Methods That Work, Harper and Row, New York, 1970.
11   IBM Scientific Subroutine Package-Programmer's Manual, IBM, White Plains, N.Y., 1966.
12   International Mathematical and Statistical Libraries Reference Manual, Houston, Texas, 1977.
13   Gear, C. W., "Algorithm 407 DIFFSUB for Solution of Ordinary Differential Equations,"Comm. ACM, Vol. 14, 1971, pp. 185-87.
14   Gear, C. W., "The Automatic Integration of Ordinary Differential Equations," Comm. ACM, Vol. 14, 1971, pp. 176-79.
15   Villadsen, J., and Michelson, M. L., Solution of Differential Equations by Polynomial Approximation, Prentice-Hall, Englewood Cliffs, N.J., 1978.

Ship Hull Vibration Analysis and Design

F. Everett Reed

Littleton Research and Engineering Corp.

Otis H. Burnside

Southwest Research Institute

INTRODUCTION

The level of propeller-excited ship hull vibration has defied analytical prediction until recently. Methods for estimating the fundamental vertical bending frequency with reasonable accuracy based on experience with previous similar ships of different dimensions have been available since the Schlick formula was first presented in 1894 [1]. The prediction of the bending frequency using available analytical methods applied to a nonuniform beam was unreliable until the effects of water inertia were explained by Frank M. Lewis in 1929 [2] and J. Lockwood Taylor in 1930 [3]. The methods for determining the natural frequencies were difficult, requiring iterative processes and clearing higher modes from the components of lower modes using the Stodola and Rayleigh-Ritz techniques.

The first analyses were based upon a beam modeled by point masses and bending flexibility only. Timoshenko [4] developed the differential equation for the beam that included bending and shear deflections and point and rotary inertias. In 1945, Prohl [5] proposed a procedure similar to the Holzer method for predicting bending natural frequencies, and Myklestad [6] applied the process to coupled bending and torsion.

During the period from 1945 to 1960, the Prohl-Myklestad methods were applied by McGoldrick and the David Taylor Model Basin staff to the bending analyses of a number of ships. The predicted results, which included shear deflections, were compared with experiments, using shakers and in normal operation. It was found that whereas the fundamental bending mode could be predicted with reasonable accuracy if shear effects were neglected, the frequencies of higher modes became increasingly influenced by the shear deflections. It was also found that although some ships such as lake ore carriers had a uniform sequence of frequencies to as high as the ninth mode, most ships showed an erratic sequence of frequencies and corresponding irregular mode shapes above the third or fourth mode. These deviations from uniformity were found to be due to local and cross-sectional resonances. Studies of ship bending vibration [7] indicated that the dynamic characteristics of the propeller-shaft system strongly influenced the response of the ship to propeller excitation.

Around 1960, procedures were being developed for predicting, by calculation from wake data and the geometry of propellers and hull, the propeller-generated excitation at the shafting and on the hull. All of these
influences are reflected in the calculation procedures discussed in the
remainder of this chapter.

CALCULATION PROCESSES

For perspective in discussing the calculation procedures and methods used
in hull vibration prediction, reference is made to Fig. 1, which is the
flow chart for propeller-excited hull vibration related to design procedures proposed in a study for the Ship Structure Committee [8].
    Attention in this presentation will be concentrated on the process
covered by blocks 4, 6, 7, 8, 9, 10, 13, 14, 15, 16, 17, 18, 19, 21, and
22. It should be noted that the procedure shows both analytical and experimental techniques for determining the excitation. In general, the
calculation procedures are less expensive and less time-consuming than
the experimental model test procedures and give a broader picture of the
excitation. Therefore, it is probably desirable to carry them through
even if detailed model tests are run. The processes will be discussed,
the available methods will be presented, and a brief discussion will be
given of the strong points and weaknesses of each.

EXCITATION CALCULATIONS

Estimate Propulsion System Longitudinal Vibration Frequencies - [Box 4]

In general, to keep propeller and hull excitation forces low, it is desirable to use many blades on the propeller. The number of blades is set
primarily by the natural frequency of the shafting and propeller in longitudinal vibration. To ascertain the probable frequency that will be
found after the design of the propulsion system and its supports is developed, it is useful to have a plot of natural frequency versus foundation stiffness. Using values of the range of foundation and thrust bearing stiffness, the range of shaft longitudinal frequency is determined.
The number of blades in the propeller is chosen so that, preferably, the
excitation frequency is less than 80 percent of a possible propulsion
natural frequency. A less desirable, but sometimes necessary, solution
is to make the excitation frequency about 30 percent above the longitudinal natural frequency.
    For making these predictions, the power and RPM of the plant must
be defined. From this, the approximate propeller diameter, propeller
weight, and the water inertia associated with longitudinal vibration can
be established. Also, the approximate diameter of the tailshaft and
lineshaft can be established. The simplest procedure is to predict on
the basis of a one-degree-of-freedom system consisting of the propeller
and water inertia plus a portion of the shaft weight vibrating against
the stiffness of the thrust bearing and its foundation. Since the shafting weighs considerably more than the propeller and adds flexibility,
this procedure is not very good.
    An improved procedure is to model the propeller and shaft as a se-
ries of concentrated masses and elastic elements and use a Holzer process
for frequency prediction. With this degree of complication it becomes
desirable to use a computer.

If a computer is used, many of the complications of defining the mass-elastic system can be avoided by using a finite element program such as ANSYS, STARDYNE, etc. However, a more accurate result can be obtained with less input (and, therefore, less chance for error) if the shaft is represented by a continuous mass and elasticity distribution. A computer program for predicting the natural frequencies of propeller and shafting systems defined by concentrated and distributed masses and stiffnesses is presented and discussed below.

Longitudinal Vibration of Shafting

Category: Longitudinal vibration of shafting
Author: F. E. Reed
          Littleton Research and Engineering Corp.
          95 Russell Street
          Littleton, Massachusetts 01460
Telephone: (617) 486-3526
Capability: Makes a plot of natural frequency of the shafting as a
          function of the stiffness of the thrust bearing and its founda-
          tion. Alternatively, if the thrust bearing stiffness is known,
          the variable may be the foundation stiffness.
Method: The propeller is represented by its weight of entrained water
          as given by Lewis and Auslaender. The shaft is represented by a
          distributed mass and elasticity. The gearing and turbines forward
          of the thrust bearing are not included.
Input: Shafting arrangement, diameters, and lengths; propeller mass,
          propeller diameter, number of blades, and developed area ratio
          (or mean width ratio)
Availability: This is a proprietary program not developed for general
          distribution. Contact author for usage.

Compute Propeller Forces - [Box 6]

Prior to about 1960, the only determination of propeller forces was by measurements on models, primarily by Frank M. Lewis [9, 10]. In the late 1950s, estimates began to be made on a quasi-steady-state basis using the procedures developed by Burrill [11] for evaluating the load- ing and efficiency of propellers whose circumferentially averaged wake varied along the propeller radii. A computer program for calculating the harmonic forces and moments generated by the propeller working in varying wakes based upon this quasi-steady-state procedure was applied by Hinterthon [12]. A similar computer program, also based on Burrill's procedure, but including the Theodorsen effects (i.e., the inertia of the fluid in responding to circulation changes resulting from changes in angle of attack), was developed by CONESCO [13]. The first program tends to give high values of harmonic forces and moments and errors in their phase because the inertia effects are neglected. The latter program tends to give low values of harmonic forces and moments because the steady-state solution allows flow over the tip, between blade sections, and interaction between blades that are not developed in the unsteady flow. Both of these programs have been superseded by improved analyses of the problem.

In 1958, Ritzer and Breslin developed a theory for the unsteady thrust and torque of a propeller in a ship wake based upon unsteady air- foil theory. This work has been continued by Tsakonas and Jacobs [14]

DESIGN

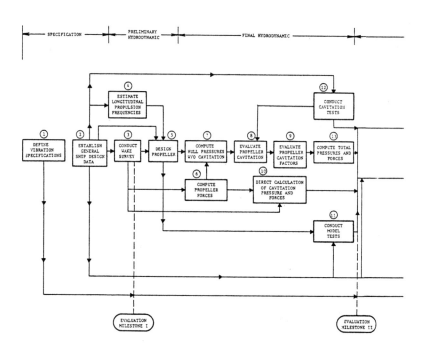

Fig. 1 Flow diagram of ship design procedures

PHASES

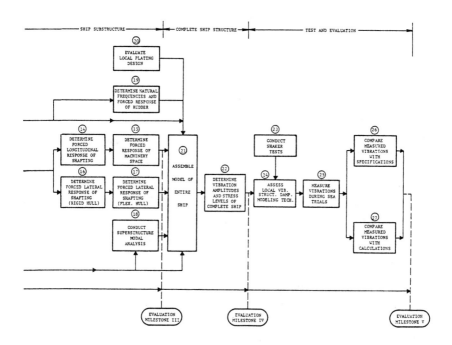

to minimize propeller-induced vibrations

and is now a fully developed program for predicting the harmonic forces
and moments exerted by a propeller on its supporting shaft, when working
in the wake behind a ship. This work is based upon lifting surface theory. Although the computations are long, they are handled easily by
computer. A description of this program is given below. This program
is widely used both in the United States and abroad.

Propeller Mean and Vibratory Forces Program

Category: Propeller mean and vibratory forces and moments, blade
     stresses, cavitation inception; lifting surface theory
Author: S. Tsakonas
     Davidson Laboratory
     Stevens Institute of Technology
     Castle Point Station
     Hoboken, New Jersey 07030
Telephone: (201) 792-2700
Capability: Furnishes the mean and vibratory blade pressure distribu-
     tion of a marine propeller operating in a nonuniform flow field
     and the resulting hydrodynamic forces and moments and blade bend-
     ing moments about the face-pitch line at various radial positions
Method: The program uses unsteady lifting-surface theory and takes into
     consideration all the relevant propeller geometry and the spatial
     nonuniformity of the inflow field.
Documentation: Contained in Ref. [14]
Input: The propeller blade geometry; the Fourier components of the spa-
     tial variation of the axial and tangential components of the wake
Output: 1. Steady and time-dependent blade loading distribution at
     multiples of shaft frequency
     2. Mean and blade frequency force and moment components in co-
efficient form for:
          a. Thrust/$\rho n^2 d^4$
          b. Torque/$\rho n^2 d^5$
          c. Transverse force/$\rho n^2 d^4$
          d. Vertical force/$\rho n^2 d^4$
          e. Transverse bending moment/$\rho n^2 d^5$
          f. Vertical bending moment/$\rho n^2 d^5$
     where
          ρ = fluid density
          n = propeller RPM
          d = propeller diameter
     3. Blade bending moments about the pitch line at various ra-
dial positions and for various orders of excitation
     4. Information for the study of cavitation inception
     5. Information for the study of blade stress analysis which is
performed by utilizing the STARDYNE-CDC finite element computer
program
Computer: CDC 6600 or CDC 7600
Availability: Program for sale for $6,000. Contact author for quotes
     on individual propeller calculations.

     The Department of Naval Architecture and Marine Engineering at the
Massachusetts Institute of Technology has also been active in the prediction of the harmonic forces and moments transmitted by a marine propeller
to its supporting shaft. Using unsteady flow theory with the propeller
blade represented as a lifting line, Neal A. Brown developed relations

for determining the periodic propeller forces [15]. Several computer programs based on this theory have been developed. More recently, Professor Justin E. Kerwin has been approaching the unsteady force problem with another procedure based on a discrete vortex method [16, 17]. Similar procedures to those developed in the United States have been developed in Europe. M. T. Murray and J. E. Tubby at the Admiralty Research Laboratory developed a computer program for determining the unsteady shaft forces from propellers [18]. The programs are described below.

Propeller Forces and Moments

Category: Harmonic propeller forces and moments; lifting line theory
Author: F. E. Reed
        Littleton Research and Engineering Corp.
        95 Russell Street
        Littleton, Massachusetts 01460
Telephone: (617) 486-3526
Capability: Program computes the harmonic forces and moments generated by a propeller in a nonuniform flow.
Method: Propeller forces are determined by lifting line theory. This is much less complex than lifting surface theory, but is considered adequate in view of uncertainties in the wake and the wide variation in service wake due to ship motions and sea action. The main reason for continuing to use the lifting line theory calculation is that it is the basis for the predictions of hull pressure and hull forces.
Input: 1. Propeller drawing
The propeller drawing should show the following information: propeller diameter, hub diameter, rake, number of blades, and propeller material; the variation with radius of chord, skewback, and pitch; propeller sections at several radii showing the variation of thickness along the chord. For propellers designed in Europe, the variation with radius of the distance from the reference line to the leading edge, trailing edge, and point of maximum thickness is acceptable in place of the variation of chord and skewback.
2. Ship speed and corresponding shaft RPM
3. Wake as measured in a model test
The results of a harmonic analysis of the measured wake are required. If the harmonic analysis results are not available, the measured inflow velocities specified at several points along the radius and at frequent points around the circumference are acceptable, and a harmonic analysis will be performed. If a measured wake is not available, it can be inferred from the available wakes of other ships.
Output: Magnitude and phase of the three components of harmonic propeller force and the three components of harmonic propeller moment; the steady vertical and horizontal forces and moments arising from first-order wake action (thrust offset)
Availability: This is a proprietary program not developed for general distribution.

Steady and Harmonic Propeller Forces and Moments

Category: Calculation of steady and harmonic propeller forces and moments by unsteady lifting line theory

Maintenance: American Bureau of Shipping
               45 Broad Street
               New York, New York 10004
Telephone: (212) 785-9800
Method: Program employs an extended version of unsteady lifting line
    theory as developed by Dr. Neal A. Brown at MIT [15]. The exten-
    sion includes the effects of propeller skew, which were not treat-
    ed in the original theory.
Input: Propeller blade geometry, Fourier coefficients of the spatial
    variation of the axial, and tangential components of wake
Output: Mean and blade-frequency components of the three forces and
    three moments acting on the propeller, and the time-varying blade
    pressure distribution at each wake harmonic. The results of this
    program are used as partial input to the ABS/SURFORCE program de-
    scribed later.
Availability: Contact Mr. Stanley G. Stiansen,
               American Bureau of Shipping,
               (212) 785-9740, for details.

Harmonic Forces and Moments in Nonuniform Flow

Category: Calculation of harmonic forces and moments generated by a
    propeller in nonuniform flow using a discrete element approach
Author: Professor Justin E. Kerwin
         Department of Ocean Engineering
         Massachusetts Institute of Technology
         Cambridge, Massachusetts 02139
Method: The program represents the propeller blade by grid points dis-
    tributed over the surface, and the wake is spatially defined (cy-
    lindrical coordinates) in three directions: longitudinal, tangen-
    tial, and radial. A distribution of vorticity is assumed over the
    surface, and by successive iteration is refined to be compatible
    with the boundary of the propeller surface and the laws of hydro-
    dynamics, Kelvin's theorem, and the Kutta requirement for flow
    continuity at the trailing edge.
        This discrete element approach appears to offer a number of
    advantages as a starting point for the computation of unsteady,
    partially cavitating flows:
        (a) It is capable of yielding accurate predictions of mean
    loading, both at design and off-design conditions.
        (b) Being a numerical procedure, blade geometry can be in-
    corporated exactly so that propellers with large skew, rake, and
    varying pitch distribution can be accommodated. This is consid-
    ered essential, since it is through the variation of these parame-
    ters that optimum propeller designs can be evolved.
        (c) Since the procedure includes all three components of
    induced velocity, there is no particular problem in including tan-
    gential and radial wake field components.
        (d) Since no loading mode functions are employed, the modi-
    fications ultimately required to include the cavities would appear
    to be feasible. Source elements presently included to represent
    blade thickness can assume the further role of representing the
    cavity volume.
        (e) A discrete element method lends itself naturally to a
    step-by-step domain solution, which is also essential for the sub-
    sequent inclusion of unsteady cavitation.

Availability: The procedures are still under development, but have been
    applied to specific cases with good results. See Refs. [16] and
    [17]. Contact author for details.

Harmonic Forces and Moments in Nonuniform Flow

Category: Calculation of harmonic forces and moments generated by a pro-
    peller in nonuniform flow by two-dimensional unsteady airfoil the-
    ory
Authors: M. T. Murray and J. E. Tubby
    Admiralty Research Laboratory
    Teddington Middlesex TW110LN
    England
Method: The calculation of the fluctuating forces on a propeller falls
    into three parts. The first part is the calculation of the varia-
    tion of the inflow velocity to the blades; the next stage involves
    the calculation of the fluctuating lift-distribution on a section
    of blade associated with this fluctuating inflow; the final stage
    is the calculation of the propeller forces and moments. The cal-
    culation of the fluctuating lift is based on two-dimensional un-
    steady airfoil theory. It ignores blade-to-blade interaction and
    the variation with radius of the various significant parameters.
    These approximations would be unacceptable for predicting the
    steady lift, but are acceptable for the unsteady lift, probably
    overestimating the lift. See Ref. [18].
Input: Shaft speed; propeller geometry, including skew, chord length,
    blade pitch angle at specific radii; wake, either in Fourier se-
    ries, amplitude-plus-phase form, or as equally spaced measurements
    of wake at the radii where the propeller geometry information is
    given. Only axial or both axial and tangential wakes may be speci-
    fied; calculations can be run for successive skew values; input
    radii may vary from 4 to 14; as many as 20 skew configurations may
    be determined; as many as 140 harmonics of the blade frequency
    forces may be calculated, but generally the number is limited to
    10; as many as 100 wake harmonics and 200 wake measurements per
    radius may be input.
Output: The input data; if wakes are given as velocity measurements,
    the harmonic values are printed (to the 71st harmonic). If given
    as Fourier components, the values listed are: the contribution to
    thrust, torque, vertical and horizontal forces, and moments from
    each specified radial section; the integrated thrust, torque,
    horizontal and vertical forces, and moments for multiples of blade
    rate harmonics.
Availability: Contact Mr. A. W. Moore at Admiralty Research Laboratory
    for details. Telephone 01-977-3231, Ext. 516.

Compute Hull Pressures and Excitations - [Boxes 7, 8, 9, and 10]

The procedures for determining the excitation on the hull are varied.
It has only recently been definitively shown by experiments [19] that
variable cavitation on a propeller influences the hull pressures and the
hull forces very strongly. The ideal way to determine the propeller-
generated hull forces would be by integrating the pressures generated by
the cavitating propeller, if this were not too difficult, because a knowledge of the pressure distribution is useful for the ship design. At the

present time this is not possible. It requires a prediction of both the cavitation growth and decay on the hull pressures. It appears that the intensity of the pressure is related to the second time derivative of the cavitation bubble volume. The problem is being studied, and there has been some progress in this field.

At the present time the procedure is roundabout and consists of predicting the hull forces generated by the propeller in the absence of cavitation and modifying the results by an empirical factor to account for cavitation effects. The factor is determined by (1) experience with full-scale measurements, (2) model tests in a cavitation towing tank, and (3) model tests in a cavitation tunnel of sufficient size to include modeling of a portion of the ship.

In a sense, the use of a factor applied to the pressures determined in the noncavitating condition is theoretically unsound because the pressures are generated by a mechanism other than that responsible for the pressures generated in the noncavitating case. The hull pressures are generated as the sum of three different processes. The first is the pressure due to propeller loads, i.e., the difference in pressure on the face and back of the blades. The second source of pressure generation is the passage of the propeller blade bulk through the water. Generally the pressures from these two sources are approximately equal in amplitude but can be quite different in phase. The third source, cavitation, is the growth and decay of cavitation bubbles as the blade moves into high wake regions. Since the growth and decay of a volume radiate pressure much more effectively than moving a volume from one place to another or introducing a flow from a source to a sink, the pressures from small cavitation volume changes can be large.

The determination of propeller-generated hull forces can be made by two processes: (1) estimation of the hull pressure and (2) an integration process involving Green's function which yields the total excitation force. Either process involves many engineering approximations for a reasonable solution. Generally the hull pressure process involves determining the pressure that would be generated by the loading and thickness of the propeller in a free field and multiplying this pressure by a factor, usually 2, to represent the pressure of the hull. This process is entirely inadequate for estimating differential pressures across narrow surfaces such as skegs or rudders. The Green's function process requires an estimate of the added mass of the hull surface for motions corresponding to each of the components of force and moment that are required [20]. Theoretical processes for predicting pressure differences across wedge- and cone-shaped surfaces [21, 22] are available but not yet programmed. A theoretical approach, the Smith-Hess procedure, for predicting the hull pressure is available, but the calculation is so long that it has not at the present time been programmed.

Procedures for predicting hull pressures and forces are presented below.

Harmonic Forces and Moments on a Ship Hull

Category: Calculation of harmonic forces and moments on the hull generated by propeller action
Author: F. E. Reed
        Littleton Research and Engineering Corp.
        95 Russell Street
        Littleton, Massachusetts 01460

Telephone: (617) 486-3526
Method: The free-field pressures (i.e., the pressures that would exist
in open water if the hull were not present) are calculated at each
hull grid point due to (1) the loading on the propeller blades
(assumed to be concentrated at the forward quarter point of the
blade chord), (2) the thickness of the propeller blade. The sum
of these two pressures, in their proper phase, is multiplied by 2
to give the reported pressure on the hull surface. The pressure
from a harmonically varying force having x, y, and z components involves the distance from the point to the location of the force.
Substituting steady and harmonic forces and distances as a function
of shaft angle yields values of the pressure. The resulting equations involve a series which under certain conditions converges
slowly. Originally only a few terms were developed. More recently the general term has been developed, allowing sufficient terms
to assure convergence. This results in pressures that correspond
to measured values. The integration for blade thickness is similar. If the cavitation volume on the blade could be defined by a
Fourier series, the same process could be applied. This has not
yet been done. See Ref. [13].
Input: The computed propeller lift distribution along the propeller
blade; the geometry of the propeller; the hull coordinates at the
points of pressure determination
Output: The harmonic hull surface pressure at blade beat frequency generated by the loaded, noncavitating propeller in the region of the
propeller (generally at grid points corresponding to underwater
intersections of buttocks and frames within 4 diameters of the propeller); by integration of the above, the blade frequency harmonic
hull forces and moments acting on the hull because of noncavitating
propeller action
Availability: This is a proprietary program not developed for general
distribution. Contact F. E. Reed for program usage.

Steady and Harmonic Pressure Fields Program

Category: Calculation of steady and harmonic pressure fields generated
by a noncavitating propeller
Author: S. Tsakonas
Davidson Laboratory
Stevens Institute of Technology
Castle Point Station
Hoboken, New Jersey 07030
Telephone: (201) 792-2700
Method: This program is a continuation of the one described earlier from
Davidson Laboratory.
Documentation: Contained in Ref. [23]
Input: The propeller blade geometry; the Fourier components of the spa-
tial variation of the axial and tangential components of the wake;
the spatial location of the points where the pressures are desired;
the steady and time-dependent blade loading distribution at multi-
ples of any shaft frequency as produced by the Davidson Laboratory
program for calculating the propeller mean vibratory forces, which
was described earlier
Output: This program furnishes the steady and harmonic components of the
pressure field generated by a noncavitating ship propeller operating in a spatially variable inflow.

Computer: CDC 6600 or CDC 7600
Availability: Program for sale for $5,000. Contact author for quotes
   on individual calculations.

Program SURFORCE

Category: Calculation of propeller-induced hull surface forces
Author: Professor W. S. Vorus
       Department of Naval Architecture and Marine Engineering
       Ann Arbor, Michigan 48109
Telephone: (313) 764-8341
Capability: This program employs the method presented by Professor
       Vorus in Ref. [20]. The conventional procedure for evaluating the
       hull forces is to integrate the propeller-generated pressures over
       the hull surface. These pressures are due to diffraction of the
       propeller-induced water flow by the hull. The diffraction problem
       and hence the pressure integration difficulties are avoided in the
       analysis and computer program by utilizing a special application
       of Green's theorem.
Input: Propeller geometry; wake distribution; stern lines and coordi-
       nates describing the sectional geometry of approximately the aft
       one-third of the ship; time-dependent geometry of propeller cavi-
       tation effects (optional); time-varying blade pressure distribu-
       tion at each wake harmonic
Output: This program computes all components of the hull force and mo-
       ment at multiples of the propeller blade rates. (In general, the
       vertical force component is the only one desired.)
Availability: Contact author or
       American Bureau of Shipping Research,
       New York, New York,
       for access to program.

    The evaluation of propeller cavitation (Box 10) is discussed in
Ref. [24]. It will be apparent that the prediction of the excitation
from a propeller is far from an exact process at the present time [25].
However, by a combination of calculations and experience, amplitude and
phase of the propeller harmonic longitudinal forces and harmonic torque
about the rotational axis can probably be estimated to a 90 percent probability that the predicted value will lie between 85 percent and 120 percent of the correct value. The accuracy for forces and moments referred
to axes normal to the rotational axes is not as good--maybe a 90 percent
probability that the predicted value will lie between 75 percent and 140
percent of the correct value. The main source for error lies in the wake
values used as input to the computer programs.
    The values of propeller-excited hull pressures and propeller-ex-
cited hull forces and moments cannot be estimated as well. In the absence of cavitation, the pressure on the hull surfaces adjacent to the
propeller tip can be estimated with, say, 90 percent probability that the
predicted value will lie between 65 percent and 150 percent of the correct value. Horizontal hull forces and moments about a vertical axis in
the noncavitating condition are generally not predicted at present. If
the prediction were of sufficient importance to justify development of
computer programs, the accuracy would probably be about the same as the
prediction for vertical forces and moments about the horizontal axis.
    When cavitation is present, assuming that the amount of cavita-
tion is not excessive from the standpoint of propeller durability and

efficiency, the accuracy of hull force predictions would probably be such that 80 percent would lie between 50 percent and 200 percent of the correct value.

RESPONSE CALCULATIONS

The prediction of excitation, it will be noted, is unique to ship vibration problems. For this reason the procedures for predicting excitation are not fully developed, but the procedures that are developed are generally used.

In the prediction of response, the procedures that can be used have wide application for structures other than ships and have generally been developed for such structures as aircraft and buildings. As a consequence, there are many computer programs that are suitable for predicting ship response, but they are not widely used. There have been some programs developed for particular aspects of ship vibration problems.

The procedure recommended in Ref. [8] is to assure that if the component substructures of the ship have suitable response characteristics, then the ship composed of these substructures will have suitable characteristics. Consider now the computer programs available for analyzing the structures discussed in the several boxes on Fig. 1.

Determine the Forced Response of the Shafting by Longitudinal Excitation - [Box 14]

By previous calculations, the longitudinal exciting force at the propeller will have been determined. The purpose of this study is to find whether the vibration level generated by this excitation will be acceptable. The propeller and the length and diameter of the shafting will be known, and the thrust bearing will probably have been selected. The unknown quantity will be the stiffness of the thrust bearing foundation. The amplitude of motion at the thrust bearing as a function of frequency for different values of foundation stiffness is required.

The stiffness of the thrust bearing foundation must be determined to assure that a shaft longitudinal vibration resonance does not fall in the operating range. For preliminary analyses, the foundation static stiffness can be determined by the use of several methods. The simplest process is to represent the foundation and bottom as a combination of frustums of wedges and beams. This procedure is described in Ref. [26]. A process requiring less engineering judgment is to use finite element methods, assuming that the machinery double bottom is supported at its edges. It is also possible to represent the machinery space double bottom as an anisotropic plate.

Generally, it will be found that the natural frequency of the bottom structure will not be far removed from the propeller blade frequency. If this happens, the propeller through longitudinal vibration of the shafting will excite engine room vibration even though the natural frequency of the shaft in longitudinal vibration determined from static stiffness considerations appears to be suitable. This aspect is considered in the following section.

Several types of computer programs are suitable for this analysis. The system can be broken down into a sequence of masses connected by springs. This can be analyzed by a Holzer Table program, of the kind developed for torsional vibration, or by a standard finite element program such as ANSYS, MARC, STARDYNE, NASTRAN, SESAM, etc. However, the

shafting, whose distributed weight is several times that of the propeller
with its associated water inertia, consists of long lengths of constant
diameter. This characteristic is encouraging to a program that represents the shaft as distributed mass and elasticity, and a few computer
programs have been developed which utilize this property. In such a
case, the system can be defined with a minimum of input variables, thus
saving time and improving accuracy and reducing the probability of erro-
neous inputs.
   The following program descriptions taken from Ref. [27] indicate
that the Maritime Administration has a program based upon the Holzer
method for determining longitudinal vibrations; that J. J. McMullen has
a program for determining longitudinal vibration where the shaft is modeled as lumped masses; and that Newport News has a program that can represent the shaft as a distributed mass system. A Littleton Research
program utilizing lumped and distributed masses and elasticities is also
described below. Reference [28] contains results of a survey for ship
structure computer programs made in 1974.

Longitudinal and Torsional Shafting Vibrations

Category: Longitudinal and torsional shafting vibrations
Descriptive Program Title: Shaft vibrational analysis using Holzer
     method
Author: Richard Siebert
         Office of Ship Construction
         Maritime Administration
         Washington, D.C. 20235
Telephone: (202) 254-7048
Date: September 1970
Capability: Calculates torsional and longitudinal critical vibration
     frequencies using the Holzer method. It was originally developed
     by NAVSEC for the IBM-7090 and subsequently converted to the CDC-
     6600 by the Maritime Administration. Double precision require-
     ments were eliminated.
Programming Language: FORTRAN IV
Documentation: Informal - complete (15 pages)
Input: Masses, inertias, and stiffness factors for each component in
     the turbine-gear-shaft-propeller system
Output: Critical frequencies in CPS and RPM for various number of
     blades
Typical Running Times: 2.57 minutes (average)

Longitudinal Shafting Vibrations

Category: Machinery shafting and bearing calculations
Maintenance: John J. McMullen Associates, Inc.
              One World Trade Center - Suite 3047
              New York, New York 10048
Method: Employs lumped mass system using "level" effect. Description
     found in Naval Ship Research and Development Report 3358, September
     1970.
Limitations and Restrictions: Computes frequencies up to four modes
Programming Language: FORTRAN IV
Documentation: Informal - User's Guide
Hardware: IBM 360/40 and IBM 1130

Program FORCE VIB

Category: Longitudinal and torsional propulsion machinery shafting and
    bearing calculations
Authors: A. S. Pototzky and F. E. Siegel
    Newport News Shipbuilding and Drydock Company
    Technical Systems Division
    4101 Washington Avenue
    Newport News, Virginia 23607
Telephone: (804) 247-7500
Capability: FORCE VIB is a computer program to calculate the steady-
    state longitudinal or torsional vibratory response of branched
    shafting systems, such as propulsion systems. The program also
    allows the varying of values to conduct parametric studies.
Method: The mechanical impedance method is used to calculate displace-
    ments, forces, and phase angles, which may be frequency dependent.
Limitations: The system may have a maximum of 35 elements consisting of
    masses, dampers, and springs, all with only one degree of freedom.
    The masses and springs may be lumped or distributed, and the damp-
    ers may be viscous or solid.
Programming Language: FORTRAN IV
Hardware: Honeywell 6080
Availability: Program not available for general distribution

Longitudinal Vibration of Shafting

Category: Longitudinal vibration of shafting
Author: F. E. Reed
    Littleton Research and Engineering Corp.
    95 Russell Street
    Littleton, Massachusetts 01460
Telephone: (617) 486-3526
Method: The propeller is represented by its mass plus entrained water
    and damping, estimated by Lewis and Auslaender's recommendations.
    The shaft is represented by a distributed mass and elasticity and
    is assumed to have a hysteretic damping (nominally 4%). The thrust
    bearing is represented as a concentrated mass elastically connected
    to a rigid hull.
Input: Shafting arrangement, diameters, and lengths; propeller mass,
    diameter, number of blades, pitch, and developed area ratio (or
    mean width ratio); harmonic thrust; the stiffness of the thrust
    bearing and its foundation; reduction gear weight
Output: A plot of the blade order harmonic force at the thrust bearing
    as a function of RPM; a plot of the amplitudes of axial motion at
    the propeller and at the thrust bearing as a function of RPM; tabu-
    lar data for above
Availability: This is a proprietary program not developed for general
    distribution. Contact author for usage.

Determine Forced Response of Machinery Space - [Box 15]

The shafting system is connected in longitudinal vibration to the machinery space double bottom through the thrust bearing. Thus, vibrations of
the shaft will be coupled with those in the machinery space, and vibrations in the machinery space bottom structure can be strongly coupled

with longitudinal vibration of the shafting. Although it might be desirable to model the double bottom as an anisotropic plate with variable
inertias for the same reasons that the distributed mass-elasticity procedure is used for the shafting, this type of model has not been developed, and it is necessary to use finite element modeling. It is desirable that the computer system that is used be compatible with that used
for the complete ship. If the final ship is to be modeled by finite
element procedures, the same system should be used for the machinery
space, which can then be incorporated in the full model as a substructure. If the complete ship is to be modeled as a Timoshenko beam with
sprung masses, any convenient finite element model can be used for the
machinery space.

Determine Forced Response of the Shafting in the Lateral Direction Assuming a Rigid Hull; i.e., Rigid Pin Support at Bearings - [Box 16]

The shaft responds laterally to the harmonic force and moment excitations about axes normal to the rotational axis. If the lateral natural
frequencies of the propeller and shaft system coincide with the blade
frequency excitation, the input to the hull through the bearings can be
strongly amplified. Calculations of ship response generally show peaks
associated with lateral frequencies of the shafting. It is, therefore,
desirable to design the shafting system so that these resonances will
not occur at the normal operating speeds. As with the longitudinal vibrations, these studies are successively made on models of increasing
complexity. The first studies are applied to the shaft simply supported
at the bearings (either at the forward and after edges or one-third of
the distance from the rear of the stern bearing). Since it is known that
the bearings are relatively flexible, this model will generally give a
frequency that is high so that if the lowest lateral frequency is less
than, say, 30 percent above the full-power blade frequency, it will probably be wise to consider relocating the bearings or modifying the shafting to raise the frequency. A finite element computer program is suitable for this analysis. It is also possible to use beam programs which
include the effects of hull flexibility. The supporting structures can
be modeled by making the supports very stiff or rigid. These programs
are discussed in the next section.

Determine the Lateral Responses of the Shafting Including the Effects of Hull Flexibility - [Box 17]

If gyroscopic effects are neglected (they are important for whirling,
but relatively unimportant at blade frequencies) and the supports are of
equal stiffness in all directions, the natural frequency and response of
the shaft will be the same in all directions. If the structure is symmetrical about a vertical axis and gyroscopic effects are neglected, the
shaft will have two natural frequencies and corresponding mode shapes,
one vertical and one horizontal. If the structure is not symmetrical,
the fundamental normal modes will be skewed to the vertical, but at right
angles to each other. The moment restraint at the bearings can have a
significant influence on the shaft frequency.
      The amount of structure to include in the stiffness calculation
is a matter for the analyst's judgment. The object is to evaluate the

stiffness to a region of a large hull mass. For a single screw ship, this may involve the structure from the afterpeak bulkhead and up to the steering gear flat. For shafts supported by struts, it will include the struts and their backup structure. If the complete hull is analyzed using a finite element analysis (Boxes 21 and 22), the validity of the modeling can be tested.

Since the structure supporting the shaft bearings is complicated, the use of finite element methods is the most feasible way of determining the support stiffness. The stiffness between the shaft and bearing of a stave bearing can be quite low if the staves are rubber. The stiffness of an oil film bearing is such that a bearing force introduces a motion having a component perpendicular to the load.

If, as a result of the calculations of shaft response, it is found that there are no shaft resonances near the operating speeds of the ship, the shafting can be considered satisfactory for this level of refinement. Later analyses of the whole ship will confirm its suitability. If, on the other hand, lateral resonances appear close to the operating speed, then by changing one or more of the following, a new propulsion system can be developed which has resonances properly located:

1. The overhang of the propeller beyond the stern bearing
2. The span between the last two bearings supporting the propeller shaft
3. The diameter of the propeller shaft
4. The support of the propeller shaft bearing
   a. The skeg and stern tube structure for a single screw ship having a skeg-supported bearing
   b. The angles, size, and manner of attachment to the bearing barrel of the arms carrying a strut bearing for open screw ships
   c. The structure supporting strut arms.
   d. Other changes as indicated by the calculations

Such changes are frequently required, and good judgment, often using analyses of simple models, is required to discover the optimum solution rapidly and inexpensively.

The following descriptions present information on two computer programs used for the analysis of transverse propeller shafting vibration.

Transverse Response of a Beam

Category: Transverse beam vibration in conceptual ship design
Maintenance: Newport News Shipbuilding and Drydock Company
            Production Computer Systems Division
            4101 Washington Avenue
            Newport News, Virginia 23607
Telephone: (804) 247-7500
Capability: Computes the steady-state transverse vibratory response of a beam with any number of intermediate flexible supports, with generalized end conditions, section properties, and loading
Programming Language: FORTRAN IV
Hardware: Honeywell 6080
Availability: Not available for general distribution

Transverse Vibration of Shafting and Propeller

Category: Transverse vibration of shafting
Author: F. E. Reed
        Littleton Research and Engineering Corp.
        95 Russell Street
        Littleton, Massachusetts 01460
Telephone: (617) 486-3526
Method: The propeller is represented by its mass, its entrained water,
    its moment of inertia about the rotational axis, its moment of in-
    ertia about an axis perpendicular to the rotational axis, the mo-
    ment of inertia of its entrained water, and the hydrodynamic damp-
    ing in its several modes of motion.
        The shaft is represented as a series of uniform beams having
    distributed mass and bending stiffness and hysteretic damping. The
    bearings are represented by their stiffness in translation in two
    directions mutually perpendicular to the shaft axis and by their
    stiffness in rotation about the same two axes. The bearings are
    assumed to bend with the shaft; however, where there is flexibility
    between shaft and bearing, e.g., rubber staves, this flexibility,
    lateral and angular, is incorporated in the strut matrix. It is
    generally acceptable to terminate the shaft at the after inboard
    lineshaft bearing.
Capability: The program computes the vibration in terms of coupled
    properties in the horizontal and vertical directions. It includes
    the influence of the steady thrust (small effect), but not that of
    the steady torque (very small).
Input: Shafting arrangement, diameters, and lengths; propeller weight
    and moment of inertia about its rotation axis, diameter, number of
    blades, pitch, and developed area ratio; stiffness or flexibility
    matrices for each bearing about axes perpendicular to the axis of
    rotation (force and rotation); horizontal and vertical harmonic
    forces and moments, and the steady thrust.
Output: Plots of bearing forces, in two normal directions, as a function
    of frequency; plots of shaft motions, in two normal directions, as
    a function of frequency, at the propeller and at other critical
    locations; plots of the shaft deflection curves at each natural
    frequency within the operating speed; plots of the steady plus har-
    monic bending moments in the shaft of the aftermost bearings; com-
    puter tables for above
Availability: This is a proprietary program not developed for general
    distribution. Contact author for usage.

Conduct Superstructure Modal Analysis - [Box 18]

In addition to substructures of the shafting and machinery spaces, it is
desirable to make a study of the superstructure as a subsystem since
resonances in this region are a frequent cause of vibration troubles.
Finite element methods are generally most suitable for modeling this
structure by considering it to be attached to a rigid strength deck.
With the high superstructures common on container ships and very long
ships, some superstructures vibrate fore and aft as a cantilever beam.
On others, the decks vibrate symmetrically within the sides, while on
still others, the decks vibrate antisymmetrically (port up, starboard
down) so that the finite element model should not be too coarse to

suitably represent the complexity of possible modes. Clearly the most
suitable programs for these analyses are finite element programs.
    It may be desirable to make substructural studies of other por-
tions of the ship such as the rudder horn subsystem or systems involving
stern crane or elevator carriers. It might also be desirable to combine
two or more smaller subsystems. For example, the lateral shaft and substructure subsystem can be connected to the longitudinal shaft and machinery space subsystem to form a larger combined subsystem.
    When the subsystems have been designed so that it is expected that
they will be free of vibration resonances, it is time to make a vibration
analysis of the complete ship. This analysis of the full ship fulfills
two important functions:

    1. It checks and confirms the validity of the boundaries assumed
for the substructures.
    2. By modeling the ship as a whole, it is possible, with the prop-
er damping, to predict the vibration levels in all parts of the ship as
a function of frequency. Comparing these predictions with established
acceptable levels allows an assessment of acceptability of the ship at a
point in construction where corrections and changes to overcome serious
difficulties can be determined and incorporated in the design.

Assemble Model of Entire Ship and Determine Vibration
Amplitudes and Stress Levels of the Complete Ship -
[Boxes 21 and 22]

Reference [8] indicates that under some conditions the complete ship may
be satisfactorily modeled as a beam structure using a Timoshenko beam as
a base. For vertical vibration, the ship may be modeled as parallel
beams elastically connected and carrying spring weights. For lateral
vibrations the bending is strongly coupled with torsion, and so a coupled
model is required. Strictly speaking, the vertical bending should be
coupled with axial vibration of the ship, and this is probably advisable
if the blade frequency approaches an estimated longitudinal frequency of
the ship. Where these conditions cannot be met, it is necessary to model
the ship by finite element methods in order to obtain reliable estimates
of response.
    Although heavy vibrations of twice and three times blade frequency
can be measured on ships, the methods of analysis that are presented in
this chapter are feasible only for the range of the fundamental blade frequency, except for the unusual cases.
    As an example of a ship modeled in terms of beams, consider Fig. 2,
an uncoupled vertical vibration model, and Fig. 3, a coupled lateral-
torsional vibration model. A finite element model for half a ship (because of symmetry, only half need be represented) is shown in Figs. 4
and 5.
    For the analysis of structures as complex as shown in Figs. 2 and
3, the computer program GBRP (General Bending Response Program) developed
at the Naval Ship Research and Development Center [29] should be used.
In the analysis of the ship hull, it can treat vertical as well as coupled lateral-torsional vibration. These capabilities and other features
of the program are described on subsequent pages.

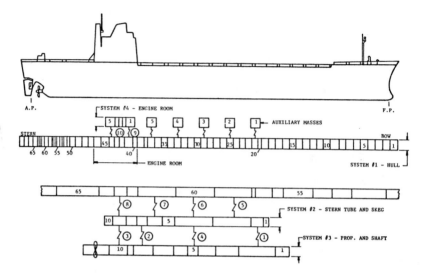

Fig. 2 Unitized and containerized ship, vertical vibration model

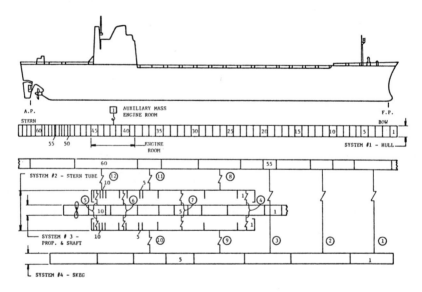

Fig. 3 Unitized and containerized ship, transverse vibration model

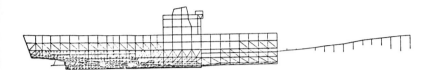

Fig. 4 Elevation view of finite element model

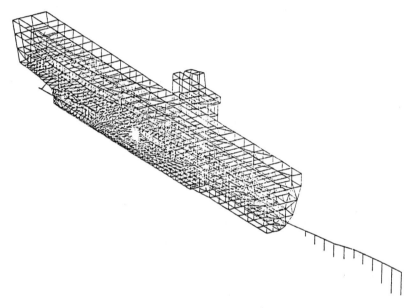

Fig. 5 Rotated view of finite element model

Program GBRP

Categories: Lateral, longitudinal, and torsional beam vibrations; bend-
          ing coupled with torsional beam vibrations; whirling vibrations of
          propeller shafts
Authors: M. E. Golden and F. M. Henderson
          Naval Ship Research and Development Center
          Bethesda, Maryland 20084
Capability: The General Bending Response Program (GBRP) consists of the
          union of three programs: General Bending Response Code 1 (GBRC1)
          for lateral, longitudinal, and torsional vibrations; GBRC2 for vi-
          brations involving bending coupled with torsion; and GBRC3 for
          whirling vibrations of propeller shafts. The latter two codes re-
          sulted from an extended application of the mathematical model used
          in the first code. The program calculates natural frequencies and

mode shapes and the response to specified harmonic driving forces
and moments. The program can represent a ship hull connected elastically to other systems such as the propulsion system and to
sprung masses. Longitudinal or torsional vibration problems can
also be solved by dividing each beam into sections connected by
springs, thus reducing the model to a mass-spring system.
Method: The program formulates the finite difference equations which
        approximate the boundary-value problem representing the steady-
        state motion of a vibrating nonuniform mass-spring system such as
        a ship hull or shafting in bending.
Programming Language: FORTRAN IV
Documentation: See Ref. [29].
Software Operation: Overlays for program subroutines; open core to opti-
        mize storage; SC 4020 plots
Hardware: CDC 6000 Series
Availability: Available for general distribution through David Taylor
        Naval Ship Research and Development Center

        To define the elastic properties of the structure, it is necessary
to define the cross-sectional elastic properties. A program and procedure for computing

I_y (Moment of inertia about transverse axis)

I_z (Moment of inertia about vertical axis)

I_{yz} (Product of inertia relative to horizontal and vertical axes)

A   (Cross-sectional area)

$K_{xz}A$ (Shear area constant vertical plane)

$K_{xy}A$ (Shear area constant transverse plane)

J_x (Torsional area constant about longitudinal axis)

$\bar{z}$ (Vertical coordinate of the neutral axis)

$\bar{y}$ (Transverse coordinate of neutral axis)

y',z' (Coordinates of the shear center of the section)

are given in Ref. [30]. This program calculates the equivalent beam parameters for the ship section properties using data tabulations obtained
from hull plans by a preestablished orderly procedure.
        U.S. Steel Engineers and Consultants, Inc., developed a program
that represents a ship as a beam on an elastic foundation. Other vibration programs based upon modeling the hull as beams have been developed
by Lloyd's Registry of Shipping and by Dr. Ing. E. Metzmeier of the
Institut für Schiffstechnik in Berlin, Federal Republic of Germany.
These programs are briefly described below.

Program SHRVS

Category: Conceptual design in ship vibration
Maintenance: U.S. Steel Engineers and Consultants
              600 Grant Street
              Pittsburgh, Pennsylvania 15230
Capability: The purpose of SHRVS is the accurate prediction of the vi-
        bratory response of a ship hull to either steady-state or transient

loads applied in the vertical centerline plane of the hull. Factors considered include cargo distribution, bulkhead location, machinery space location, as well as the flexural and shear stiffness of the main-hull girder and of the double-bottom structure. See Ref. [31].

Programming Language: FORTRAN IV
Hardware: CDC 6500
Program Size: 160K Octal words
Typical Running Times: 3 minutes
Availability: Contact F. R. Griffith,
                 Manager-Sales, Computer Services,
                 U.S. Steel Engineers and Consultants, Inc.

Program Hull Vibration LR57P

Category: Eigenvalues and eigenvectors of lower ship hull modes
Maintenance: Lloyd's Registry of Shipping
                 71, Fenchurch Street
                 London EC3, England
Date: Latest revision April 1976
Capability: Computes the eigenvalues and eigenvectors of any structure that can be represented by a free-free beam
Program Language: FORTRAN IV
Documentation: Contained in Lloyd's Registry Development Unit Report No. 131 [32]
Hardware: IBM 370/158
Availability: Program available as a service from Lloyd's Registry - contact Mr. Geoffrey H. Sole, Structural Engineer.

Program FREIS, ERZS

Category: Eigenvalues, eigenvectors, steady-state, transient response of a ship hull
Author: Prof. Dr.-Ing. E. Metzmeier
         Institute für Schiffstechnik
         Technische Universität Berlin
         Federal Republic of Germany
Date: 1974
Capability: Computes the eigenvalues, eigenvectors, steady-state, and transient response of a ship hull
Method: Finite difference method
Limitations and Restrictions: 41 degrees of freedom (dof) for longitudinal, 82 dof for vertical, and 164 dof for coupled horizontal-torsional vibrations
Programming Language: FORTRAN
Hardware: CDC 6500
Availability: Contact author for usage.

The factors that enter into the choice of the number and location of the subdivisions of the hull structure are considered in Ref. [8]. The advantage of representing a ship by a beam model is that the computer analysis is more direct, more easily interpreted, and considerably less expensive than that with a finite element analysis for a structure that is as well defined. The disadvantages are that for many ship vibration

problems, particularly where the decks are open so that the vibration
across the width of the ship is important, the beam representation of
the ship is inadequate and a finite element process is required for satisfactory modeling.

The use of finite element methods for predicting ship vibrations
is becoming widespread. Some organizations have developed finite element
programs specifically for ship applications. Among these that should be
mentioned are SESAM-69 developed by Det norske Veritas, the Norwegian
classification society [33], and DASH developed by the Netherlands Ship
Research Center. Bureau Veritas, the French classification society, has
made many finite element analyses of ship structures, and they use finite
element programs such as ASKA, NASTRAN, SAP, STRUDL, or transfer matrix
programs. The Electric Boat Division of General Dynamics Corporation
developed and maintains a finite element computer program GENSAM for use
on submarine vibration problems. Information on these programs is presented below.

Program SESAM-69

Category: General purpose finite element program
Maintenance: A/S Computas (subsidiary of Det norske Veritas)
              Veritasveien 1
              Post Office Box 310
              N-1322 Hovik, Norway
Date: System became operative in 1969.
Capability: SESAM stands for Super Element Structural Analysis program
    Modules. The modules consist of various applications of programs
    which can analyze piping systems, solids, thin/thick shells, axi-
    symmetric bodies, superelements, three-dimensional frames, two-
    and three-dimensional membranes, and stationary nonlinear tempera-
    ture problems. See Ref. [33].
Programming Language: FORTRAN
Documentation: Users' manuals, maintenance manuals, operators' manuals,
    modeling manuals
Hardware: SESAM-69 was developed previously for the UNIVAC 1108. Major
    parts of the program have been converted to the CDC and IBM operat-
    ing systems.
Availability: The program is available to the maritime industry on a
    usage, lease, or purchase basis. For details contact Knut T.
    Skaar, Senior Research Engineer, Research Division, Det norske
    Veritas.

Program DASH

Category: Finite element program for the dynamic analysis of ship hulls
    (DASH)
Author: Dr. S. Hylarides
         Netherlands Ship Model Basin
         P. O. Box 28
         Wageningen, The Netherlands
Date: 1970, latest revision 1975
Capability: Computes the eigenvalues, eigenvectors, steady-state, and
    transient response of a ship hull
Method: Finite element method with the ship represented as a collection
    of beams and plates. See Ref. [34].

Programming Language: ALGOL
Availability: Program is not available for purchase. Contact Netherlands Ship Model Basin for information on program use.

Program GENSAM

Category: General purpose finite element program
Maintenance: Electric Boat Division
            Advanced Engineering Department
            General Dynamics Corporation
            Eastern Point Road
            Groton, Connecticut 06340
Date: Initial completion 1967; Version 13, January 1976
Capability: Can model general structures consisting of beams, plates,
    shells, axisymmetric shells and continua, and three-dimensional
    continua. Capable of solving the following types of problems: normal
    mode prediction, shock spectrum response, steady-state vibration
    response, mechanical impedance and mobility, modal transient re-
    sponse, direct transient response, random vibration response (power
    spectral density and root-mean-square), fluid-structure interac-
    tion, electroelastic vibration, and wave propagation.
Programming Language: 99 percent FORTRAN V, 1 percent machine language
Documentation: Consists of GENSAM User's Manual, Command Manual, Element
    Manual, RJE User's Manual, and Production Analysis Program User's
    Manual.
Hardware: UNIVAC 1106, 1108, 1110; EXEC 8 operating system
Availability: This is a proprietary program with availability determined
    on a case basis. Contact Dr. Henno Allik or Mr. Philip Cacciatore.

Since the cost of developing, maintaining, and updating a large finite element computer program is high, it is common to apply general purpose computer programs to ship vibration problems. In particular NASTRAN
is used by Lloyd's Registry of Shipping, the American Bureau of Shipping,
Littleton Research and Engineering Corp., and probably by other organizations. This program was developed for the analysis of large structures
and readily applies to ships. It is being continually updated to improve
the representation of structural elements and the processing efficiency.
Since ship applications constitute only a small part of NASTRAN usage,
the program does not contain a subroutine for determining an added mass
matrix associated with the entrained water. Because it was developed for
large projects, NASTRAN carries high overhead structure. Most ship finite element studies involve models that are large enough to benefit from
the generality provided by the overhead, but for many small studies that
will not later be incorporated in the large model, it may be desirable
to use other finite element programs such as STARDYNE, ANSYS, MARC,
STRUDL, or SAP.

SUMMARY

This chapter has shown that there are many computer programs available for
predicting the loading and response of a ship due to propeller-induced
excitations. The choice of a particular program is largely a matter of
availability, user experience, and degree of sophistication desired in
the analysis.

For the most part, the present programs can adequately predict the excitation and response, with the exception being in the analytical prediction of cavitation pressures on the hull surface. Unfortunately, these cavitation effects can be significant, and continued research in this area is required.

In the area of overall design philosophy, there seems to be some reluctance on the part of shipbuilders to fully employ the analytical techniques available or on the part of shipowners to insist that the techniques be used to minimize vibrations in the design stage. These analytical procedures must be utilized on a routine basis with a feedback mechanism to compare measured and predicted calculations and response so their accuracy can be evaluated and, if necessary, improved. Only through a logical design process can ships be consistently built which possess acceptable vibration characteristics.

ACKNOWLEDGMENTS

The authors wish to thank all individuals and companies which furnished information about their computer programs. Because this particular field is the subject of many active research programs throughout the world, it is not possible to recognize each on an individual basis. A special appreciation is extended to the Ship Research Committee, which has offered many valuable comments and suggestions throughout the project associated with this chapter.

REFERENCES

1 Schlick, O., "Further Investigations of the Vibrations of Steamers," Trans. Institution of Naval Architects, London, Vol. 35, 1894.

2 Lewis, F. M., "The Inertia of Water Surrounding a Vibrating Ship," Trans. SNAME, Vol. 37, 1929.

3 Taylor, J. L., "Vibration of Ships," Trans. Institution of Naval Architects, London, Vol. 72, 1930.

4 Timoshenko, S., Vibration Problems in Engineering, D. Van Nostrand Co., New York, 1937.

5 Prohl, M. A., "A General Method of Calculating Critical Speeds of Flexible Rotors," ASME, Journal of Applied Mechanics, Vol. 12, No. 3, 1945.

6 Myklestad, N. O., "New Methods of Calculating Natural Mode of Coupled Bending - Torsion Vibration of Beams," Trans. ASME, Vol. 67, No. 1, Jan. 1945.

7 Reed, F. E., "The Design of Ships to Avoid Propeller-Excited Vibrations," Trans. SNAME, Vol. 79, 1971.

8 Burnside, O. H., Kana, D. D., and Reed, F. E., "A Design Procedure for Minimizing Propeller-Induced Vibration in Hull Structural Elements," Final Report, SR240, Department of Transportation, U.S. Coast Guard, Contract No. DOT-CG-61907-A, April 1979.

9 Lewis, F. M., "Propeller Vibration," Trans. SNAME, Vol. 43, 1936.

10 Lewis, F. M., "Propeller Vibration," Trans. SNAME, Vol. 44, 1936.

11 Burrill, L. C., "Calculation of Marine Propeller Characteristics," Northeast Coast Institute of Engineers and Shipbuilders, Vol. 60, 1943-44.

12 Hinterthon, W. B., "Propeller-Excited Vibratory Forces for the Tanker SS ESSO Gettysburg Calculated from Wake Surveys," Naval Ship Research and Development Rept. 2870, Aug. 1968.

13   Reed, F. E., and Bradshaw, R. T., "Ship Hull Vibrations II. Distribution of Exciting Forces Generated by Propellers," CONESCO Report to Bureau of Ships, F-101-2, Index No. NS712-100ST2, June 1960.
14   Tsakonas, S., and Jacobs, W. R., "Documentation of a Computer Program for the Pressure Distribution Forces and Moments on Ship Propellers in Hull Wakes," Stevens Institute of Technology, Davidson Laboratory Rept. SIT-DL-76-1863.
15   Brown, N. A., "Periodic Propeller Forces in Non-Uniform Flow," Massachusetts Institute of Technology, Department of Naval Architecture and Marine Engineering Rept. 64-7, 1964.
16   Frydelund, O., and Kerwin, J. E., "The Development of Numerical Methods for the Computation of Unsteady Propeller Forces," Symposium on Hydrodynamics of Ship and Offshore Propulsion Systems, Det norske Veritas, Oslo, Norway, March 1977.
17   Kerwin, J. E., "Computer Techniques for Propeller Blade Section Designs," International Shipbuilding Progress, Vol. 20, No. 227, July 1973.
18   Murray, M. T., and Tubby, J. E., "Blade-Rate Force Fluctuations of a Propeller in Non-Uniform Flow," Admiralty Research Laboratory, ARL/M/P33A, June 1973.
19   Van Oossanen, P., and van der Kooy, J., "Vibratory Hull Forces Induced by Cavitating Propellers," Trans. Royal Institute of Naval Architects, Vol. 115, 1973.
20   Vorus, W. S., "A Method for Analyzing the Propeller-Induced Vibratory Forces Acting on the Surface of a Ship Stern," Trans. SNAME, Vol. 82, 1974.
21   Yildiz, M., and Mawardi, O. K., "On the Diffraction of Multiple Fields by a Semi-Infinite Rigid Wedge," Journal Acoustical Society of America, Vol. 32, No. 12, Dec. 1960.
22   Yildiz, M., and Mawardi, O. K., "Diffraction of a Dipole Field by a Rigid Cone (Abstract)," Journal Acoustical Society of America, Vol. 32, No. 12, 1960.
23   Tsakonas, S., Jacobs, W. R., and Ali, M. R., "Documentation for the Complete Program for the Pressure Field Generated by a Propeller in a Variable Inflow," Stevens Institute of Technology, Davidson Laboratory Rept. 1910, May 1977.
24   Van Oossanen, P., "Theoretical Prediction of Cavitation on Propellers," Marine Technology, Vol. 14, No. 4, 1977.
25   Schawanecke, H., "Comparison of Methods for the Calculation of Wake Induced Propeller Blade Exciting Forces," International Towing Tank Conference, Ottawa, Canada, Paper No. 13, 1975.
26   The Society of Naval Architects and Marine Engineers, "Longitudinal Stiffness of Main Thrust Bearing Foundations," SNAME Technical and Research Report R-15, Sept. 1972.
27   "The National Shipbuilding Research Program - Research on Computer Applications to Shipbuilding VII, Catalog of Program Abstracts" U.S. Department of Commerce, Maritime Administration, in cooperation with Avondale Shipyards, Inc., May 1975.
28   Jones, R. F., Jr., "Ship Structures," Structural Mechanics Computer Programs, ed. W. Pilkey et al., University Press of Virginia, Charlottesville, 1974.
29   Golden, M. E., and Henderson, F. M., "An Updated Guide to the Use of General Bending Response Program (GBRP)," Computation and Mathematics Department Research and Development Rept. 4601, Naval Ship Research and Development Center, Bethesda, Md., April 1975.
30   Leibowitz, R. C., and Harder, R. L., "Mechanized Computation of Ship Parameters," David Taylor Model Basin Rept. 1841, June 1965.

31 Kline, R. G., Clough, R. W., and Kavlio, D., "Propeller-Excited Vibrations," SNAME, Northern California Local Section, March 1971.

32 Lloyd's Registry of Shipping, Development Unit Report No. 131.

33 Egeland, O., and Araldsen, P. O., "SESAM-69 - A General Purpose Finite Element Method Program," Computers and Structures, Vol. 4, Pergamon Press, 1974, pp. 41-68.

34 Hylariades, Ir. S., "DASH, Computer Program for Dynamic Analysis of Ship Hulls," Netherlands Ship Research Center Rept. No. 159/S, NSMB Publication 367, Sept. 1971.

Piping Engineering

Wallace B. Wright

Arthur D. Little, Inc.

INTRODUCTION

This chapter is an update of one written five years ago by the author
on piping systems analysis [1]. This earlier chapter put emphasis on
delineating the analytical capabilities of various programs available
to and actually used by the technical community for evaluation of design.
The analytical capabilities were summarized in chart form and a person
to contact was listed for the readers who wished more information.

This chapter performs the same function as its predecessor, but a
second section has been introduced to emphasize a change in the business
of software development. This second section reflects the way software
developers are optimizing the use of existing computers, new hardware,
rapidly decreasing hardware cost, "distributed data processing," and
new numerical techniques to assist in the process of piping engineering.

The phrase "the business of software development" was purposefully
used above to reflect the rapidly increasing cost of software development versus the decreasing cost of computer hardware. Since any business seeks a unique niche to make it different and appealing, this
second section is written in a free style format where the developer was
asked to describe current or planned software enhancements. Some chose
to respond to this invitation by providing a summary of planned activities, others provided brochures that amplify on the basic capabilities
described in the first section, while still others preferred not to
respond because they feel this type of information is proprietary. However, the response of those asked to contribute, either directly or
indirectly, was quite good, and their contribution is appreciated.

The second section should provide the reader with insight into the
diverse areas of development, and, keeping in mind that there is always
a reason for development, some trends will be noted. The trends are
consistent with any positive contribution to technology--contributions
that allow man to do more with less.

CAPABILITY STATEMENT

The requirements of software in piping engineering are multifaceted, but there are a number of basic industry needs; and, hence, all programs do have a number of similar capabilities. To define and show these capabilities, a table was generated in a matrix form. An x in a location indicates that the program in that row has the capability indicated on that line. A blank space indicates a lack of the capability in that program. The table starts on page 194.

While many programs exhibit similar characteristics, this means only that they should be considered candidates for further investigation by the potential user and not automatically deemed equivalent. Inherent in each program is a series of requirements placed on the user, and it is advisable to investigate the true meaning of implementing a particular analytical capability.

The capability statement is divided into eight categories: types of loading, modeling capability, preprocessing features, intermediate data, postprocessing, documentation level, computer hardware requirements, and program development.

The "types of loading" category describes the time-independent (static) loadings and the time-dependent (dynamic, thermal) loadings. The "modeling capability" describes the structural elements (pipe elements, elbows, and so on) that are available to describe a piping/structural system and the types of restraints (partial, skew, etc.) that may be placed on the system. "Preprocessing" is of practical importance in input deck debugging, and this category gives an indication of preprocessing capability. "Intermediate data," coupled with preprocessor error diagnostics, provides one of the best methods of evaluating input data, intermediate mathematical manipulations, and computations. Normally, the intermediate data may be selectively requested so the analyst can retrieve meaningful data for scrutiny. "Postprocessing" normally contains the information which is used to determine the adequacy of the design by evaluating load, deflection, and stress values against established criteria. "Documentation level" is important in defining the program's established and documented level of reliability. "Operational-on" indicates the computer system's generic name by hardware manufacturers and does not attempt to define the machine versions or operating systems on which the machine has been implemented. However, this information does provide an indication of the program's machine dependence or independence. "Program development" and "program availability" listings provide a quick assessment of the program's current activity and the method(s) of procurement.

SOFTWARE SUPPLIERS' COMMENTS ON THEIR PRODUCTS' DEVELOPMENT AND FEATURES

ADLPIPE

ADLPIPE has recently become a subset of a large piping engineering
Design Information System (DIS) which is a development of Arthur D.
Little, Inc. DIS performs two tasks: first, it greatly simplifies
input for stress analysis, and second, it may be used for other engineering tasks such as drawing generation, interference checking, and
bills of material. All of the tasks operate from a common data base.
Communication with DIS may be either batch or interactive or a combination of the two.
     Two developments to be completed in the first half of 1979 are
a hydraulic analysis capability and a nonlinear capability. Both will
operate as subsets of DIS. The hydraulics capability will analyze
steady-state flow characteristics of piping systems. The structural
nonlinear capability includes large deformation theory, nonlinear material properties and restraints, and multiple time-dependent forcing
functions for dynamics problems and single acting restraints for
static problems.
     For further information contact:
I. W. Dingwell   (617) 864-5770 ext 892
Arthur D. Little, Inc.
Acorn Park
Cambridge, Massachusetts 02140

ANSYS[1]

The ANSYS engineering analysis computer program is a large-scale general
purpose computer program employing finite element technology for the
solution of several classes of engineering analysis problems. The program capabilities include structural analyses (static and dynamic;
elastic, plastic, creep, and swelling; small and large deflections), and
heat transfer analyses (steady-state and transient; conduction, convection, and radiation). Structural and heat transfer analyses may be made
in one, two, or three dimensions, including axisymmetric and plane problems. Coupled thermal-fluid flow capability, coupled thermal-elastic
capability, and wave motion analysis capability are also available.
     ANSYS may be run in either the interactive or the batch mode.
Interactive running is suited to low-speed terminal operations.
Prompting commands are returned by the program in the interactive mode.
Free-format data input is allowed in either mode.
     In addition to the general mesh generation routine, a preprocessing
routine is also available to generate boundary conditions from a minimum
of input data. Several thousand data sets may be readily generated for
transient dynamic analysis.
     A preprocessing routine that converts standard piping system data
to ANSYS input data is available.
     Further capability is documented by:

_____

[1]Information excerpted from brochures supplied by the developer to
the author.

Table 1   Capabilities of Software in Piping Engineering

Program Name	ADLPIP	ANSYS	DYNAFLEX	MARC	ME101	NUPIPEII
Types of Loading						
Static: Wind	x	x	x	x	x	x
Thermal	x	x	x	x	x	x
Deadweight	x	x	x	x	x	x
Externally Applied Loads	x	x	x	x	x	x
Dynamic: Response Spectra	x	x	x		x	x
Time Dependent:						
Dynamic Linear Elastic:	x	x		x		x
Transient	x	x		x		x
Steady State Oscillatory		x				x
Dynamic Nonlinear Elastic/Plastic:		x		x		
Large Deformation		x		x		
Gap Restraints		x		x		
Plasticity/Creep		x		x		
Modeling Capability						
Straight Pipe as a: Beam	x	x	x	x	x	x
Shell		x		x		
Elbow as a: Modified Curved Beam	x	x	x	x	x	x
Shell		x		x		
Tee as a: Beam Intersection	x	x		x	x	x
Modified Beam Intersection	x	x	x		x	x
Intersection of Two Shells		x		x		
Stiffness Elements and Restraints:						
6 x 6 Stiffness Matrix	x	x				x
To Ground	x	x		x	x	x
Between Elements	x	x		x	x	x
Spring Hangers	x	x	x	x	x	x
Anchor (Ground) Restraints: Partial Restraint	x	x	x	x	x	x
Full Restraint	x	x	x	x	x	x
Skew (Ground) Restraint: Guided	x	x	x	x	x	x
Preprocessing						
Input Data Preparation: Specifically for Piping	x	x	x	x	x	x
General		x		x		
Input Data Error Diagnostics: Nonfatal	x	x	x	x	x	x
Fatal	x	x	x	x	x	x
Plotting: Dimensional Isometrics	x	x	x	x		
Dimensioned Orthographics		x		x		
Stress Isometrics	x	x		x		x
Stereoptics						
Intermediate Data						
Input data printed in interpreted form	x	x	x	x	x	x
Mathematical manipulations may be called for evaluation	x	x	x	x	x	x
Forces and moments are printed: Static	x	x	x	x	x	x
Time Dependent	x	x		x		x
Deflections and rotations are printed: Static	x	x	x	x	x	x
Time Dependent	x	x		x		x
Nonlinear accumulated strains/deflections are printed		x		x		

Table I (cont.)

PIPEDYNII	PIPESD	PIPESTRESSII	PIRAX	PISTAR	PISYS	SAP4G	STALUM	SUPERPIPE	TMRPIPE	WECAN
x			x				x			x
x	x	x	x	x	x	x	x	x	x	x
x	x	x	x	x	x	x	x	x	x	x
x	x	x	x	x	x	x	x	x	x	x
x	x			x	x	x	x	x	x	x
x							x		x	x
x			x	x	x	x	x	x	x	x
x						x	x		x	x
										x
										x
			x							x
x	x	x	x	x	x	x	x	x	x	x
						x				x
x		x		x	x	x	x	x	x	x
			x			x				x
	x		x		x	x	x	x		x
x		x		x			x	x	x	x
						x				x
x		x								x
x		x		x	x	x	x	x	x	x
x		x		x	x	x	x	x		x
x	x	x	x	x	x	x	x	x	x	x
x	x	x	x	x	x	x	x	x	x	x
x		x	x	x	x	x	x	x	x	x
x	x	x	x	x	x	x	x	x	x	x
x	x	x	x	x	x	x	x	x	x	
					x	x	x			x
x		x		x	x	x	x	x	x	x
		x		x	x	x	x	x	x	x
x					x	x	x		x	x
x							x		x	x
								x		x
	x	x	x	x	x	x	x	x	x	x
x							x	x	x	
x	x	x	x	x	x	x	x	x	x	x
x			x	x	x	x	x	x	x	x
x	x	x	x	x	x	x	x	x	x	x
x			x	x	x	x	x	x	x	x
			x							x

Table 1 (cont.)

Program Name	ADLPIPE	ANSYS	DYNAFLEX	MARC	ME101	NUPIPEII	PIPEDYNII
Postprocessing							
Stresses are computed to meet:							
B31.1.0 Power Piping	x	x	x		x	x	x
B31.2 Fuel Gas Piping	x		x			x	
B31.3 Petroleum Refinery Piping	x		x			x	
B31.4 L. P. Transportation Piping	x		x				
ASME Section III, Nuclear Components Code, Class 1	x	x	x		x	x	x
Class 2	x	x	x		x	x	x
Class 3	x	x	x		x	x	x
Plotting: Static Deformation		x			x	x	
Dynamic: Mode Shapes		x			x		
Displacement Time History		x	x		x	x	x
Strain Time History					x		
Force Time History		x	x		x		
Documentation Level:							
Data Preparation Manual	x	x	x		x	x	x
Programmer's Manual		x			x	x	
Mathematical Formulation	x	x	x		x	x	x
Numerical Techniques	x	x	x		x	x	x
Comparative Sample Problem Solutions	x	x	x		x	x	x
Listing Available	x		x		x	x	x
Operational On:							
IBM	x	x	x		x	x	x
CDC	x	x	x		x	x	x
UNIVAC	x	x	x		x	x	x
PRIME	x				x		
DEC			x		x		
Other		x			x		x
Program Development:							
The program is under active development	x	x	x		x	x	x
The program is actively maintained by author	x	x	x		x	x	x
by others		x	x				x
Program Available Commercially: Purchase		x	x		x	x	x
License	x	x	x		x	x	x
Utility Network (Use Basis)	x		x			x	
Total Program Capability: Reported Here	x		x		x	x	x
Reported Elsewhere in Book							

Table 1 (cont.)

Program Name	PIPESD	PIPESTRESSII	PIRAX	PISTAR	PISYS	SAP4G	STALUM	SUPERPIPE	TMRPIPE	WECAN
Postprocessing										
Stresses are computed to meet:										
B31.1.0 Power Piping	x			x		x		x	x	x
B31.2 Fuel Gas Piping	x	x								
B31.3 Petroleum Refinery Piping										
B31.4 L.P. Transportation Piping										
ASME Section III, Class 1	x			x	x	x		x	x	x
Class 2	x			x	x	x		x	x	x
Class 3	x			x	x	x		x		x
Plotting: Static Deformation	x				x	x				x
Dynamic: Mode Shapes	x			x	x	x	x			x
Displacement Time History				x	x	x				x
Strain Time History										x
Force Time History	x			x	x	x				x
Documentation Level										
Data Preparation Manual	x	x	x	x	x	x		x	x	x
Programmer's Manual			x			x				
Mathematical Formulation		x	x	x		x		x	x	x
Numerical Techniques				x		x		x	x	x
Comparative Sample Solutions	x		x	x	x	x		x	x	x
Listing Available						?				
Operational On:										
IBM		x	x							
CDC	x	x	x	x				x		x
UNIVAC						x				
PRIME										
DEC					x					
Other					x					
Program Development										
The program is under active development	x	x		x	x	x		x	x	x
The program is actively maintained by author	x			x	x	x		x	x	x
by others	x	x		x			x			x
Program Available Commercially: Purchase		x							x	
License	x	x		x				x	x	
Utility Network	x	x		x			x	x	x	
Total Program Capability: Reported Here	x				x		x			
Reported in Book	x					x		x		

1. ANSYS User's Manual
2. ANSYS Example Manual
3. ANSYS Introductory Manual
4. ANSYS Verification Manual
5. ANSYS Theoretical Manual
6. ANSYS Capability Sheets
7. ANSYS Minicomputer Brochure

For further information contact:
Gabriel J. Desalvo   (412) 746-3304
John A. Swanson
Swanson Analysis Systems, Inc.
P.O. Box 65
Houston, Pennsylvania   15342

DYNAFLEX

For further information contact:
W. Koff   (201) 494-8787
Auton Computing Corp.
One Metro Plaza
505 Thornall Street
Edison, New Jersey   08817

MARC

MARC is an internationally known general purpose finite element program
designed, developed, and built specifically for nonlinear analysis. Nonlinearities considered include plasticity, large strains, large rotations,
and large displacements. MARC may be used for the analysis of structures in the static, dynamic, and thermal regimes. Its extensive element library makes it useful in elastic analysis, and its broad coverage
of the structural mechanics field makes it an invaluable tool for nonlinear analysis.
    In addition to the commonly used finite elements, MARC has two
elements specifically designed for the analysis of piping systems. The
first is a straight, closed-section beam element with sixteen numerical
integration points around the circumference for the default circular
cross section (MARC Type 14). This element provides a very accurate
implementation of Euler-Bernouilli beam theory to model pipe runs.
    The second special piping element (MARC Type 17) is used to model
pipe bends. This elbow element is basically a superposition of a modified axisymmetric shell element and a beam with constant stretch and
curvatures. This formulation admits ovalization of the cross section.
The pipe bends are modeled using several sections of element Type 17.
The elbow elements are coupled together and into the straight beam
elements by use of special tying (linear constraint equations). Thus,
a complete pipe bend might be modeled as several sections of elbow elements tied together, each section being built from several elements,
all sharing a common "elbow" node, and having the usual two nodes on the
shell surface.
    Other elements in the MARC element library typically used to model
a piping system include point masses, linear and nonlinear springs, and
gap elements to model friction, sliding, and nonlinear force-displacement

mechanisms.

A pipe mesh generator preprocessor (MARC-PIPE) is available to facilitate model generation.

Analyses which may be performed on the piping system using MARC include:

1. Deadweight
2. Thermal
3. Anchor motion
4. Transient response

These analyses may include nonlinear effects (plasticity, creep, large displacements, etc.).

A comprehensive graphic capability includes undeformed and deformed models, variable versus variable, and contour plots.

All model and solution data may be written to files accessible by user-written programs for further postprocessing.

The resources at MARC Analysis Research Corporation are available to assist in or to perform the piping analysis.

For further information contact:
H. Dale Seamons   (415) 326-7511
MARC Analysis Research Corporation
260 Sheridan Avenue
Suite 200
Palo Alto, California 94306

ME 101

For further information contact:
M. Z. Jeric   (213) 864-6011
Bechtel Power Corporation
P. O. Box 60860
Terminal Annes
Los Angeles, California 90060

NUPIPE II

For further information contact:
Doug P. Munson   (408) 446-2500
Nuclear Services Corporation
1700 Dell Avenue
Campbell, California 95008

PIPEDYN II

For further information contact:
Yung-Lo Lin   (215) 448-1204
Franklin Research Center
The Benjamin Franklin Parkway
Philadelphia, Pennsylvania 19103

PIPESD

In order to keep pace with the expanding analytical needs of the piping engineer, future versions of PIPESD will incorporate three major enhancements. These enhancements will significantly expand the current capabilities of the program.
      The first addition will be a full out-of-core solution capability. With this enhancement the benefit to the user will be that virtually any size problem can be handled in one run. Next, in order to keep pace with the industry requirements for detailed structural dynamics investigations, a time history analysis capability with both mode super-position and direct integration schemes will be added. Finally, in an effort to keep the analysis of piping programs cost effective in partic-ular dynamic analyses, PIPESD will offer the user the ability to perform restarts with both data and/or computational results as the third major enhancement.
      Along with the implementation of the aforementioned enhancements many of the existing features of the program will be improved. First, the plotting capability of the program will be made more user-oriented and expanded to include the plotting of response spectra and time histories. The existing preprocessing and error diagnostics will also be expanded to help the user in the data checking of the model. Along with the out-of-core solver comes the added advantage to the user that there be no practical limitation on the number of material and cross-sectional properties, pipe elements, load cases and load combinations, and Class 2, B31.1 or B31.3 analysis load sets.
      Thus, with the addition of the previously mentioned enhancements and the improvement of many of the existing features, along with its existing reputation as a user-oriented program, future versions of PIPESD will remain an effective tool to aid the engineer in meeting the demands and challenges of doing sound engineering analyses of piping systems.

      For further information contact:
Richard W. White   (612) 482-2471
Control Data Corporation
Engineering Applications
Applications Resource Center
4201 Lexington Avenue North
Arden Hills, Minnesota 55112

PIPESTRESS II

For further information contact:
R. J. Pearl   01-730 4544
Service in Informatics & Analysis Limited
Ebury Gate
23 Lower Belgrave Street
London SW1W ONW
England

PIRAX

For further information contact:
J. M. Corum   (615) 574-1000
Oak Ridge National Lab
P.O. Box Y
Oak Ridge, Tennessee 37830

PISTAR

For further information contact:
R. E. Keever   (408) 629-9800
Nutech
145 Martinvale Lane
San Jose, California 95119

PISYS and SAP4G

For further information contact:
Gerald Mok
Nuclear Energy Division
General Electric Company
175 Curtner Avenue
Mail Code 775
San Jose, California 95125

STALUM

For further information contact:
Kenneth K. Yoon   (804) 384-5111
Applied Mechanics
M. J. Yan
Babcock & Wilcox
Power Generation Group
P. O. Box 1260
Lynchburg, Virginia 24505

SUPERPIPE[2]

SUPERPIPE is a comprehensive computer program for stress and code compliance analysis of piping systems, with an emphasis on nuclear power
piping applications. The program was developed from an extensive review
of piping analysis procedures, engineering applications, and existing
program capabilities, with the aim of providing the most current analytical tools to the piping engineer, while reducing the overall engineering cost and the potential for analytical errors. The program has many
analytical capabilities not found in other production-oriented piping
analysis programs and affords the engineer considerable problem-solving
flexibility.
    SUPERPIPE is structured to perform the analysis in phases, if
desired, with restart capability after each phase. Partial or intermediate results can be stored for use at a later date. In addition, the
output is divided into independent sections, each with "stand-alone"
documentation and built-in quality assurance sign-off sheets for ease in
summarizing and distributing results to other engineering groups.
    SUPERPIPE input is designed for flexibility and engineering conven-
ience in describing the piping problem for analysis. This allows the
engineer to prepare the problem in the most convenient frame of refer-

---

[2]Information excerpted from brochures supplied by the developer to
the author.

ence and to identify standard material and component designations, in
order to reduce the number of input errors.

Output of SUPERPIPE is designed for inclusion in certified stress
reports or stress summaries. Extensive summary table features are provided for ease in reviewing results and supplying design input to other
engineering disciplines. The output may be separated into functional
groups for simultaneous review without compromising traceability or com-
pleteness of documentation.

For further information contact:
Leonard J. Swec, Jr.   (415) 544-8000
Structural Engineering Division
EDS Nuclear, Inc.
220 Montgomery Street
San Francisco, California   94104

TMRPIPE

For further information contact:
Alan G. Beardsley   (617) 890-3350 ext. 155
Teledyne Engineering Services
303 Bear Hill Road
Waltham, Massachusetts   02154

WECAN

For further information contact:
S. E. Gabrielse   (412) 256-5040
Westinghouse Research and Development Center
Churchill
Pittsburgh, Pennsylvania   15235

CLOSURE

The technical community is using the computer to perform a number of
tasks other than the traditional stress analysis. The comments made by
software suppliers indicate several things: a procedural management of
data may be embedded in a software system, data management is becoming
an integral part of the analytical procedure, data base systems are
expanding current functional software capabilities, and the number of
interactive computer systems that prompt the user is increasing.

These new areas of analytical capability are not amenable to the
standard benchmark methods [2-5] of program verification. Instead,
correct management of computer-generated data now introduces the requirements of data base management to the technical community. This
type of mangement will demand unique requirements to assure program
verification for correctness of information.

REFERENCES

1 Wright, W. B., "Piping Systems," ed., W. Pilkey, K. Saczalski,
and H. Schaeffer, Structural Mechanics Computer Programs, University
Press of Virginia, Charlottesville, 1974, pp. 143-49.

2 Tuba, I. S., and Wright, W. B., Pressure Vessel and Piping 1972
Computer Programs Verification: An Aid to Developers and Users, ASME,
New York, 1972.

3 Tuba, I. S., Selby, R. A., and Wright, W. B., Pressure Vessels and Piping: Analysis and Computers, ASME, New York, 1974.
4 Corum, J. M., and Wright, W. B., Pressure Vessels and Piping: Verification and Qualification of Inelastic Analysis Computer Programs, ASME, New York, 1975.
5 Dietrich, D. E., Pressure Vessels and Piping Computer Program Evaluation and Qualification, ASME, New York, 1977.

Fracture Mechanics

Jaroslav Mackerle

Billy Fredriksson

Linköping Institute of Technology

INTRODUCTION

The amount of software for stress analysis in fracture mechanics has
increased rapidly during the last few years. Both special purpose
programs and options for stress analysis in fracture mechanics in
general purpose programs have been developed. Many programs exist, some
that are available commercially, and some that are for internal use.
It is not possible in a review chapter like this to survey them all.
The reader is referred to Ref. [2, 3, and 16] where more programs are
surveyed in detail. Reference [16] gives a detailed survey of stress
analysis programs for fracture mechanics and also for fatigue. In
Refs. [2] and [3], finite element programs and finite elements respectively are surveyed. These references are periodically brought up
to date.
    A number of different methods for stress analysis, both analytical
and numerical, are frequently used. In this survey we concentrate on
the application of the finite element method in fracture mechanics.
Both general purpose and special purpose programs are surveyed. The
boundary element method is briefly discussed. First we introduce some
definitions and nomenclature in a very brief theoretical part. In this
part we discuss the stress state, energy considerations, crack extension
work, energy release rates, the J-integral, linear and nonlinear fracture
mechanics, fracture criteria, stress intensity factor calculation methods,
energy methods for stress intensity calculation, J-integral calculations,
singular elements, the boundary element method, and fatigue analysis.
A descriptive survey of the different programs is then presented. Next,
some information about the programs is given in a tabular survey.
Finally, a large number of references to theoretical papers and applications are given.

STRESS STATE

Stress analysis in fracture mechanics is concerned with the proper
solution of stress and displacement fields at the crack-tip region.
Fig. 1 shows a typical crack geometry with a definition of the coordinate
system and the basic deformation modes used in fracture mechanics.

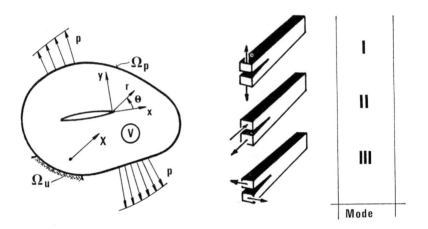

Fig. 1   Coordinate system and basic deformation modes

The stresses σ_{ij} and displacements u_i in the vicinity of the crack-
tip could, when linear elasticity is assumed, be written

$$\sigma_{ij} = \frac{1}{(2\pi r)^{1/2}} [K_I f_{ij}(\theta) + K_{II} g_{ij}(\theta) + K_{III} h_{ij}(\theta) + \dots]$$

$$u_i = \frac{1}{2G} \left(\frac{r}{2\pi}\right)^{1/2} [K_I \tilde{f}_{ij}(\theta) + K_{II} \tilde{g}_{ij}(\theta) + K_{III} \tilde{h}_{ij}(\theta) + \dots]$$

(1)

K_I, K_{II}, and K_{III} are the stress intensity factors in modes I, II, and
III respectively. Functions defining the variation in θ are f, g, and
h. For instance, for a crack loaded in mode I, only the stress
σ_{yy} and displacement u_y are written [4-6]

$$\sigma_{yy} = \frac{1}{(2\pi r)^{1/2}} \left[K_I \cos \frac{\theta}{2} \left(1 + \sin \frac{\theta}{2} \sin \frac{3\theta}{2} \right) \right] \tag{2}$$

$$u_y = \frac{1}{2G} \left(\frac{r}{2\pi} \right)^{1/2} \frac{1}{2} K_I \left[(2\kappa + 1) \sin \frac{\theta}{2} - \sin \frac{3\theta}{2} \right]$$

$\kappa = 3 - 4\nu$ for plane strain and $\kappa = (3 - \nu)/(1 + \nu)$ for plane stress conditions.

ENERGY CONSIDERATIONS

The study of the energy balance at the crack-tip presents many useful methods for computational fracture mechanics. Since Griffith used energy considerations for elastic material in the 1920s, the area has been extended to include plasticity, dynamic effects, and crack closure.

Consider a virtual crack growth from state 1 to state 2. The material is assumed to be elastic-plastic, and crack closure under friction is possible. The energy balance could then be expressed as [7, 8]

$$-U' - K' - D_p - D_c = G \tag{3}$$

U' is the change in total potential energy, and K' is the change in kinetic energy during the crack growth. D_p and D_c are energy dissipated due to the plasticity and friction at closure and defined as

$$D_p = \lim_{\Delta A \to 0} \frac{1}{\Delta A} \int_V \left(\int_1^2 \sigma_{ij} \, d\varepsilon_{ij}^P \right) dV \tag{4}$$

$$D_c = \lim_{\Delta A \to 0} \frac{1}{\Delta A} \int_{S_c} \left(\int_1^2 P_\alpha \, dv_\alpha \right) dS \tag{5}$$

A is the fracture area; S_c is the surface of contact; p_α is the shear stress, and v_α is the slip between the cracked surfaces in contact.

G in Eq. (3) is the energy dissipated at the fracture process zone [7] during formation of the new surface. It is called crack extension work. In forms of local stresses at a crack-tip, it could be written

$$G = - \lim_{\Delta A \to 0} \frac{1}{\Delta A} \int_{S_{cr}^+} \left(\int_1^2 q_i \, du_i \right) dS \tag{6}$$

S_{cr}^{+} is the newly formed crack surface, and $-q_i$ is the stress vector acting from the continuum on the fracture process zone. For linear elastic material with quasi-static loading and no closure, Eq. (3) yields

$$-U' = G \tag{7}$$

G expresses the energy release rate. In Eqs. (3-7) it was assumed that the extension was described by the fracture area A as a single parameter. For multiparametric situations Eqs. (3-7) are used tentatively, for instance, in assuming different propagation directions to detect the growth.

The so-called J-integral is widely used in fracture mechanics. It is for coplanar extension defined by

$$J = \oint_C (U_e \, dy - T_i \, \frac{\partial u_i}{\partial x} \, ds) \tag{8}$$

C is an arbitrary path surrounding the crack tip; U_e is the strain energy per unit volume; T_i is the traction according to the outward normal along C; and u_i is the displacement. The J-integral is path-independent for elastic materials. The following relationship holds for an elastic material and coplanar extension.

$$J = G \tag{9}$$

$$J = \frac{\kappa + 1}{8G} (K_I^2 + K_{II}^2) + \frac{1}{2G} K_{III}^2 \tag{10}$$

or

$$J = \frac{\kappa + 1}{8G} K_e^2 \tag{11}$$

The effective stress intensity factor K_e is then defined as

$$K_e^2 = K_I^2 + K_{II}^2 + \frac{4}{\kappa + 1} K_{III}^2 \tag{12}$$

The J-integral has been generalized for combined extension by Strifors [11]. When the crack is assumed to virtually advance as in Fig. 2, the generalized J-integral J_α is

$$J = \frac{\kappa + 1}{8G} [K_e^2 \cos \alpha - 2K_I K_{II} \sin \alpha] \tag{13}$$

Strifors [11] has also proposed a further generalization that includes a rotation of the crack.

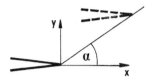

Fig. 2   Parallel extension of crack

LINEAR AND NONLINEAR FRACTURE MECHANICS

Linearity in Eq. (3) is obtained if D_p (and for closure problems D_c) is zero. For most engineering materials this will result in fracture loads that are much too low. In linear fracture mechanics $D_p \neq 0$ is included. The yielding is localized to the vicinity of the crack tip so that the description is independent of the external fields and geometry [7]. For linear fracture mechanics methods to hold, thickness requirements should be satisfied. It is then possible to introduce a material parameter called fracture toughness, K_{IC}, which could be used in fracture criteria.

If the thickness requirements are not satisfied, the testing for the material parameter must be done at the same thickness as in the structure to be studied. Then the methods for linear fracture mechanics could be used.

When conditions for linear fracture mechanics are not met, for instance when substantial yielding occurs, the fracture mechanics are nonlinear.

FRACTURE CRITERIA

Many different fracture criteria exist. We mention here only some of them.

For linear fracture mechanics, fracture is assumed to take place when

$$K_e = K_{IC} \tag{14}$$

for coplanar extension, and when [6]

$$K_{e\alpha} = K_{IC} \tag{15}$$

$$K_{e\alpha} = \sqrt[4]{K_e^4 + 4K_I^2 \overline{K_{II}^2}} \qquad (16)$$

for noncoplanar extension, as defined by Fig. 2. K_e is given by Eq. (12).
For nonlinear fracture mechanics there are rarely any widely used
and accepted criteria. The most frequently used are the J-integral
criterion and the COD criterion.
Crack extension is initiated when

$$J = J_{IC} \qquad (17)$$

There is some experimental evidence that J_{IC} is a material constant. J
should be computed for a path far from the plastic zone. Here also,
some thickness requirements do exist.
The crack opening displacement (COD) criterion in nonlinear fracture
mechanics specifies that crack extension is initiated when the COD
takes a critical value. The opening COD of the crack tip is not well
defined, and difficulties arise both in measuring and computing the
COD.

COMPUTATIONAL FRACTURE MECHANICS

A large number of methods for calculating stress intensity factors,
J-integrals,and energy release rates exist. In this chapter, we shall
concentrate on the finite element method (FEM) and the boundary element
method (BEM), which are widely used as numerical tools in stress analysis
in fracture mechanics.

Stress Intensity Factor Calculations

When using FEM as the calculation tool, K can be calculated from nodal
point displacements by extrapolation. As an example, study mode I.
From Eq. (2) for symmetric conditions we obtain

$$2u_y(r,\pi)/(r)^{1/2} = \frac{\kappa + 1}{G(2)^{1/2}} K_I \qquad (18)$$

By extrapolation to r = 0 (where Eq. (2) is correct) from nodal point
displacements in Fig. 3a we obtain u(0,π), which defines the computed
value of K_I. Similar computations are made for other modes.
The stress intensity factor can be obtained from extrapolation
of stresses in a similar way by using Eq. (2) and the FEM stresses.
See Fig. 3b.

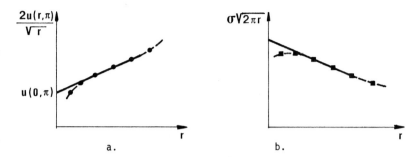

Fig. 3   Stress intensity factors from extrapolation of
         (a) displacements and (b) stresses

Energy Methods

To calculate stress intensity factors, computations of energy release
rates or crack extension work G have been very popular in recent years.
From Eqs. (3), (6), (7), (9), and (10), the definition of G and the
connections to global energy quantities, J-integral, and stress intensity factors are given. By using FEM it is possible to calculate G
effectively in linear, nonlinear, and dynamic problems.

By using the definition of G from Eq. (6), it is possible to calculate G by node relaxation. See Fig. 4. When relaxing the nodes, the
work done by the nodal force P(u) on the displacement u is calculated
(the shaded area in Fig. 4). For linear problems the relaxation presents no difficulties. The nodal force for node i is calculated, and
node i is then released and the displacement calculated. As linearity
holds, the incremental work ΔW is given by

$$\Delta W = \frac{1}{2} u_i P_i \qquad (19)$$

If the increment in the fracture area is ΔA, we obtain

$$G = \Delta W / \Delta A \qquad (20)$$

G can be calculated from two loading cases (for symmetry only one) by
applying unit loads at crack-tip nodes.

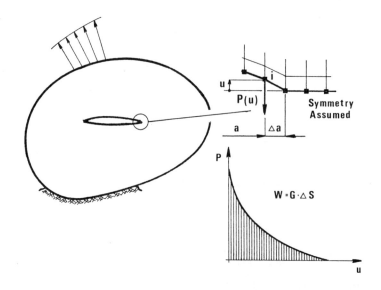

Fig. 4   Energy release rate by node relaxation

Problems arise in combined modes. It is not obvious how to separate
stress intensity factors in Eqs. (9)and(10). It is also possible to
calculate G from global relations given by Eq. (3) or Eq. (7). A
very effective method to calculate $\overline{\Delta U}$ at virtual crack extension is the
stiffness derivative method. The change in stiffness $\Delta[k]$ due to
changed conditions at the crack-tip nodes is calculated and

$$\Delta U = \frac{1}{2} \{u\}^t \Delta[k] \{u\} \qquad\qquad\qquad (21)$$

G is then obtained from Eq. (7) by dividing by ΔA.
    For nonlinear problems the relaxation must be performed incre-
mentally and the crack extension work calculated as the integral sum.
    The FEM has also been used to study dynamic problems [9, 10].
For linear elastic material, Eq. (3) yields

$$-U' - K' = G \qquad\qquad\qquad (22)$$

For dynamic problems it is not physically obvious how to relax nodes at a crack-tip. Methods of relaxation are proposed by Keegstra [9] and Rydholm et al. [10].

J-integral

The J-integral is calculated either by energy release methods and the equality given by Eq. (9) or directly from the definition of J given by Eq. (8). When Eq. (8) is used, numerical integration is performed through an integration path in the finite element model. The integration path is through either nodal points or integration points of the elements.

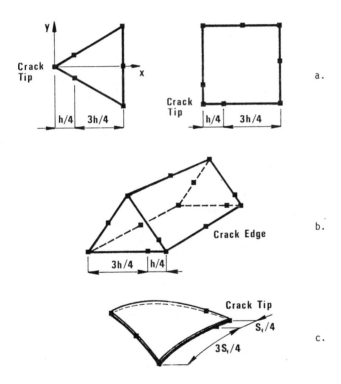

Fig. 5   Examples of quarter-point elements: (a) two-dimensional, (b) three-dimensional, (c) shell element

Singular Elements

As described earlier, the elasticity solution to the crack problem presents a singularity ($r^{1/2}$) in stresses. In order to increase the accuracy in computations, so-called singular elements, which are used in FEM models at crack-tips, have been introduced. Several different types of singular elements have been proposed [3]. They could be categorized as follows [1]: (1) use of displacements assumption with proper near field displacements, Eqs. (1-2); (2) define a circular core which contains the appropriate equations, Eq. (1); (3) centered fan elements with ($r^{1/2}$) displacement assumption in radial direction; (4) use of Muskhelishvilis stress function. For these methods the stress intensity factor is used as a nodal parameter and obtained as a solution of the system of equations. Elements for both two- and three-dimensional problems exist [115-18]. Hybrid elements are also used.

In recent years the isoparametric elements have been very popular in crack analysis. See, for instance, Barsoum [63-68]. By distorting the quadratic isoparametric element by moving the midside node to the quarterpoint, it can be shown that the square root singularity is obtained. Examples of quarterpoint elements are given in Fig. 5.

Distortion of cubic isoparametric elements also presents the proper singularity [14]. The singularity is obtained by collapsing the quadrilateral into a triangle and placing the two side nodes of each side of the triangle at 1/9 and 4/9 points. See Fig. 6.

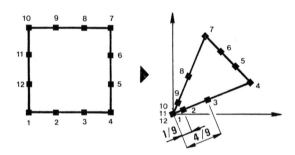

Fig. 6   Collapsed cubic isoparametric element

Boundary Element Method (BEM)

Recently the BEM has been used rather extensively to calculate stress intensity factors for both two- and three-dimensional crack problems. See, for instance, the work by Lange [12]. In the BEM the solution to the continuum problem is given in the form of a boundary integral. This is obtained by using the fundamental solution to the problem. On the surface the displacement is assumed to be in a piecewise manner as in the FEM. The surface integral is then solved numerically, resulting in a system of equations to solve for unknown displacements.

The advantages of this method as compared to the FEM are that

singularities are more easily dealt with and there is a reduction of
dimensionality (3D to 2D). For calculating stress intensity factors
extrapolation of displacements and stresses can be used. The J-integral
can be calculated from definition. The CETIM program covered in the
survey in this chapter is a BEM program.

FATIGUE

Fatigue analysis is often performed through postprocessing of the
stress intensity factor calculations. A number of different crack propagation laws exist. We will only mention two methods here, the Paris
and Formans crack propagation laws.

Assume that the loading is such that a variation in stress intensity is ΔK_I during a loading cycle. If the minimum stress is negative,
it is set to zero. The Paris law states that the crack advance per
cycle N is

$$\frac{da}{dN} = C(\Delta K_I)^n \tag{23}$$

C and n are material constants. Furthermore, it is stated that when
ΔK_I is less than the threshold value, ΔK_{th}, no crack advance takes
place. When ΔK_I is close to K_{IC} very rapid advance takes place.

Formans law for crack propagation is an extension of the Paris
law to include the stress ratio R for the nominal stress $\sigma_{0\ min}$
and $\sigma_{0\ max}$, $R = \sigma_{0\ min} / \sigma_{0\ max}$. Formans law states that propagation
takes place according to

$$\frac{da}{dN} = \frac{M(\Delta K_I)^q}{(1 - R)\ K_{IC} - \Delta K_I} \tag{24}$$

M and q are constants. Aamodt [15] has presented an interesting method
for studying two ψ parametric crack extension. He is studying the
propagation of elliptical cracks with half-axes a and c. The Paris
law is generalized to be used for propagation in the a- (y-) direction
and c- (x-) direction. The strain energy U_e is a function of the
loading, and a and c are calculated by FEM and functional fitting.
When U_e is known, the stress intensities K_{Ix} and K_{Iy} are computed
assuming plane strain. The propagation is then obtained from
generalization of the Paris law:

$$\frac{dc}{dN} = C_1(\Delta K_{Ix})^{n_1} \tag{25}$$

$$\frac{da}{dN} = C_2(\Delta K_{Iy})^{n_2} \tag{26}$$

DISCRIPTIVE SURVEY

This part describes fracture mechanics possibilities in some general
purpose finite element programs and special purpose programs for fracture
mechanics applications. As mentioned earlier in the theoretical section,
there exist several solution methods used for stress analysis in fracture
mechanics. Recently, much activity has been concentrated on applying the
finite element method to the fracture mechanics stress analysis problem
solution. Only the programs based on the finite element method are surveyed here. More programs and programs based on the other solution
methods are described in Ref. [16].
     Programs presented in this chapter are listed in Table 1 and Table 2.
Short descriptions are given in the following sections. Program information was obtained from questionnaires sent to different program developers, and is applicable to the fracture mechanics capabilities of these
general purpose finite element programs.

ANSYS [17-20]

Contact: Swanson Analysis Systems, Inc.
           P.O. Box 65
           Houston, PA   15342
           USA
General Information: Program has been used commercially since 1970. The
     documentation consists of a theoretical manual, user's manual,
     examples manual, and verification manual. A programmer's manual is
     not scheduled. Training seminars are available through SASI service
     and through CDC centers. The program is very general, applicable
     to linear and nonlinear static and dynamic problems. It is also
     implemented on minicomputers. Free-field input, coordinate, and
     element generators are available.
Capability for fracture mechanics: Elements used - 8 node planar, 8
     node solid, and 20 node solid, displacement formulation. The ele-
     ments become singular with a midside node at quarter point. Stress
     intensity factor calculation: stresses and strains are computed at
     the centroid of the element. The distance from the centroid to the
     crack tip is also given. Nonlinear fracture mechanics: Plasticity
     and geometric nonlinearity. Dynamic fracture mechanics and fatigue
     are not included in the program.

ASAS [21-23]

Contact: Atkins On-line Ltd.
           Fourmost House 12-22 West Street
           Epsom
           Surrey KT18 7RH
           England
General Information: Development started in 1970 by Atkins R & D. The
     program consists of ASAS-G, ASAS Heat, ASDIS, and a number of pre-
     and postprocessor programs. Applicable only to linear problems.
     The documentation appears to be very good; it consists of a user's
     manual, theoretical manual, comparative sample problems, and program-
     mer's manual. Training courses are available. Users group exists.

Table 1   Information about General Purpose Programs for Stress Analysis in Fracture Mechanics

GENERAL - PURPOSE PROGR.		ANSYS	ASAS	ASKA ★	BERSAFE	FESAP	MARC	NASTRAN ★	PAFEC 75	PLANS	SESAM 69	TITUS ★
RANGE OF APPLICAT.	Fracture mech. linear statics	●	●	●	●	●	●	●	●	●	●	●
	Fracture mech. nonlinear statics	●			●		●		●			
	Fracture mech. linear dynamics		●						●	●		
	Fatigue		●				●			●	●	
ELEMENT LIBRARY	Nonsingular element	●	●	●	●	●		●	●	●	●	●
	Singular element		●	●	●		●	●				
FORMULAT.	Force											
	Displacement	●	●	●	●	●	●	●	●	●	●	●
	Hybrid							●				
	Mixed											
STRUCTURE GEOMETRY	Two-dimensional	●	●	●	●	●	●	●	●			●
	Three-dimensional	●	●	●	●	●	●		●		●	●
	Membrane, plane stress	●	●	●	●	●	●	●	●			●
	Membrane, plane strain	●	●	●	●	●	●		●			●
	Axisymmetric	●			●		●		●			●
	Plate bending		●		●	●	●					
	Shell				●	●	●					
LOADING	Static	●	●	●	●	●	●	●	●	●	●	●
	Function of time		●					●	●	●		
	Mode I	●	●	●	●	●	●	●	●	●	●	●
	Mode II	●	●		●	●	●	●				●
	Mode III		●		●	●	●		●			●
	Combined modes	●	●		●	●		●				●
	Initial stresses / strains	●	●			●		●	●	●	●	●
SURFACE CRACK GEOMETRY	Straight	●	●	●	●	●	●	●	●			●
	Curved	●	●	●	●	●	●	●	●			●
	Circular	●	●	●	●	●	●		●			●
	Elliptic	●	●	●	●	●	●		●		●	●
	Multiple	●	●		●	●	●	●	●			●
INTERNAL CRACK GEOMETRY	Straight	●	●	●	●	●	●		●	●		●
	Curved	●	●	●	●	●	●		●			●
	Circular	●	●		●	●	●		●			●
	Elliptic	●	●		●	●	●		●		●	●
	Multiple	●	●		●	●	●		●			●
CRACK CLOSURE, BRANCHING	Closure frictionless	●	●		●	●			●	●	●	●
	Closure with friction	●			●							
	Branching				●							
RUNS ON	CDC	●	●			●	●	●	●	●		●
	IBM	●	●	●	●	●	●	●	●	●		
	Univac	●	●		●	●		●	●		●	●
	Others	●	●		●				●			

★ Not available in original version, completed by users

Table 2   Information about Special Purpose Programs for Stress Analysis in Fracture Mechanics

SPECIAL – PURPOSE PROGR.		BROWN UNIV.	CAMBRIDGE	CETIM	GEORGIA	LEHIGH	LOCKHEED-G	NLR	NTH	OSAKA	PIFEM	SMART	SWANSEA	TEPSA	TWENTE	WASHINGTON
RANGE OF APPLICAT.	Fracture mech. linear statics	●	●	●	●	●	●	●	●	●	●	●	●	●	●	●
	Fracture mech. non linear statics	●	●	●	●			●	●	●	●	●	●	●	●	●
	Fracture mech. linear dynamics		●		●	●						●	●			●
	Fatigue		●		●			●	●			●	●	●	●	●
ELEMENT LIBRARY	Nonsingular element		●	●				●	●	●	●	●	●	●	●	●
	Singular element				●	●	●						●		●	
FORMULAT.	Force															
	Displacement	●	●	●				●	●	●	●	●	●	●	●	●
	Hybrid				●											●
	Mixed															
STRUCTURE GEOMETRY	Two - dimensional	●	●	●	●	●	●	●	●	●	●	●	●	●	●	●
	Three-dimensional				●				●				●	●		●
	Membrane, plane stress		●	●	●			●	●	●	●	●	●			●
	Membrane, plane strain	●	●	●	●			●	●	●	●	●	●			●
	Axisymmetric	●	●	●					●		●	●	●			
	Plate bending				●								●			
	Shell															●
LOADING	Static	●	●	●	●	●	●	●	●	●	●	●	●	●	●	●
	Function of time		●			●	●					●	●			●
	Mode I	●	●	●	●	●	●	●	●	●	●	●	●	●	●	●
	Mode II	●	●	●	●			●	●				●	●	●	●
	Mode III				●							●	●		●	●
	Combined modes		●	●	●			●	●				●			●
	Initial stresses/strains	●	●	●	●			●	●			●	●			●
SURFACE CRACK GEOMETRY	Straight	●	●	●	●	●	●	●	●	●	●	●	●	●		●
	Curved			●	●	●	●						●	●		●
	Circular	●		●	●		●						●	●		●
	Elliptic			●	●		●						●	●		●
	Multiple	●		●	●		●						●	●		●
INTERNAL CRACK GEOMETRY	Straight	●	●	●	●	●	●	●	●			●	●	●	●	●
	Curved			●	●	●							●	●	●	●
	Circular	●	●	●	●								●	●	●	●
	Elliptic			●	●	●							●	●		●
	Multiple	●	●	●	●								●	●		●
CRACK CLOSURE BRANCHING	Closure frictionless		●		●			●		●			●	●		
	Closure with friction				●									●		
	Branching			●	●		●		●		●		●	●		●
RUNS ON	CDC			●	●		●	●	●			●	●	●		●
	IBM		●								●		●			
	Univac						●		●			●				
	Others									●			●	●	●	●

There are annual users conferences.
Capability for fracture mechanics: Singularity modeling both by isoparametric stress elements and stress based elements with explicit
singularity of the Westergaard type. Displacement formulation.
Square, 11 nodes planar membrane crack-tip element, and membrane crack-
tip element for symmetrical fracture mechanics applications. Stress
intensity factor calculation. Extrapolation of displacements.
Energy release from stiffness changes. J-integral calculation. Nonlinear fracture mechanics is not available. Dynamic fracture
mechanics: K_I, K_{II}, and K_{III} computation for stationary cracks.
Fatigue studies possible. Type of law for propagation is user
specified. Fatigue data can be used as a data base for endurance
calculations.

ASKA [24-32]

Contact for original version: IKO Software Service GmbH
Veihinger Str. 49
7 Stuttgart 80
West Germany
Also available from: Routines for fracture mechanics applications have
been developed by M. J. Broekhoven, Dept. of Mechanical Engineering,
Delft University of Technology, Delft, Holland, and at NLR, Structures
Department, Anthony Fokkerweg 2, Amsterdam 1917, Holland.
General Information: Development started in 1965. Fracture mechanics
part is not included in the official version. The program has been
completed at Delft University of Technology and NLR, the Netherlands,
to include fracture mechanics. The official program system consists
of ASKA I, ASKA II, ASKA III - 1, ASKA III - 2, and of several pre-
and postprocessor programs. Documentation includes user's manual,
theoretical manual, and programmer's manual. ASKA is very flexible,
and is used for solving linear and nonlinear problems. Free-format
input. Annual congresses in Baden-Baden, West Germany. No users
group.
Capability for fracture mechanics: Delft University version: The ASKA
program is used for both 2D and 3D LEFM computations. Postprocessor
routines have been developed using the global energy method
(stresses and displacements in crack-plane nodal points), Park's
stiffness derivative procedure, and the displacement method. Especially full advantage is taken of the substructuring facility in
the ASKA program. Efforts to apply a modified element to obtain
crack-tip$\sqrt{r}$ singularities are underway.
National Aerospace Lab. - NLR version: The ASKA program is
used for 3D LEFM calculations. An effective method of energy release rate calculation is applied. Stress intensity factors are
found. Standard ASKA elements are used. Fatigue studies possible.

BERSAFE [33-49]

Contact: Central Electricity Generating Board
R & D Dept.
Berkeley Nuclear Laboratory
Berkeley, Gloucestershire GL13 9PB
England

General Information: Development started in 1967. The program consists
of BERSAFE and BERDYNE and several pre- and postprocessor programs.
The program is used for solution of linear and nonlinear problems.
It is documented in user's, programmer's, and theoretical manuals.
There is a users group.
Capability for fracture mechanics: Special 2D and 3D singularity elements
are available. Displacement formulation. Any loading system may
be applied in 2D and 3D, hence with an arbitrary crack front any
combination of modes can arise. K_i values with i = I, II, or III
can be obtained by extended substitution methods (K^*) or by VCE
(virtual crack extension) method. J-integrals may be calculated for
LEFM and nonlinear plasticity or creep. Nonhomogenous material and
thermal gradients may be applied. Dynamic fracture mechanics is
not included in the program. Fatigue studies are possible. The
Paris law with threshold values of ΔK is used.

FESAP [50-52]

Contact: Applied Mechanics Section, R & D Division
           Alliance Research Center
           The Babcock & Wilcox Co.
           P.O. Box 835
           Alliance, Ohio 44601
           USA
General Information: FESAP is a general purpose program for linear
static and dynamic analysis. The core of the program is based upon
SAP and SAP IV, developed for the University of California at
Berkeley.
Capability for fracture mechanics: Isoparametric continuum element,
quarterpoint quadratic isoparametric singularity. Displacement
formulation. Stress intensity factor is calculated by extrapolation
of displacements. J-integral calculation is done via a separate
subroutine, JSAP. Nonlinear fracture mechanics and dynamic fracture
mechanics calculations are not possible.

MARC [53-68]

Contact: Marc Analysis Co.
           314 Court House Plaza
           260 Sheridan Avenue
           Palo Alto, California 94306
           USA
General Information: Well-known program, widely used via CDC computer
centers. It is a very general purpose program for linear and
nonlinear static and dynamic computations. The program is documented
in the user's information manuals. In the users manual references
are given to the theory for the different procedures. Marc Analysis
Co. provides consulting and software services. It publishes a quarterly newsletter.
Capability for fracture mechanics: Crack-tip elements are the quarter-
point elements. Displacement formulation. Stress intensity factor
is computed by extrapolation of displacements or from the J-integral
using differential stiffness method. Nonlinear fracture mechanics:
K_I, K_{II}, and K_{III} calculations for stationary cracks. Fatigue

studies are not possible.

NASTRAN [69-77]

Contact: MacNeal - Schwendler Co.
           7442 North Figueroa Str.
           Los Angeles, CA 90041
           USA
General Information: Development sponsored by NASA started in 1966.
    Today there are three versions of NASTRAN (Cosmic, MSC, Sperry
    Univac). The documentation is very extensive. It consists of a
    user's manual, theoretical manual, programmer's manual, and
    demonstration problem manuals. Several users groups exist.
    Annual users conferences are held in USA and Europe. Several dif-
    ferent pre- and postprocessor programs have been developed for NAS-
    TRAN by users.
Capability for fracture mechanics: No rigid format is available for
    fracture mechanics computation. Usually the users develop new
    routines. Lockheed Missiles, California, has performed extensive
    NASTRAN modifications including several new functional and matrix
    modules. For fracture problems, the system is used in conjunction
    with specialized singular cracked elements. They are based on the
    stress function approach. Singular stress terms as well as higher-
    order stress terms were included. The stress-free boundary condi-
    tion was enforced on the crack surface. A program package has been
    developed to be executed in tandem with the NASTRAN system with
    the interfacing accomplished using the DMAP feature. Linear frac-
    ture mechanics applications only. The stress intensity factors K_I
    and K_{II} are provided directly, as part of the output.

PAFEC 75 [78-83]

Contact: Pafec Ltd.
           Thane Road
           Lenton Industrial Estate West
           Nottingham NG 7 2TG
           England
General Information: Development started in 1965 in the Mechanical
    Engineering Department at the University of Nottingham. The
    first commercially available version was produced in 1970 and
    was known as PAFEC 70. Version PAFEC 75 uses new data base methods
    that improve reliability and reduce the time needed to code new
    facilities into PAFEC. Fully integrated system. The program is
    used for linear and nonlinear static and dynamic calculations.
    Documentation consists of the following PAFEC 75 manuals: Easydata,
    Data Preparation, Theory, Results, and Systems. A users group exists.
Capability for fracture mechanics: Isoparametric elements are distorted
    to produce singularity. Stress intensity factor calculation by
    extrapolation of displacements. Dynamic fracture mechanics: K_I,
    K_{II}, K_{III} calculations for stationary cracks. Quasi-static
    propagation using user-defined steering program. Fatigue studies
    possible. User-defined law for crack propagation. Nonlinear part
    is not included in program.

PLANS ⌊84-88]

Contact: Grumman Aerospace Co.
           Applied Mechanics Section
           Bethpage, New York 11714
           USA
General Information: This program is designed and developed specifically
    for nonlinear analysis. PLANS is a collection of special purpose
    programs or modules, each associated with a distinct physical pro-
    blem class. Each module is an independent program with its asso-
    ciated element library that can be individually loaded and used.
    The development of nonlinear structural analysis techniques at
    Grumman Aerospace Co. started in 1965. General distribution of
    the program started in 1974.
Capability for fracture mechanics: Elements used are constant and linear
    strain triangles, 4- and 5-node transition triangles (membrane
    stress only), and isoparametric quadrilaterals (4-8 nodes). Dis-
    placement formulation is combined with conformal mapping techniques.
    Stress intensity factor is calculated by energy release from node
    relaxation. Nonlinear fracture mechanics calculations take elastic-
    plastic behavior into consideration. Ideally plastic and linear
    and nonlinear hardening are treated using kinematic hardening
    theory of plasticity. K_I, K_{II} calculation is made for stationary
    cracks. Not usable for fatigue studies.

SESAM-69 [89-105]

Contact: A/S Computas
           P.O. Box 310
           1322 Høvik
           Norway
General Information: Development started in 1968. This is a modular
    system containing a number of programs which either can be used as
    autonomous programs or can be integrated in the general multilevel
    superelement program. Program for solution of fracture mechanics
    problems developed in cooperation with the Norwegian Institute of
    Technology, Trondheim, SESAM-69 was the first program utilizing the
    multilevel substructuring technique.
Documentation: User's manuals, and maintenance manuals. Users group
    established in 1977.
Capability for fracture mechanics: Program NV 344 uses a 20-node iso-
    parametric solid element. There is a displacement formulation.
    Strain energy release rate for determining stress intensity factors.
    Energy release is automatically calculated from node relaxation.
    Fatigue studies possible. Paris law for crack growth is used.
    Other laws may be introduced easily. The program does not include
    a routine for nonlinear fracture mechanics calculations.

TITUS [106-111]

Contact: VOUILLON, CITRA
           13 Avenue Morane Saulnier
           78-Velizy
           France
       for the fracture mechanics routine contact:

Creusot-Loire
Att: J. Heliot
Div. Chaudronnerie
15, Rue Pasquier
75 008 Paris
France
General Information: Development started in 1968. Program is designed
    for computation of 2D and 3D linear elastic and heat transfer pro-
    blems. Free-format input, plotting facilities.
Capability for fracture mechanics: Fracture mechanics is not included
    in the original program version. It was developed and is used by
    Creusot-Loire. Element library contains 6- and 8-node isoparametric
    elements for 2D problems and solid isoparametric elements for 3D
    problems. The stress intensity factor is calculated by crack
    closing method for mode I and mode II problems, or it is calculated
    from stiffness changes. Program permits the calculation of 2D and
    3D weight functions, but it cannot be used for dynamic and nonlinear
    fracture mechanics. Fatigue studies are possible. Crack propaga-
    tion law used is: $\Delta a = f(\Delta K)$ for mode I, II, and III; $\Delta a = f(G)$
    for mixed mode problems. The program can calculate crack extension
    when the direction of the extension is known.

Special Purpose Programs for Fracture Mechanics Applications

BROWN UNIVERSITY [112-118]

Contact: D. M. Parks, R. M. McMeeking, D. M. Tracey, J. R. Rice
           Brown University
           Providence, RI   02912
           USA
Program Characteristics: Displacement formulation. J-integral evaluation
    by virtual crack extension. Stress intensity factor calculated from
    stiffness changes. Nonlinear fracture mechanics: elastic-plastic
    material. Power law or linear hardening for small strains. Iso-
    parametric hardening for large strain. Dynamic fracture mechanics
    and fatigue studies are not possible. Program is not in form suit-
    able for public use.

CAMBRIDGE UNIVERSITY [119-124]

Contact: Cambridge University
           Engineering Department
           Att: A. P. Kfouri
           Trumpington Str.
           Cambridge CB2 1PZ
           England
Program Characteristics: The element library contains isoparametric
    plane stress, plane strain, or axisymmetric 4-node quadrilateral
    elements. Displacement formulation. The program is essentially
    two-dimensional. The elastic-plastic analysis is based upon the
    incremental, initial stress approach. The type of nonlinear
    calculations performed are plasticity, creep, moderate geometry
    changes. Strain hardening can be included in the form of linear

strain hardening, with or without an initial nonhardening stage, or
in the form of a Ramberg Osgood type stress-strain curve. The
material can also be nonhardening. A subroutine is available for
the direct calculation of the J-integral by summation along a simple
path through the center of the elements, but it is assumed that no
yielding has taken place in these elements. Dynamic fracture
mechanics: K_I and K_{II} calculations for stationary cracks. Quasi-
static analysis for moving cracks. Fatigue studies: Analyses involving a few cycles are possible.

CETIM [125-129]

Contact: CETIM
          Att: J. M. Boissenot
          52, Avenue Felix-Louat
          60 300 Senlis
          France
General Information: Isoparametric triangular element, nonsingular
    2D elements. Displacement formulation. Stress intensity factor
    calculated by extrapolation of displacements. J-integral calculated
    from arbitrary contour surrounding the crack front, or Strifors
    integral. Nonlinear fracture mechanics: elasto-plasticity. Strifors
    integral criterion. Dynamic fracture part is not included in the
    program. The program is a part of the CA. ST. OR. system. Boundary
    element method.

GEORGIA [130-148]

Contact: Prof. S. N. Atluri
          School of Engineering Science and Mechanics
          Georgia Institute of Technology
          Atlanta, GA 30332
          USA
Program Characteristics: Four different programs have been developed,
    identified as A, B, C, D.
    Program A is for 2D elastic plane problems. Exact solutions em-
        bedded in 8-node singular element. Hybrid-displacement formula-
        tion. Stress intensity factor calculated by extrapolation of
        stresses and displacements. 2D orthotropic and isotropic crack
        problems. It is not possible to do nonlinear and dynamic fracture
        mechanics calculations.
    Program B is for 3D elastic problems. Exact solution embedded in 20-
        node singular element. Hybrid-displacement formulation. Stress
        intensity factor calculated by extrapolation of stresses and
        displacements. 3D homogeneous and bimaterial crack problems.
        It is not possible to do nonlinear and dynamic fracture mechanics
        calculations.
    Program C is for 2D elastic-plastic plane problems. Asymptotic solu-
        tions embedded in singularity cone elements. Hybrid-displacement
        formulation. Stress intensity factor calculated by extrapolation.
        of stresses and displacements. Global energy balance. Energy flow
        rate into the process zone. Geometrical nonlinearity by updated
        Lagrangian formulation. Material nonlinearity with power law. In-
        cremental formulation with iterative equilibrium corrections.
        Fatigue studies are possible.

Program D is for 2D elastic plate bending problems. Exact solutions embedded in a singularity element. Hybrid stress formulation. Stress intensity factor calculated by extrapolation of stresses and displacements. It is not possible to do nonlinear and dynamic fracture mechanics.

LEHIGH UNIVERSITY [149-150]

Contact: S. G. Papaioannou
           Lehigh University
           Bethlehem, PA 18015
           USA

Program Characteristics: Constant strain triangle for region and higher-order circular crack-tip element. The special element technique is used with a standard FEM program. Stress intensity factor calculation by extrapolation of displacements and stresses. Dynamic fracture mechanics: K_I calculation for stationary cracks. A non-linear fracture mechanics part is not available.

LOCKHEED - GEORGIA [151-171]

Contact: Lockheed - Georgia Co.
           Att: J. A. Aberson
           Dept. 72-26, Zone 459
           Marietta, Georgia
           USA

The program is also available through COSMIC

General Information: Singular symmetric and unsymmetric through-crack elements developed by using the William's series. Displacement formulation. Stress intensity factors extracted from William's series expansion for displacements obtained by integrating strain series. Dynamic fracture mechanics: stress intensity factors K_I, K_{II}, calculations for stationary cracks. Limited capabilities for handling running cracks. Fatigue studies are possible. Interfaces with crack growth program. Paris, Walker's, and Forman's law are available. Nonlinear fracture mechanics parts is not included in the program.

NLR [172-174]

Contact: National Aerospace Laboratory
           Att: A. U. de Koning
           Voorsterweg 31, NOP
           Emmeloord
           The Netherlands

Program Characteristics: Linear and quadratic displacement elements, displacement formulation. The method of stress intensity factor calculation is through energy release by node relaxation or energy release from differential stiffness. J-integral calculated from the contour integral. Nonlinear fracture mechanics: material nonlinearity. Small-strain plasticity including strain hardening and Bauschinger effect. The program cannot be used for dynamic fracture mechanics. Fatigue studies are possible (method unknown).

NTH [175-181]

Contact: Dept. of Applied Mechanics
           Att: I. Lotsberg
           The Norwegian Inst. of Technology
           Trondheim
           Norway
Program Characteristics: Two programs are available, identified as A and B.
     Program A: Analysis of internal cracks in three-dimensional bodies.
     20-node isoparametric hexahedral. Displacement formulation.
     Stress intensity factor calculation by global energy release from
     stiffness changes. Fatigue studies are the main object of the
     program. Generalized form of the Paris law. Endurance calcula-
     tions possible. The program is not for nonlinear and dynamic frac-
     ture mechanics.
     Program B: Nonlinear analysis of through cracks in plates. Con-
     stant strain and linear strain elements. Displacement formulation.
     Stress intensity factor calculation: extrapolation of displace-
     ments and stresses. Energy release from stiffness changes or from
     node relaxation. J-integral calculations. The nonlinear routine
     handles flow theory of plasticity. Dynamic fracture mechanics
     is not included. Fatigue studies are not possible.

OSAKA UNIVERSITY [182-187]

Contact: Dept. of Mechanical Engineering
           Att: K. Ogura, K. Ohji
           Osaka University
           Osaka 565
           Japan
Program Characteristics: Constant strain triangular element. Displace-
     ment formulation. Nonlinear fracture mechanics calculations in-
     clude elastic-plastic analysis based upon von Mises yield criterion
     and associated flow rule. Program is specially developed for fatigue
     crack growth study. Dynamic fracture mechanics is not included.

PIFEM [188-190]

Contact: Dept. of Mechanical Engineering
           Att: J. Bäcklund
           Linköping Institute of Technology
           Fack
           581 83 Linköping
           Sweden
Program Characteristics: 8-node isoparametric plane element. Singularity
     by element distortion. Displacement formulation. Stress inten-
     sity factor by extrapolation of displacements. J-integral by
     numerical integration along path through integration points of
     elements. The nonlinear fracture mechanics calculation made is
     plasticity, J_{IC} as initiation criterion for crack growth. Fatigue
     studies possible. Dynamic fracture mechanics is not included in
     the program.

SMART [191-194]

Contact: Institut für Statik und Dynamic der Luft- und Raumfahrtkonstr.
Pfaffenwaldring 27
7 Stuttgart 80
West Germany

Program Characteristics: Originally developed for the analysis of prestressed concrete pressure vessels. As special features comprehensive creep and ultimate load packages were incorporated, whereby
the latter provides extensive capabilities for analyzing cracking
and fracturing of the components. The ultimate approach is based
upon refined strength of material concepts in which crack formation
and propagation are smeared in the form of degrading stiffness models
with pronounced softening regimes up to brittle post-failure behavior. Discrete cracks in the sense of fracture mechanics cannot
be treated directly, except along the line of linear or stationary
fracture mechanics. The element library contains the isoparametric
approach, quadratic interpolation, compatible family of line, surface, and volume elements. Displacement formulation. The stress
intensity factor calculation is made by extrapolation of stresses
and displacements. Energy release is by node relaxation. Material
nonlinearities for metals and concrete. In the area of dynamic
fracture mechanics, K_I, K_{II}, K_{III} calculations are made for stationary cracks. It is not possible to do fatigue studies.

SWANSEA [195-198]

Contact: Dept. of Civil Engineering
Att: A. R. Luxmoore
University College
Swansea SA2 8PP
U. K.

Program Characteristics: Three programs have been developed: a 2D
and 3D elastic program with crack-tip elements; a 2D and 3D
elastic-plastic program with crack extension and a J-integral routine; and a 2D and 3D elastic program for dynamic crack propagation.
The element library has a wide range of element types, including
linear, parabolic, and cubic isoparametric elements. Special
analytic crack-tip elements are available. There are front and
banded solution routines. Various methods for stress intensity
factor calculation are available, including extrapolation of
stresses and displacements. Superposition methods. Energy release
by node relaxation. J-integral by contour relaxation. Nonlinear
fracture mechanics subroutines handle material nonlinearity such as
elastoplasticity,   viscoelasticity, and viscoplasticity. Dynamic
fracture mechanics programming allows K_I, K_{II}, K_{III} calculations for
stationary cracks. Stress intensity for prescribed motion crack
arrest possible. There are routines for fatigue studies and various
types of propagation laws.

TEPSA [199-205]

Contact: Dept. of Mechanical Engineering
          Att: T. R. Hsu
          The University of Manitoba, Winnipeg
          Manitoba, Canada R3T 2N2

Program Characteristics: The program was originally formulated for nuclear
     reactor fuel analysis. The element library includes triangular and
     quadrilateral elements which are both axisymmetric and planar.
     Displacement formulation. Stress intensity factor calculation by
     extrapolation of stresses. Energy release from stiffness changes.
     Nonlinear fracture mechanics calculations are made for material
     and geometric nonlinearity. Dynamic fracture mechanics is not
     included in the program. Fatigue studies are possible. Cumulative
     residual strain used for crack propagation investigation.

TWENTE INSTITUTE OF TECHNOLOGY [206-207]

Contact: Dept. of Mechanical Engineering
          Engineering Mechanics Group
          Att: C de Pater
          Twente Institute of Technology
          P.O. Box 217
          Enschede
          The Netherlands

Program Characteristics: Element library includes triangular and
     quadrilateral isoparametric elements and special crack-tip elements.
     Displacement formulation. Stress intensity factor is calculated
     by extrapolation of displacements. Energy release from stiffness
     changes. Nonlinear fracture mechanics includes both material and
     geometric nonlinearities. Fatigue studies are possible using
     Paris law for crack propagation. Dynamic fracture mechanics routine
     has not been developed.

UNIVERSITY OF WASHINGTON [208-233]

Contact: Dept. of Mechanical Engineering
          Att: A. S. Kobayashi
          University of Washington
          Seattle, Washington 98105
          USA

Program Characteristics: Three programs have been developed, identified
     as A, B, and C.
     Program A does static 2D elastic-plastic analysis. Assumed displace-
         ment hybrid finite element with large deformation. Stress inten-
         sity factor is directly computed as the strength at the singular
         terms. Extrapolation of displacements. Energy release by node
         relaxation. J-integral calculation. The nonlinear part does
         calculations of plasticity and K_{IC} or J_{IC} for initiation of
         crack growth. No criteria for stability studies. Fatigue studies
         possible, arbitrary laws for crack propagation.
     Program B does dynamic 2D elastic analysis. HONDO code has been
         modified for fracture dynamics. Finite difference method is
         used for pipe and shell codes. Stress intensity factor calcu-

lated by extrapolation of displacements. Energy release by node relaxation. K_{ID} calculated for stationary cracks and prescribed crack-front velocity. Crack arrest studies are possible. Program C does static 3D elastic analysis. Assumed displacement hybrid finite element with K_I, K_{II}, K_{III} varying quadratically along crack front. Alternating method is used for embedded and partially embedded elliptical cracks. Stress intensity factor calculated directly as the strength of singular terms. Extrapolation of displacements. Nonlinear and dynamic fracture mechanics is not included in the program. Fatigue studies are not possible.

TABULAR SURVEY

In Tables 1 and 2 concentrated information about the programs is given.

ACKNOWLEDGMENT

The authors are grateful to the program developers for their help in filling out the questionnaires about their program.

REFERENCES

1 Benzley, S. E., and Parks, D. M., "Fracture Mechanics," Structural Mechanics Computer Programs, ed. Pilkey, Saczalski, Schaeffer, University Press of Virginia, Charlottesville, 1974.
2 Fredriksson, B., and Mackerle, J., "Structural Mechanics Finite Element Computer Program," Report AEC-L-001, Advanced Engineering Corporation, S-580 03 Linköping, Sweden, 1977.
3 Fredriksson, B., and Mackerle, J., "Finite Element Review," Report AEC-L-003, Advanced Engineering Corporation, S-580 03 Linköping, Sweden, 1978.
4 Knott, J. F., Fundamentals of Fracture Mechanics, Butterworths, London, 1973.
5 Carlsson, J., "Brottmekanik," Ingenjörsförlaget, Stockholm, 1976, (in Swedish).
6 Bäcklund, J.,"Brottmekanik," Report IKP-S-073, Linköping Institute of Technology, 1977, (in Swedish).
7 Hellan, K., "Energy Considerations in Static Fracture Mechanics," Publ. No. 73:6, Inst. for Mekanikk, University of Norway, Trondheim, Nov. 1973.
8 Fredriksson, B., "Elastic Contact Problems in Fracture Mechanics," Proc. 4th Int. Conf. on Fracture, Waterloo, Canada, June 1977.
9 Keegstra, P. N. R., "A Transient Finite Element Crack Propagation Model for Nuclear Pressure Vessel Steels," Inst. Nuc. Eng., Vol. 17, No. 4, 1976.
10 Rydholm, G., Fredriksson, B., and Nilsson, F., "Numerical Investigations of Rapid Crack Propagation," Proc. Int. Conf. on Numerical Methods in Fracture Mechanics, Swansea, England, Jan 1978.
11 Strifors, H., "The Apparent Crack Extension Force as a Criterion for Crack Growth in Solids," Royal Inst. of Tech., Strength of Materials Div., Publ. No. 195, Stockholm, 1973.
12 Lange, D., "3-D Fracture Analysis Using the Boundary Integral Equation Method," Proc. Int. Conf. on Numerical Methods in Fracture Mechanics, Swansea, England, Jan. 1978.

13 Byskov, E., "The Calculation of Stress Intensity Factors Using the Finite Element Method with Cracked Elements," Int. J. Fracture Mechanics, Vol. 6, No. 2, 1970.

14 Pu, S. H., Hussin, M. A., and Lorensen, W. E., "The Collapsed Cubic Isoparametric Element as a Singular Element for Crack Problems," Int. J. Num. Meth. Engr., Vol. 12, 1978, pp. 1727-42.

15 Aamodt, B., and Mo. O., "Elasto-Plastic Analysis Using an Efficient Formulation of the Finite Element Method," and Aamodt, B., "Efficient Formulations of the Finite Element Method in Linear and Nonlinear Fracture Mechanics," Publication No. 92, Feb. 1976, Det Norske Veritas, Oslo, Norway.

16 Fredriksson, B., and Mackerle, J., "Stress Analysis Programs for Fracture Mechanics," Advanded Engineering Co., AEC-L-004, Linköping, Sweden, Sept. 1979.

17 De Salvo, G. J., and Swanson, J. A., "ANSYS Engineering Analysis System User's Manual," Swanson Analysis Systems Inc., Houston, PA, March 1975, Revision 3, Aug. 1978.

18 "ANSYS Examples Manual," Swanson Analysis Systems Inc., Houston, PA, April 1978.

19 "ANSYS Verification Manual," Swanson Analysis Systems Inc., Houston, PA, June 1976.

20 "ANSYS Theoretical Manual," Swanson Analysis Systems Inc., Houston, PA, Revision 3, Jan. 1977.

21 "ASAS User Manual," Atkins R. D., Epsom, Surrey, England, Nov. 1976.

22 Henrywood, R. K., and Sheffield, J. D., "ASAS - A General Purpose Finite Element Analysis System," Computer Aided Design, Vol. 8, No. 1, Jan. 1976, pp. 2-8.

23 Knowles, N. C., "ASAS - Progress Towards Acceptability," CAD 76, Second Int. Conf. on Computers in Engineering and Building Design, Imperial College, London, March 1976, pp. 234-40.

24 Argyris, J. H., "ASKA-User's Reference Manual," ISD Rep. No. 73, Stuttgart, 1971.

25 Brönlund, O. E., Bühlmeier, J., "DYNAN User's Reference Manual," ISD Rep. 97, Stuttgart, 1971.

26 "ASKA III-1, Material Nonlinearities User's Reference Manual," ASKA UM 207, Stuttgart, 1972.

27 "ASKA III-2, Linear Buckling, User's Reference Manual," ASKA UM 212, Stuttgart, 1974.

28 Argyris, J. H., and Schrem, E., "ASKA, Software Engineering for the Seventies in Structural Analysis," 2nd SMIRT Conf., Berlin, Sept. 1973, Paper M1/4.

29 Meijers, P., "Review of the ASKA Program," Numer. and Computer Meth. in Struct. Mech., ed. S. G. Fenves, Academic Press, New York, 1973, pp. 123-49.

30 Schrem, E., "A Short Description of ASKA," Int. Short Course on Finite Elem. Linear and Nonlinear Analysis, Milan, June 1974, Also Rep. ISD UM 215, Stuttgart, 1974.

31 Spaas, H. A. C. M., and Broekhoven, M. J. G., "Application of the Finite Element Technique to a Complex 3D Elastic Problem: Nozzle Junction with Cracks," Finite Elem. Congress, IKOSS, Baden-Baden, West Germany, Nov. 1974.

32 Broekhoven, M. J. G., "Computation of Stress Intensity Factor for Nozzel Corner Cracks by Various Finite Element Procedures," 3rd Int. SMIRT Conf., London, Sept. 1975, Paper G4/6.

33 Hellen, T. K., "BERSAFE, A Computer System for Stress Analysis, Part 1: User's Guide," Rep. CEGB, RD/B/N/ 1761, Berkeley Nuclear Lab., England.

34 Hellen, T. K., "BERSAFE, A Computer System for Stress Analysis, Part 2: Advice and Sample Problems," CEGB Rep. RD/B/N 1813, Berkeley Nuclear Lab., England.

35 Hellen, T. K., "A User's Guide to BERSAFE Phase II," CEGB Rep. RD/B/N/ 2508, Berkeley Nuclear Lab., England, 1974.

36 Hellen T. K., and Protheroe, S. J., "The BERSAFE Finite Element System," Computer Aided Design, Vol. 6, No. 1, Jan. 1974, pp. 15-24.

37 Jerram, K., and Hellen, T. K., "The Use of Finite Element Techniques in Fracture Mechanics," CEGB Rep. RD/B/N 2478, Berkeley Nuclear Lab., England, 1972.

38 Hellen, T. K., "The Calculation of Stress Intensity Factors Using Refined Finite Element Techniques," CEGB Rep. RD/B/N 2583, Berkeley Nuclear Lab., England, March 1973.

39 Reynen, J., "Analysis of Cracked Pressure Vessel Nozzles by Finite Elements," 3rd Int. SMIRT Conf., London, Sept. 1975, Paper G 5/1.

40 Hellen T. K., and Blackburn, W. S., "The Use of a Path Independent Integral in Nonlinear Fracture Mechanics," 4th Int. SMIRT Conf., San Francisco, Aug. 1977, Paper G 3/3.

41 Hellen, T. K., and Blackburn, W S., "The Calculation of Stress Intensity Factors in Two and Three Dimensions Using Finite Elements," CEGB Rep. RD/B/N 3378, Berkeley Nuclear Lab., England, 1975.

42 Hellen, T. K., and Dowling, A. R., "Three-Dimensional Crack Analysis Applied to an LWR Nozzle-Cylinder Intersection," Int. J. Press. Vess. Piping, Vol. 3, 1975, pp. 57-74.

43 Hellen, T. K., et al., "Fracture Analysis of Thermally Stressed Bodies," CEGB Rep. RD/B/N 3451, Berkeley Nuclear Lab., England, 1975.

44 Blackburn, W. S., "Calculation of Stress Intensity Factors at Crack Tips Using Special Finite Elements," The Mathematics of Finite Elements and Its Applications, Academic Press, New York, 1972, pp. 327-36.

45 Blackburn, W. S., and Hellen, T. K., "Calculation of Stress Intensity Factors for Elliptical and Semi-Elliptical Cracks in Blocks and Cylinders," CEGB Rep. RD/B/N 3103, Berkeley Nuclear Lab., England, July 1974.

46 Blackburn, W. S., and Hellen, T. K., "Calculation of Stress Intensity Factors in Three Dimensions by Finite Element Methods," Int. J. Num. Meth. Engineering, Vol. 11, No. 2, 1977, pp. 211-29.

47 Hellen, T. K., "The Finite Element Calculation of Stress Intensity Factors Using Energy Techniques," 2nd Int. SMIRT Conf., Berlin, Sept. 1973, Paper G 5/3.

48 Hellen, T. K., "The Use of the J-Integral for Non-Linear Fracture Mechanics," CEGB Rep. RD/B/N 3770, Berkeley Nuclear Lab., England, 1976.

49 Hellen, T. K., "On Special Isoparametric Elements for Linear Elastic Fracture Mechanics," Int. J. Num. Meth. Engineering, Vol. 11, 1977, pp. 200-205.

50 Van Fossen, D. B., "FESAP - Design Program for Static and Dynamic Structural Analysis," 2d SAP User's Conf., June 1977.

51 Bloom, J. M., and van der Sluys, W. A., "Determination of Stress Intensity Factors for Gradient Stress Fields," J. Press. Vess. Technol., Paper 76-WA/PVP-10, 1976.

52 Heckmer, J. L., and Bloom, J. M., "Determination of Stress Intensity Factors for the Corner-Cracked Hole Using the Isoparametric Singularity Element," Int. J. Fracture, Oct. 1977.

53 "MARC-CDC, Nonlinear Finite Element Analysis Program, User
Information Manual, Vol. I," Control Data Co., Minneapolis, 1974.
54 "MARC-CDC, Program Input Manual, Vol. II," Control Data Co.,
Minneapolis, Minn.
55 "MARC-CDC, Demonstration Problem Manual, Vol. III," Control Data
Co., Minneapolis, Minn.
56 Ayres, D. J., "Elastic-Plastic Dynamic Analysis of Opening Area
of an Axial Crack in a Pipe under Pressure," 3rd Int. SMIRT Conf., London,
Sept. 1975, Paper L 7/6.
57 Levy, N., et al., "Progress in Three Dimensional Elastic-Plastic
Stress Analysis for Fracture Mechanic," Nuclear Engng. Design, Vol. 17,
1971, pp. 64-75.
58 Schmitt, W., et al., "Calculation of Stress-Intensity Factors
of Cracks in Nozzles," Int. J. Fracture, Vol. 12, No. 3, 1976, pp. 381-90.
59 Prij, J., "Two- and Three-Dimensional Finite Element Analysis of
a Central Cracked Crackgrowth Test Specimen," 4th Int. SMIRT Conf., San
Francisco, Aug. 1977, Paper G 4/2.
60 Ayres, D. J., "Determination of the Largest Stable Suddenly
Appearing Axial and Circumferential Through-Cracks in Ductile Pressurized
Pipe," 4th Int. SMIRT Conf., San Francisco, Aug. 1977, Paper F 7/1.
61 Marcal, P. V., "Three-Dimensional Finite Element Analysis for
Fracture Mechanics," In the Surface Crack: Physical Problems and Computat.
Solutions, ASME Winter Annual Meet., New York, 1972, pp. 187-202.
62 Marcal, P. V., et al., "Elastic-Plastic Behaviour of a Longitudinal Semi-Elliptic Crack in a Thick Pressure Vessel," Proc. 6th Annual
Informat. Meet., Heavy Section Steel Technol. Program, Oak Ridge, Tenn.
1972.
63 Barsoum, R. S., "Application of Quadratic Isoparametric Finite
Elements in Linear Fracture Mechanics," Int. J. Fract., Vol. 10, No. 4,
1974, pp. 603-5.
64 Barsoum, R. S., "Further Application of Quadratic Isoparametric
Finite Elements to Linear Fracture Mechanics of Plate Bending and General
Shells," Int. J. Fracture, Vol. 11, No. 1, 1975, pp. 167-69.
65 Barsoum, R. S.,"A Degenerate Solid Element for Linear Fracture
Analysis of Plate Bending and General Shells," Int. J. Num. Meth. Engng.,
Vol. 10, No. 3, 1976, pp. 551-64.
66 Barsoum, R. S., "Application of Triangular Quarter-Point Elements
as Crack Tip Elements of Power Law Hardening Material," Int. J. Fracture,
Vol. 12, No. 3, 1976, pp. 463-66.
67 Barsoum, R. S., "On the Use of Isoparametric Finite Elements
in Linear Fracture Mechanics," Int. J. Num. Meth. Engng., Vol. 10, No. 1
1976, pp. 25-37.
68 Barsoum, R. S., "Triangular Quarter-Point Elements as Elastic and
Perfectly Plastic Crack Tip Elements," Int. J. Num. Meth. Engng., Vol. 11,
No. 1, 1977, pp. 85-98.
69 "MSC/NASTRAN, Basic Training Manual," MacNeal-Schwendler Co.,
Los Angeles.
70 "MSC/NASTRAN, Demonstration Problem Manual," MacNeal-Schwendler
Co., Los Angeles.
71 "MSC/NASTRAN, User's Manual," MacNeal-Schwendler Co., Los Angeles.
72 Nagy, L. I., "Evaluation of NASTRAN from the User's Point of
View," JSAE Symp. on Anal. and Design of Automobile Body Structure,
Tokyo, Nov. 1973.
73 MacNeal, R. N., and McCormick, C. W., "The NASTRAN Computer Program for Structural Analysis," Computer Structure, Vol. 1, 1971, pp. 389-
412.
74 MacNeal, R. N., "Some Organizational Aspects of NASTRAN," Nucl.
Engng. and Design, Vol. 29, 1974, pp. 254-65.

75 Tocher, J. L., and Herness, E. D., "A Critical View of NASTRAN," Numer. and Computer Meth. in Struct. Mech., ed. S. J. Fenves, Academic Press, New York, 1973, pp. 151-74.

76 Hussain, M. A., et al., "The Quarter-Point Quadratic Isoparametric Element as a Singular Element for Crack Problems," NASTRAN User's Experiences, NASA TM-X-3428, Oct. 1976, p. 419.

77 Chu, C. S., "Finite Element Computer Program to Analyse Cracked Orthotropic Sheets," Lockheed-Georgia Co., NASA Rep. NASA-CR-2698, July, 1976.

78 "PAFEC 75 - Theory, Results," PAFEC Ltd, Nottingham, England.

79 "PAFEC 75 - EASIDATA," PAFEC Ltd, Nottingham, England.

80 "PAFEC 75 - Get Started," PAFEC Ltd, Nottingham, England.

81 "PAFEC 75 - Data Preparation," PAFEC Ltd, Nottingham, England.

82 "PAFEC 75 - Systems," PAFEC Ltd, Nottingham, England.

83 Henshell, R. D., and Shaw, K. G., "Crack Tip Finite Elements are Unnecessary," Int. J. Num. Meth. Engng., Vol. 9, No. 3, 1975, pp. 495-507.

84 Pifko, A., Levine, H. S., and Armen, H., "PLANS - A Finite Element Program for Nonlinear Analysis of Structures, Vol. 1 - Theoretical Manual," Grumman Aerospace Co., Research Dept., Rep. RE-501, Nov. 1975, 180 p.

85 Pifko, A., et al., "PLANS - A Finite Element Program for Nonlinear Analysis of Structures, Vol. II - User's Manual," Grumman Aerospace Co., Research Dept. RM-633, May 1977.

86 Armen, H., et al., "Nonlinear Crack Analysis with Finite Elements," Numer. Solution of Nonlinear Struct. Problems, ed. R. F. Hartung, ASME, Vol. 6, 1973.

87 Newman, J. C., and Armen, H., "Elastic-Plastic Analysis of a Propagating Crack under Cyclic Loading," AIAA/ASME/SAE 15th Struct. Dynamics and Mater. Conf., Las Vegas, Paper 74-366, April 1974.

88 Newman, J. C., "A Finite Element Analysis of Fatigue Crack Closure," NASA, Langley Research Center, VA, Sept. 1974, 34 p.

89 Engja, H., et al., "Finite Element Program for Piping System Analysis, User's Manual NV 323," Det Norske Veritas, Oslo 1972.

90 Kråkeland, B., et al., "Thin Shell Analysis, User's Manual NV 331," Det Norske Veritas, Oslo, 1974.

91 Wergeland, J. H., "Thick/Thin Shell Analysis, User's Manual NV 332," Det Norske Veritas, Oslo, 1974.

92 Aasen, E., et al., "Analysis of Solids, User's Manual NV 333," Det Norske Veritas, Oslo, 1974.

93 Sandsmark, N., and Egeland, O., "Plastic and Visco-Elastic Stress Analysis of Solids of Revolution, User's Manual NV 334," Det Norske Veritas, Oslo, 1972.

94 Kråkeland, B., et al., "General Superelement Program, User's Manual NV 336," Det Norske Veritas, Oslo, 1974.

95 Bjørnstad, H., "3-Dimensional Frame Analysis, User's Manual NV 337," Det Norske Veritas, Oslo, 1973.

96 Kråkeland, B., et al., "Membrane Analysis, User's Manual NV 339," Det Norske Veritas, Oslo, 1974.

97 Bergan, P. G., and Aamodt, B., "NV 344 Crack Analysis Program, User's Manual," Det Norske Veritas, Oslo.

98 Bergan, P. G., and Aamodt, B., "NV 344 Crack Analysis Program, Maintenance Manual," Det Norske Veritas, Oslo.

99 Aamodt, B., et al., "Calculation of Stress Intensity Factors and Fatigue Crack Propagation of Semi-Elliptical Part through Surface Cracks," Proc. 2nd Int. Conf. Press. Vess. Technol., San Antonio, Texas, Oct. 1973, pp. 911-21.

100   Aamodt, B., "Application of the Finite Element Method to Problems in Linear and Nonlinear Fracture Mechanics," NTH Trondheim, Rep. 74-1, Norway, June 1974.
101   Aamodt, B., and Bergan, P. G., "Numerical Techniques in Linear and Non-Linear Fracture Mechanics," Computat. Fracture Mech., ed. E. F. Rybicki, ASME, New York, 1974, pp. 199-216.
102   Aamodt, B., "Efficient Formulations of the Finite Element Method in Linear and Non-Linear Fracture Mechanics," Det Norske Veritas, Publ. 92, Oslo, Feb. 1976.
103   Aamodt, B., and Klem, F., "Application of Numerical Techniques in Practical Fracture Mechanics," Conf. Fracture Mech. in Engng. Practice, Univ. of Sheffield, Sept. 1976.
104   Bergan, P. G., and Aamodt, B., "Finite Element Analysis of Crack Propagation in Three Dimensional Solids under Cyclic Loading," 2nd Int. SMIRT Conf., Berlin, Sept. 1973; also Nuclear Engng. and Design, Vol. 29, No. 2, Dec. 1974, pp. 180-88.
105   Bergan, P. G., and Lotsberg, I., "Damage Analysis for Fatigue Growth of Internal Cracks," Int. Symp. on Pract. Design in Shipbuilding Tokyo, Oct. 1977.
106   "TITUS - Presentation Sommaire," CITRA, Velizy, France.
107   "TITUS - Notice D'Emploi," CITRA, Velizy, France.
108   Launay, G., et al., "Three-Dimensional Thermoelastic Computer Code TITUS," 1st Int. SMIRT Conf., Berlin, 1971.
109   Heliot, J., and Vagner, J., "Use of the Weight Function Concept and the Crack Closing Method for Calculating Stress Intensity Factors in Plane or Axisymmetric Problems," Fracture 1977, Vol. 2, ICF 4, Waterloo, Ontario, Canada, June 1977.
110   Labbens, R., "Practical Method for Calculating Stress Intensity Factors through Weight Functions," Mechanics of Crack Growth, ASTM STP 590, 1976, pp. 368-84.
111   Labbens, R. C., et al., "Weight Functions for Three-Dimensional Symmetrical Crack Problems," Crack and Fracture, ASTM STP 601, 1976, pp. 448-70.
112   Parks, D. M., "A Stiffness Derivative Finite Element Technique for Determination of Elastic Crack Tip Stress Intensity Factors," Int. J. Fracture, Vol. 4, No. 4, Dec. 1974, pp. 487-502.
113   Parks, D. M., "Virtual Crack Extension: A General Finite Element Technique for J-Integral Evaluation," Int. Conf. Num. Meth. Fract. Mech., Univ. College of Swansea, Wales, Jan. 1978, pp. 464-78.
114   McMeeking, R. M., "Finite Deformation Analysis of Crack Tip Opening in Elastic Plastic Materials and Implications for Fracture Initiation," Brown University, Div. of Engng., May 1976, 70 p.
115   Tracey, D., and Cook T. S., "Analysis of Power Type Singularities Using Finite Elements," Int. J. Num. Meth. Engng., Vol. 11, No. 8, 1977, pp. 1225-35.
116   Tracey, D. M., "Finite Elements for Determination of Crack Tip Elastic Stress Intensity Factors," Engng. Fract. Mech., Vol. 3, 1971, pp. 255-65.
117   Tracey, D, M., "Finite Elements for Three-Dimensional Elastic Crack Analysis," Nuclear Engng. and Design, Vol. 26, 1974, pp. 282-90.
118   Tracey, D., "3D Elastic Singularity Element for Evaluation of K along an Arbitrary Crack Front," Int. J. Fracture, Vol. 9, 1973, pp. 340-43.
119   Kfouri, A. P., "Stress Displacement, Line Integral and Closure Energy Determinations of Crack Tip Stress Intensity Factors," Int. J. Press. Vess. and Piping, Vol. 2, No. 3, 1974, pp. 179-91.

120 Kfouri, A. P., and Miller, K. J., "Crack Separation Energy Rates in Elastic-Plastic Fracture Mechanics," Proc. Inst. Mech. Engng., Vol. 190, 48/76, 1976, p. 571.
121 Kfouri, A. P., and Rice, J. R., "Elastic Plastic Separation Energy Rate for Crack Advance in Finite Growth Steps," Fracture 1977, Vol. 1, ICF 4, Waterloo, Canada, June 1977, pp. 43-59.
122 Miller, K. J., "Application of Fracture Mechanics to Fatigue at Notches," Int. J. Fract., Vol. 9, No. 3, 1973, pp. 326-28.
123 Miller, K. J., and Kfouri, A. P., "Elastic-Plastic Finite-Element Analysis of Crack Tip Fields under Biaxial Loading Conditions," Int. J. Fracture, Vol. 10, No. 3, 1974, pp. 393-404.
124 Miller, K. J., and Kfouri, A. P., "A Comparison of Elastic-Plastic Fracture Parameters in Biaxial Stress States," ASTM Symp. on Elastic-Plastic Fracture, Atlanta, Ga., Nov. 1977.
125 Boissenot, J. M., and Dubois, M., "Study of Directional Criteria of Crack Instability," J. de Mécanique Appliquée, Vol. 1, No. 2, 1977.
126 Boissenot, J. M., and Serres, D., "Determination of the Apparent Crack Extension Force Using 3-D Boundary Integral Equation Method," Int. Conf. Num. Meth. Fract. Mech., Swansea, 1978, pp. 422-33.
127 Dubois, M., and Lachat, J. C., "The Integral Formulation of Boundary Value Problems," Variat. Meth. in Engng., Univ. of Southampton, 1972.
128 Lachat, J. C., and Watson, J. O., "A Second Generation Boundary Integral Equation Program for Three Dimensional Elastic Analysis," Appl. Mech. Div., ASME, New York, 1975.
129 Lachat, J. C., "A Further Development of the Boundary Integral Technique for Elastostatics," Ph.D. Thesis., Univ. of Southampton, 1975.
130 Atluri, S. N., Kobayashi, A. S., and Nakagaki, N., "Application of an Assumed Displacement Hybrid Finite Element Procedure to Two-Dimensional Problems in Fracture Mechanics," AIAA Paper No. 74-390, April 1974.
131 Atluri, S. N., Kobayashi, A. S., and Nakagaki, M., "Fracture Mechanics Application of an Assumed Displacement Hybrid Finite-Element Procedure," AIAA J., Vol. 13, No. 6, 1975, pp. 734-39.
132 Atluri, S. N., Kobayashi, A. S., and Nakagaki, M., "An Assumed Displacement Hybrid Finite Element Model for Linear Fracture Mechanics," Int. Journ. of Fracture, Vol. 11, No. 2, 1975, pp. 257-71.
133 Atluri, S. N., Kobayashi, A. S., and Nakagaki, M., "A Finite Element Program for Fracture Mechanics Analysis of Composite Materials," Fracture Mechanics of Composites, ASTM Stp 593, Nov. 1975, pp. 86-98.
134 Atluri, S. N., Kathiresan, K., and Kobayashi, A. S., "Three-Dimensional Linear Fracture Mechanics Analysis by a Displacement-Hybrid Finite-Element Model," 3rd Int. Conf. on Struct. Mech. in React. Technol., London, Sept. 1975, Paper L/3.
135 Atluri, S. N., and Kathiresan, K., "An Assumed Displacement Hybrid Finite Element Model for Three-Dimensional Linear Fracture Mechanics Analysis," Proc. 12th Annual Meet. of the Soc. Engr. Science, Univ. of Texas, Austin, Texas, Oct. 1975.
136 Atluri, S., and Nakagaki, M., "Post-Yield Analysis of a Three Point Bend Fracture Test Specimen," Develop. in Theoret. and Applied Mech., Vol. 8, ed. R. P. McNitt, Virginia Polytech. and State Univ., Blacksburg, April 1976, pp. 106-25.
137 Atluri, S., and Nakagaki, M., "J-Integral Estimation Procedures for Strain Hardening Materials in Ductile Fracture," Proceed. of AIAA/ASME/SAE 17th Struct., Structural Dynamics and Mater. Conf., Valley Forge, PA., May 1976, pp. 140-52.

138 Atluri, S. N., Nakagaki, M., and Chen, W. H., "Fracture Analysis under Large-Scale Yielding: A Finite Deformation Embedded Singularity, Elastic-Plastic Incremental Finite Element Solution," ASTM Special Technical Publication, 1976.

139 Atluri, S. N., and Kathiresan, K., "On a 3D Singularity Element for Computation of Combined-Mode Stress Intensities," NASA Special Tech. Publicat., Proceed. of 13th Ses Meet., 1976, pp. 257-64.

140 Atluri, S. N., "On the Formulation and Application of Rational Numerical Methods for Problems with Non-Removable Singularities," Proceed. of Int. Symposium on Innovative Numerical Methods in Applied Science, Versailles, France, 1977.

141 Atluri, S. N., and Tong, P., "On Hybrid Techniques in Fracture Analysis," Int. Conf. on Fracture Mech. and Technology, Hong Kong, March 1977.

142 Atluri, S. N., and Nakagaki, M., "Stress Analysis of Crack in the Elasto-Plastic Range," 4th Quadrennial Int. Conf. on Fracture, Waterloo, Canada, June 1977.

143 Atluri, S. N., and Kathiresan, K., "Analysis of Crack in Adhesively Bonded Structures," ASME Winter Annual Meet., Atlanta, Ga., Nov. 1977.

144 Atluri, S. N., and Kathiresan, K., "Cracks near Fastener Holes and Surface Flaws in Plates: Direct Computation of Stress Intensities," 18th AIAA/ASME/SAE Structures, Struct. Dynam. and Mater. Conf., San Diego, March 1977.

145 Atluri, S. N., Nakagaki, M., and Rhee, H. C., "Fracture Analysis of Structures under Combined Models Loading," ASCE Confer., Raleigh, N.C., May 1977.

146 Atluri, S. N., and Kathiresan, K., "Outer and Inner Surface Flaws in Thick-Walled Pressure Vessels," 4th Conf. on Struct. Mech. in React. Technol., San Francisco, Aug. 1977, Paper G 5/4.

147 Atluri, S. N., "Inner Surface Crack in an Internally Pressured Cylinder Analysis by a Three Dimensional Displacement-Hybrid Finite Element Method," 3rd Int. Conf. on Pressure Vessel Technol., Tokyo, Japan, April 1977.

148 Atluri S. N., "Hybrid Finite Element Models for Linear and Nonlinear Fracture Mechanics," Proc. Int. Conf. on Num. Meth. in Fracture Mech., Swansea, Jan. 1978, pp. 52-66.

149 Papaioannou, S. G., "A Finite Element Method for Calculating Stress Intensity Factors and Its Application to Composites," M.S. Thesis, Mech. Engng., Lehigh Univ., Bethlehem, 1972.

150 Papaioannou, S. G., et al., "Finite Element Method for Calculating Stress Intensity Factors and Its Application to Composites," Engng. Fract. Mech., Vol. 6, No. 4, 1974, pp. 807-23.

151 Aberson, J. A., and Anderson, J. M., "Cracked Finite Elements Proposed for NASTRAN," Third NASTRAN User's Colloquium, NASA Tms-2893, NASA Langley Research Center, Langley, Va., 1973, pp. 531-50.

152 Aberson, J. A., "Development of Cracked Finite Elements at the Lockheed-Georgia Company," LG73ER007, Lockheed-Georgia Company, May 1973.

153 Aberson, J. A., "Effects of Compressive Overloads on Fatigue Crack Growth," presented at the AIAA/ASME/SAE 15th Structures, Structural Dynamics and Materials Conference, Las Vegas, Nevada, April 17-19, 1974; also in the AIAA Journal of Aircraft, Feb. 1974, p. 100.

154 Aberson, J. A., "Analysis of a Spliced Joint Containing a Crack," Fifth Canadian Congress of Applied Mechanics, Univ. of New Brunswick, Fredericton, N.B., Canada, May 26-30, 1975.

155 Aberson, J. A., "Characterization of Crack Growth in Bonded Structure," Proc. of the 12th Ann. Meet. of the Soc. of Engng. Science, Univ. of Texas at Austin, Oct. 20-22, 1975.

156 Aberson, J. A., "Finite Element Analysis of Crack Structures Subjected to Shock Loads," Computational Fracture Mechanics, ed. E. F. Rybicki and S. E. Benzley, ASME, New York, 1974, pp. 173-84.

157 Aberson, J. A., "Fracture Control for Composite Laminates," The Army Symposium on Solid Mechanics, 1976-Composite Materials: The Influence of Mechanics of Failure on Design, Cape Cod, Mass., Sept. 14-16, 1976.

158 Aberson, J. A., "Fracture in Composites," Lockheed-Georgia Report SMN 391, Feb. 1976.

159 Aberson, J. A., "Development of Load-Interaction Model," Lockheed-Georgia Report SMN 390, Feb. 1976.

160 Aberson, J. A., "Finite Element Analysis of Dynamic Fracture," Advances in Engineering Science, Proceedings of 13th Annual Meeting of the Society of Engineering Science, NASA CP-2001, Nov. 1976, Hampton, VA., pp. 215-26.

161 Aberson, J. A., "Finite Element Computer Program to Analyze Cracked Orthotropic Sheets," National Aeronautics and Space Administration, NASA CR-2628, Hampton, VA., 1976.

162 Aberson, J. A., "User's Guide for Finite Computer Programs to Analyze Cracked Orthotropic Sheets," National Aeronautics and Space Administration, Hampton, VA., 1976.

163 Aberson, J. A., "Residual Strength Analysis of Primary Aircraft Structure Damaged Due to Projectile Impact and Penetration," Air Force Armament Laboratory - AFATL-TR-77-16, Vols. 1 and 2, Eglin Air Force Base, Fla., 1977.

164 Aberson, J. A., "Green's Function for a Thru-Crack Emanating from Fastener Holes," The Fourth International Conference on Fracture, University of Waterloo, Ontario, Canada, June 19-24, 1977.

165 Aberson, J. A., "Interaction Effects of Multiple Cracks," AIAA/ASME/SAE 17th Structures, Structural Dynamics and Material Conference, King of Prussia, Pa., May 5-7, 1976; also in AIAA Journal, March, 1977.

166 Aberson, J. A., "Fracture Mechanics Methodology and Analytical Procedures," Lockheed-Georgia Report SMN 366B, Feb. 1977.

167 Aberson, J. A., "Dynamic Analysis of Cracked Structures Using Singularity Finite Elements," Mechanics of Fracture IV: Elastodynamic Crack Problems, ed. G. C. Sih, Noordhoff International, Leyden, 1977, pp. 249-94.

168 Aberson, J. A., "Singularity Element Simulation of Crack Propagation," Fast Fracture and Crack Arrest, ed. G. T. Hahn and M. F. Kanninen, ASTM STP 627, American Society for Testing Materials, 1977, pp. 123-34.

169 Aberson, J. A., "A Finite-Element Analysis of an Impact Test," Fracture 1977: Proceedings of 4th International Conference on Fracture, Vol. 3, June 1977, Waterloo, Canada, pp. 85-90.

170 Anderson, J. M., et al., "Finite Element Analysis of Cracked Structures Subjected to Shock Loads," Computat. Fracture Mech., ed. E. F. Rybicki and S. E. Benzley, ASME, New York, 1975, pp. 173-84.

171 Chu, C. S., "Finite Element Computer Program to Analyse Cracked Orthotropic Sheets," Lockheed-Georgia Co., NASA Tech. Rep. NASA-CR-2698, July 1976.

172 De Koning, A. U., and Sanderse, A., "A Computer Programme for Elastic-Plastic Calculations with Use of TRIM 6 Finite Elements," Rep. NLR TR 72 144, Nat. Aerospace Lab., Amsterdam, 1972.

173 De Koning, A. U., "Result of Calculations with TRIM 6 and TRIAX 6 Elastic-Plastic Elements," Int. J. Fracture, Vol. 9, No. 3, 1973, pp. 313-15.

174 De Koning, A. U., et al., "Energy Dissipation during Stable Crack Growth in Aluminum Alloy 2024-T3," 1st Conf. on Numer. Meth. in Fract. Mech., Swansea, Jan. 1978, pp. 525-36.

175 Hellan, K., and Lotsberg, I., "On Absolute Convergence of the Separation Work as Calculated by Release of Nodes in a Finite Element Model," Int. J. Fracture, Vol. 13, 1977, pp. 539-43.

176 Lotsberg, I., "Finite Element Analysis of Some Problems in Fracture Mechanics," Div. of Struct. Mech., The Norwegian Inst. of Technol., Rep. 77-5, Trondheim, Nov. 1977.

177 Lotsberg, I., and Bergan, P. G., "Calculation of Fatigue Growth of Internal Cracks," Nucl. Engng. and Design, Aug. 1977.

178 Lotsberg, I., "Crack Analysis Program, Internal Cracks - User's Manual," Div. of Struct. Mech., The Norwegian Inst. of Technol., Univ. of Trondheim, Feb. 1977.

179 Lotsberg, I., "Crack Analysis Program, Internal Cracks - Maintenance Manual," Div. of Struct. Mech., The Norwegian Inst. of Technol., Univ. of Trondheim, Feb. 1977.

180 Lotsberg, I., "Nonlinear Crack Analysis Program - User's Manual," Div. of Struct. Mech., The Norwegian Inst. of Technol., Univ. of Trondheim, 1977.

181 Lotsberg, I., "Crack Growth Simulation by the Finite Element Method," Proc., 1st Conf. on Numer. Meth. in Fract. Mech., Swansea, Jan. 1978, pp. 496-507.

182 Ogura, K., and Ohji, K., "FEM Analysis of Crack Closure and Delay Effect in Fatigue Crack Growth under Variable Amplitude Loading," Engng. Fract. Mech., Vol. 9, 1977, p. 471.

183 Ogura, K., Ohji, K., and Honda, K., "Influence of Mechanical Factors on the Fatigue Crack Closure," Proc. Int. Conf. on Fracture, Waterloo, Canada, Vol. 2, 1977, p. 1055.

184 Ohji, K., Ogura, K., and Ohkubo, Y., "Finite Element Approach to the Critical Cyclic Stress Required to Propagate a Crack," Japan Congr. on Mater. Res., Osaka, Aug. 1972, Soc. of Mater. Sci., Kyoto, 1973, pp. 45-58.

185 Ohji, K., Ogura, K., and Ohkubo, Y., "On the Closure of Fatigue Cracks under Cyclic Loading," Int. J. of Fracture, Vol. 10, 1974, p. 123.

186 Ohji, K., Ogura, K., and Ohkubo, Y., "Fatigue Crack Growth under Biaxial Loading," Int. J. of Fracture, Vol. 10, 1974, p. 609.

187 Ohji, K., Ogura, K., and Ohkubo, Y., "Cyclic Analysis of a Propagating Crack and Its Correlation with Fatigue Crack Growth," Engineer. Fracture Mech., Vol. 7, No. 3, 1975, pp. 457-64.

188 Bäcklund, J., Wennerström, H., and Axelsson, K., "PIFEM - A Computer Program for Analysis of Elasto-Plastic Structures," Swedish Ship Research Foundation, Rep. No. 125, Gothenburg, 1976.

189 Bäcklund, J., and Aronsson, C. G., "Effects of Geometrical Imcompatibilities on Stress Intensity Factors Calculated by the Finite Element Method," Proceed. 1st Internat. Conf. on Numer. Meth. in Fracture Mechanics, Swansea, Jan. 1978.

190 Bäcklund, J., and Sjöström, S., "Finite Element Analysis of Fatigue Crack Growth in Aircraft Components," Proc. 1st Int. Conf. on Numer. Meth. in Fract. Mech., Swansea, Jan. 1978, pp. 787-97.

191 Argyris, J. H., "Recent Developments in the Finite Element Analysis of Prestressed Concrete Reactor Vessels," 2d Cong. on Struct. Mech. in Reactor Technol., Berlin 1973; also in Nucl. Eng. Design, Vol. 28, 1974, pp. 42-75.

192 Argyris, J. H., Faust, G., and William, K. J., "Limit Load Analysis of Thick-Walled Concrete Structures. A Finite Element Approach to Frac-

ture," ISD-166, Stuttgart University, Inst. fur Statik und Dynamik der Luft- und Raumfahrtkonstr., 1975; also in Computat. in Appl. Mech. and Engng., Vol. 8, 1976, pp. 215-43.

193 Argyris, J. H., "Unified Concept of Constitutive Modeling and Numerical Solution Methods for Concrete Creep Problems," Comp. Meth. Appl. in Mech. Engng., Vol. 10, 1977, pp. 199-246.

194 Argyris, J. H., "Finite Elementberechnung von Spannbeton-Reaktordruckbehältern," Deutscher Ausschuss für Stahlbeton, Heft 279, 1977.

195 Luxmoore, A. R., Light, M. F., and Evans, W. T., "A Comparison of Energy Release Rates, the J-Integral and Crack Tip Displacements," Int. J. Fract., Vol. 13, 1977, pp. 257-59.

196 Light, M. F., Luxmoore, A., and Evans, W. T., "Prediction of Slow Crack Growth by a Finite Element Method," Int. Journ. of Fracture, Vol. 11, No. 6, 1975, pp. 1045-46.

197 Light, M. F., Luxmoore, A. R., and Evans, W. T., "Some Further Results on Slow Crack Growth Prediction by a Finite Element Method," Int. Journ. of Fract., Vol. 12, No. 3, 1976, pp. 503-6.

198 Light, M. F., and Luxmoore, A. R., "Application of the Front Solution to Two- and Three-Dimensional Elasto-plastic Crack Problems," Int. J. Num. Meth. Engng., Vol. 11, No. 2, 1977.

199 Hsu, T. R., Bertels, A. W. M., Arya, B., and Banerjee, S., "Application of the Finite Element Method to the Non-Linear Analysis of Nuclear Reactor Fuel Behaviour," Proceedings of the First International Conference on Computational Method in Non-Linear Mechanics, Sept. 1974,

200 Hsu, T. R., and Bertels, A. W. M., "An Improved Approximation of Constitutive Elasto-Plastic Stress Strain Relationship for Finite Element Analysis," AIAA Journal, Vol. 12, No. 10, Oct. 1974, pp. 1450-52.

201 Hsu, T. R., and Bertels, A. W. M., "Propagation and Opening of a Through Crack in a Pipe Subject to Combined Cyclic Thermo-Mechanical Loadings," Journal of Pressure Vessel Technol., ASME Transaction, Feb. 1976.

202 "Stress Analysis on Cracked Plates by Finite Element Method," Thermomechanics Lab., Rep. 73-UN-1, March 1973, Univ. of Manitoba.

203 "On Computational Efficiency of TEPSA Code," Part I - Theory and User's Manual, Thermomech. Lab. Rep. 77A-9, Part II - Code Listing, Rep. 77-A-10, June 1977, Univ. of Manitoba.

204 "Transient Thermal Elasto-Plastic Stress Analysis," Part I - Exp. Verification of TEPSA Code, Part II - Kinematic Hardening Rule, Part III - Code Listing, Thermomech. Lab., Rep., Nos. 77-A-11 to 13, 1977, Univ. of Manitoba.

205 "Finite Element Elasto-Plastic Stress Analysis of Solids by Finite Strain Theory," Part I - Theory and User's Manual, Part II - Code Listing, Thermomech. Lab., Rep. Nos. 77-A-14, 15, 1977, Univ. of Manitoba.

206 Marse, J., "Crack Closure Related to Fatigue Crack Propagation," Twente Univ. of Technol., Rep., Dept. of Mech. Engng., Enschede, The Netherlands.

207 Spiering, R. M. E. J., and de Pater, C., "On the Cracked Element Approach for the Computation of Stress Intensity Factors," 4th Int. SMIRT Conf., San Francisco, Aug. 1977, Paper G 5/7.

208 Kobayashi, A. S., Maiden, D. E., Simon, B. J., and Iida, S., "Application of Finite Element Analysis to Two-Dimensional Problems in Fracture Mechanics," ASME Paper 69-WA/PUP-12, Nov. 1969.

209 Kobayashi, A. S., and Maiden, D. E., "Stress Intensity Factors for a Straight Crack Approaching a Circular Hole," Proc. of Air Force Conf. on Fatigue and Fracture of Aircraft Struct. and Materials, Sept. 1970, pp. 217-24.

210 Kobayashi, A. S., Chiu, S. T., and Beeuwkes, R., "Elastic-Plastic State in a Plate with an Extending Crack," Proc. of the Army Symp. on Solid Mech. Light Weight Struct., Vol. 4., Dec. 1970, pp. 85-98.

211 Kobayashi, A. S., Chiu, S. T., and Beeuwkes, R., "A Numerical and Experimental Investigation on the Use of J-Integral," Engineering Fracture Mechanics, Vol. 5, 1973, pp. 293-305.

212 Kobayashi, A. S., "Stress Intensity Factors and Plasticity Correction Factors, Finite Element Techniques in Fracture Mechanics," Int. J. Fracture, Vol. 9, No. 3, 1973, p. 317.

213 Kobayashi, A. S., and Shah, R. C., "Elliptical Crack Embedded in a Plate Subjected to Tensile and Bending Loading," J. of Pressure Vessel Technology, Trans. of ASME 96, Series J (1) 47-54, Feb. 1974.

214 Kobayashi, A. S., Johnson, B. N., and Wade, B. G., "Crack Approaching a Hole," Fracture Analysis, ASTM Special Technical Publication 560, 1974, pp. 53-68.

215 Kobayashi, A. S., Polvanich, N., Emery, A. F., and Love, W. J., "Stress Intensity Factor of a Surface Crack in a Pressurized Cylinder," Computational Fracture Mechanics, ed. E. F. Rybicki and S. E. Benzley, ASME, New York, 1975, pp. 121-32.

216 Kobayashi, A. S., Atluri, S. N., and Nakagaki, M., "An Assumed Displacement Hybrid Finite Element Model for Linear Fracture Mechanics," Int'l. J. of Fracture, Vol. 11, No. 2, April 1975, pp. 257-71.

217 Kobayashi, A. S., Enetanya, A. N., and Shah, R. C., "Stress Intensity Factors for Elliptical Cracks," Prospects of Fracture Mechnics, ed. G. C. Sih, H. C. Van Elst, and D. Broek, Noordhoff International, Leyden, 1974, pp. 525-44.

218 Kobayashi, A. S., "Criteria for Crack Branching and Crack Arrest," Progress in Experimental Mechanics - The Durelli Anniversary Volume, ed. V. J. Parks, The Catholic University of America, 1975, pp. 83-97.

219 Kobayashi, A. S., Atluri, S. N., and Kathiresan, K., "Three-Dimensional Linear Fracture Mechanics Analysis by a Displacement-Hybrid Finite Element Model," Trans. of the 3rd Int. Conf. on Structural Mechanics in Reactor Technology, London, Sept. 1-5, 1975, Vol. 5, Paper L 1/3, p. 13.

220 Kobayashi, A. S., Atluri, S. N., and Nakagaki, M., "Application of an Assumed Displacement Hybrid Finite Element Procedure to Two-Dimensional Problems in Fracture Mechanics," Proc. of the 15th Structures, Structural Dynamics and Materials Conf., April 17-19, 1974, Las Vegas, Nevada; also in AIAA Journal, Vol. 13, No. 6, June 1976, pp. 734-39.

221 Kobayashi, A. S., and Enetanya, A. N., "Stress Intensity Factor of a Corner Flaw," Mechanics of Crack Growth, ASTM STP 590, 1976, pp. 477-95.

222 Kobayashi, A. S., Emery, A. F., and Love, W. J., "Elastic Crack Propagation along a Pressurized Pipe," J. of Pressure Vessel Technology, Trans. of ASME, Vol. 98, No. 1, Feb. 1976, pp. 2-7.

223 Kobayashi, A. S., Polvanich, N., Emery, A. F., and Love, W. J., "Corner Flaw at a Hole in a Turbine Disk," J. of Engineering for Power, Trans. of ASME, Vol. 98, No. 4, Oct. 1976, pp. 465-77.

224 Kobayashi, A. S., Emery, A. F., and Mall, S., "Dynamic Finite Element and Dynamic Photoelastic Analysis of Two Fracturing Homolite-100 Plates," Experimental Mechanics, Vol. 16, No. 9, Sept. 1976, pp. 321-28.

225 Kobayashi, A. S., "Crack Opening Displacement in a Surface Flawed Plate Subjected to Tension or Plate Bending," Proc. of the 2nd Int. Conf. on Mechanical Behavior of Materials, Boston, Aug. 16-29, 1976, pp. 1073-77.

226 Kobayashi, A. S., Emery, A. F., Polvanich, N., and Love, W. J., "Surface Flaw in a Pressurized and Thermally Shocked Hollow Cylinder," Int. Journal of Pressure Vessels and Piping, Vol. 5, No. 2, April 1977, pp. 103-22.

227 Kobayashi, A. S., Emery, A. F., Polvanich, N., and Love. W. J., "Inner and Outer Surface Cracks in Internally Pressurized Cylinders," Journal of Pressure Vessel Technology, Trans. of ASME, Vol. 99, No. 1, Feb. 1977, pp. 83-89.

228 Kobayashi, A. S., Emery, A. F., and Mall, S., "Dynamic Finite Element and Dynamic Photoelastic Analysis of Crack Arrest in Homolite-1000 Plates," Fast Fracture and Crack Arrest, ASTM STP 627, 1977.

229 Kobayashi, A. S., Emery, A. F., Neighbors, P. K., and Love, W. J., "Stress Intensity Factors in Edge-Cracked Plates Subjected to Transient Thermal Singularities," Journal of Pressure Vessel Technology, Trans. of ASME, Vol. 99, Series J, No. 1, Feb. 1977, pp. 100-105.

230 Kobayashi, A. S., and Mall, S., "Dynamic Finite Element and Dynamic Photoelastic Analyses of an Impacted Pretensioned Plate," Fracture 1977, Proc. of the Fourth Int. Conf. on Fracture, June 19-24, 1977, Waterloo, Canada, Vol. 3, pp. 79-84.

231 Kobayashi, A. S., Polvanich, N., Emery, A. F., and Love. W. J., "Corner Crack at a Nozzle," Proc. of the 3rd Intern. Conf. on Pressure Vessel Technology, Tokyo, April 19-22, 1977, pp. 507-16.

232 Kobayashi, A. S., Cheng, J. S., and Atluri, S. N., "Assumed Displacement Finite Element Method for Non-Linear Elastic and Elastic-Plastic Analysis," A Collection of Technical Papers on Structures and Materials, Vol. A, AIAA/ASME, 18th Structures, Structural Dynamics and Materials Conf., San Diego, Calif. March 21-23, 1977, pp. 279-89.

233 Kobayashi, A. S., Polvanich, N., Emery, A. F., and Love, W. J., "Stress Intensity Factors of Corner Cracks in Two Nozzle-Cylinder Intersection," 4th Int. Conf. on Structural Mechanics in Reactor Technology, San Francisco, Calif. Aug. 15-19, 1977.

Part III

REVIEWS OF COMPUTATIONAL MECHANICS TECHNOLOGY

Finite Element Mesh Optimization and Enrichment Techniques

Lawrence L. Durocher

University of Bridgeport

Robert J. Stango

University of Illinois

INTRODUCTION

Mesh optimization and optimal mesh refinement concepts are closely related; however, the aims and techniques used in each are quite distinct. While mesh optimization algorithms focus on obtaining the best solution accuracy for a given type and number of elements, optimal mesh refinement strategies focus on introducing more degrees of freedom (more nodes and elements) into the model in the regions that will benefit more from mesh refinement.

Many users of commercial software are not even aware that a rearrangement of the mesh pattern can change the solution accuracy, and have little or no information on which to base a refinement sequence. Not only are there many programs in this area, but the timeliness of the review is further emphasized by the fact that a general purpose program (MARC) now offers the user an option of displaying an energy measure that can be used to identify areas that will benefit, or will not benefit, from mesh enrichment.

In this chapter, the basic concepts of mesh optimization are reviewed, mesh optimization procedures are discussed, and several examples of mesh optimization are presented. More promising developments related to adaptive mesh refinement techniques are discussed along with unresolved problem areas associated with automated procedures for mesh optimization and refinement.

MESH OPTIMIZATION

Literature Review and Theory

An optimal mesh is generally defined to be a mesh pattern that yields the greatest solution accuracy for a given number and type of finite elements. An optimal mesh is obtained by changing the nodal positions so as to achieve maximum solution accuracy.

Apparently, Carroll [1] and Marcal and McNeice [2] were the first investigators to consider mesh selection procedures as a valuable aid to analysts who normally select initial grids with a lack of experience, or conflicting experiences [3], with somewhat similar problems. Although Marcal and McNeice obtained near-optimal meshes by manual adjustment of the nodal coordinates and Carroll used an automated approach, the criterion (minimizing the potential energy) and the derived governing equations for optimal meshes are identical. Carroll [1, 4], in addition, formally proved the existence of an optimal grid arrangement although no guarantee of uniqueness could be given. Simultaneously, or shortly thereafter, similar approaches [5-7] to different elastostatic problems appeared in the literature. Turcke and McNeice [7-10], again using the minimum potential energy criterion, developed an automated procedure for determining an optimal mesh geometry. While Carroll [1, 4] used an in-direct search algorithm [11] that necessitates the calculation of derivatives of the potential energy function, Turcke and McNeice employed a direct search approach [12] that attempts to minimize the potential energy on the basis of a past history of successful and unsuccessful changes in nodal coordinates. A successful nodal move is defined as one that reduces the potential energy.

Previous work was confined to elastostatic problems; Carroll [13-16] generalized the variational basis of the mesh optimization formulation by employing Hamilton's principle and considered free vibration and buckling problems. For discussion purposes, Carroll's development will be presented in an abbreviated form.

Hamilton's principle requires that

$$\int_{t_1}^{t_2} \delta(T-V)dt + \int_{t_1}^{t_2} \delta W_{nc} \, dt = 0 \tag{1}$$

where T = kinetic energy of the system, V = potential energy stored in the system plus the potential of conservative externally applied actions, and W_{nc} = work done by nonconservative generalized forces. Normally, a finite element solution to Eq. (1) is based on a fixed mesh pattern of elements and associated nodes. That is, the mesh is assumed to be unalterable and Hamilton's principle is satisfied by proper adjustment of the nodal values of the displacement components. Hence in the standard finite element approach, the unknown quantities are simply the nodal values of displacements.

If one recognizes that the energy terms in Eq. (1) are functions of the nodal coordinates (idealization parameters) as well as the nodal displacements, then Hamilton's principle requires the following Euler-Lagrange equations be satisfied:

$$\frac{d}{dt}\left(\frac{\partial L}{\partial \dot{u}_i}\right) + \frac{\partial L}{\partial u_i} + \frac{\partial W_{nc}}{\partial u_i} = 0 \quad i = 1,2,\ldots, N \tag{2}$$

$$\frac{d}{dt}\left(\frac{\partial L}{\partial \dot{q}_j}\right) + \frac{\partial L}{\partial q_j} + \frac{\partial W_{nc}}{\partial q_j} = 0 \quad j = 1,2,\ldots, M \tag{3}$$

where $L = T-V$, t = time, $\dot{u}_i = du_i/dt$, $\dot{q}_j = dq_j/dt$, u_i = nodal displacement components, q_j = idealization parameters or nodal coordinates, N = total number of nodal displacements, and M = total number of nodal coordinates or idealization parameters. Typical definitions of u_i and q_j are shown in Fig. 1.

The first set of Lagrange equations, Eq. (2), is more recognizable if cast in matrix notation. For elastodynamic problems, Eq. (2) becomes [15]

$$[M] \left\{\ddot{U}\right\} + [K] \left\{U\right\} - \left\{F\right\} = \left\{0\right\} \quad (4)$$

where $[M]$ = mass matrix, $[K]$ = global stiffness matrix, (F) = global load vector, (U) = column vector of nodal displacements. Thus, the first set of Lagrange equations is the usual equations of motion associated with the body or structure, which for static problems are simply the nodal equilibrium equations

$$[K] \left\{U\right\} = \left\{F\right\} \quad (5)$$

Equations (4) and (5) are the standard elastodynamic and elastostatic finite element formulations for a fixed idealization of nodes and elements. Satisfaction of these equations does not ensure that one will obtain the most accurate solution for a given number and type of finite elements. Since a rearrangement of the mesh pattern, holding the number of elements constant, can have a dramatic influence on the solution accuracy, nodal coordinates or idealization parameters must also be considered as variables.

Thus, Hamilton's principle requires that Eq. (3) be simultaneously satisfied. In more familiar matrix notation, Eq. (3) becomes

$$\left\{\dot{U}\right\}^T \frac{\partial [M]}{\partial q_j} \left\{\dot{U}\right\} + \left\{U\right\}^T \frac{\partial [K]}{\partial q_j} \left\{U\right\} - 2 \frac{\partial \{F\}}{q_j}^T \left\{U\right\} = 0 \quad (6)$$

Note that Eqs. (4) and (6) constitute a set of coupled nonlinear equations since the mass, stiffness, and load terms are functions of the nodal coordinates. While Carroll [14,15] has considered free vibration and buckling problems, another computational hurdle arises in such problems because each eigenvalue has an optimal grid associated with it. For elastostatic problems, Eq. (6) degenerates

$$\frac{1}{2} \left\{U\right\}^T \frac{\partial [K]}{\partial q_j} \left\{U\right\} - \frac{\partial \{F\}}{\partial q_j}^T \left\{U\right\} = r_j, \quad j = 1,2,\ldots, M \quad (7)$$

where it has been recognized that in an iterative solution to Eqs. (5) and (7), the right-hand sides of Eqs. (7) will not be identically zero. The residuals or errors, r_j, are a measure of the error associated with the idealization geometry and, as shown by Carroll [4], must vanish when an optimal subdivision (for a fixed number of elements) exists and/or the finite element solution is exact. For elastostatic problems, the residuals are derivatives of the potential energy function, and the sign of each r_j establishes the direction in which q_j should be moved so as to minimize the potential energy [2].

In summary, two approaches have been used to obtain optimal meshes for elastostatic problems. Turcke and McNeice [7-10] employed a direct approach in which each nodal coordinate is changed, the equilibrium

equations are reformulated and resolved, and the potential energy is
monitored to determine whether or not the nodal movement improved the
solution.   In such an approach, Rosenbrock's method [12] is employed to
determine how much and in what direction a node should be moved. An
advantage of the direct search approach is that it can be used, with very
little change from one element type to another, for virtually any type of
elastostatic problem. The primary disadvantage is the enormous amount of
computer time required to continually reformulate and resolve the equilibrium equations after every change in nodal coordinates.
     Carroll's approach [4] may be classified as an indirect approach in
that an optimal mesh is found by monitoring the residuals, which are
gradients of the potential energy, rather than the potential energy.
After solving the equilibrium equations (Eq. (5)) for a fixed
geometry, the residuals are calculated from Eqs. (7) and a gradient search
routine [11] is used to determine new coordinates; the reformulation and
calculation of residuals is continued until the residuals fall below some
prescribed tolerance. Note that the calculation of residuals requires that
one calculate derivatives of the stiffness matrix with respect to changes
in the nodal coordinates. An exact calculation of such derivatives is
obviously very element—dependent, and the ease with which such calculations can be made will vary radically from one element type to another.
In addition, the disadvantage associated with Turcke and McNeice's
approach, namely, enormous computational effort to obtain an optimal grid,
is also required in Carroll's indirect scheme.
     The CPU time (DEC System-10 computer) required to obtain optimal
meshes ranges from 10 minutes for a very simple problem (say less than 30
degrees of freedom) to many hours for a realistic idealization of a
typical engineering problem. In fact, the computational effort is so
great that to the authors' knowledge no optimization problem having over
60 degrees of freedom has been solved. Computer time increases very
rapidly as one attempts to optimize meshes having more nodes; moreover,
mesh optimization of higher-order elements proves to be even more costly
[17].
     Although considerable effort [8, 10, 15, 16] has been devoted to
developing guidelines that would allow the user to construct near-optimal
meshes without using formal optimization procedures, the published guidelines [8, 10] are somewhat vague and certainly open to interpretation.
It has been the authors' experience [17] that direct application of such
guidelines to new problems is cumbersome, if not impossible, and generally
yields marginal improvements. Application [17] of the proposed guidelines
[8, 10] to several types of beam problems yielded somewhat improved displacement and stress values compared to a uniform grid, but nowhere near
as great an improvement as the computer-optimized solution (see, for
example, Fig. 1).

                        Mesh Optimization Examples

To illustrate the radical restructuring of mesh geometry and the resultant improvements in displacements and stresses obtained via mesh optimization, several examples will be considered. Figure 1 presents an initial
uniform grid, a manually optimized grid obtained using the guidelines
suggested by Turcke and McNeice [8, 10], and a computer-optimized grid
[17], along with the corresponding maximum displacements and bending
stresses. A direct search approach [17] was used to establish the
computer—optimized meshes. The linear displacement, plane stress triangle
(CST) was used in each of the analyses. This element has proved to be

popular in grid optimization studies due to the speed with which each element stiffness can be calculated, an important factor when many reformulations must be expected due to nodal repositioning.

Note that the manually optimized grid (MOG) has a pattern somewhat similar to the computer-optimized grid (COG). However, the computer optimized grid is shifted so as to distribute more elements closer to the wall. The displacements from the MOG are no closer to the exact solution than the uniform mesh, and in fact, the predicted tip displacement is worse. The MOG bending stress at most points along the beam is also poorer than the initial grid; a notable exception is at the wall. The COG displacements and stresses represent substantial improvements over the uniform grid values. No attempt was made to limit the aspect ratios of the triangles during the optimization process. The optimization was assumed to have converged when the nodal coordinates remained unchanged within three significant figures. Note that the initial mesh was symmetric and the optimized mesh is very close to being symmetric; the primary deviation is in the vicinity of the applied load. If the midside nodal coordinates at the tip are assumed to be unalterable, then the optimized mesh will be symmetric.

If the initial mesh is nonsymmetric, then the optimized mesh is also nonsymmetric [17].

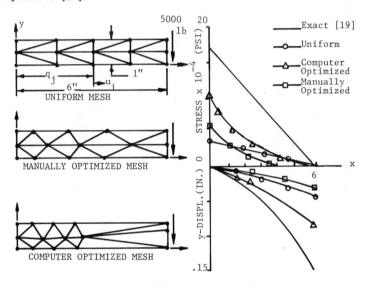

Fig. 1   CST optimization of cantilever beam

To demonstrate the effect of element type on the optimization process, the same problem was reanalyzed [17] using the eight-degree-of-freedom linear isoparametric elements [18]. An initial uniform mesh, a computer-optimized mesh, a mesh obtained by replacing the optimized CST elements (Fig. 1) with linear isoparametric elements, and the associated displacements and stresses are shown in Fig. 2. The CST replacement was considered as a measure that might make the optimization process more economical if lower-order elements could be used to generate patterns for

higher-order elements. Since the two element types are based on the
same displacement assumption except for the mixed quadratic term (xy),
this replacement was deemed a natural test for element substitution. The
isoparametric mesh optimization takes approximately ten times the CPU time
required for CST elements; hence, a substantial cost savings could be
achieved if element replacement provided accuracy.

Figure 2 clearly illustrates that the optimized isoparametric grid is
somewhat similar to the replacement mesh; however, the COG elements tend
to remain more rectangular. While the stresses in the COG and replacement analyses are very similar, the displacement predictions are obviously
quite different. On the basis of this and other problems [17], it appears
that such replacements are not completely satisfactory. Note that the
percentage of improvement in displacements and stresses of the COG analysis
is not as great as that obtained in the CST optimization. Clearly, the
percentage of improvement obtained by optimization must decrease if the element type and/or fineness of mesh is such that the initial grid produces
displacements and stresses that are already somewhat close to exact values.

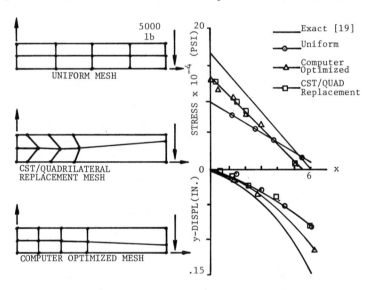

Fig. 2   Quadrilateral optimization of beam

As a final example of mesh optimization, consider the uniformly
distributed edge load acting on a unit thickness plate, Boussinesq's
problem [19]. This problem was analyzed [17] using CST, linear, and
parabolic isoparametric elements [18]. For discussion purposes, the CST
results are shown in Fig. 3. Note that the uniform mesh displacements and
stresses differ significantly from the exact solution. The optimized
analysis yields displacement and stress distributions that have essentially the same shape and numerical values as the exact solution. While
mesh refinement would certainly improve the uniform grid predictions of
displacement, considerable refinement might be required to reproduce the
stress predictions of the optimal grid. It should also be mentioned that

the authors attempted to use the guidelines of Turcke and McNeice to manually construct a near-optimal mesh for this problem; the required isoenergetic (constant strain energy density) contours were so erratic as to make manual optimization extremely difficult.

When approaching grid optimization with parabolic isoparametric elements, midside nodes must be restrained to remain approximately midway between the corner nodes. This requirement was met most easily, from a computational viewpoint, by permitting only linear distortions of the element sides during mesh optimization. The initial and optimized results for the Boussinesq problem are shown in Fig. 4. Again, dramatic improvements in the displacements and stress predictions are evident.

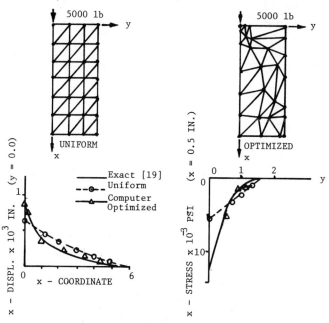

Fig. 3 CST optimization of Boussinesq problem

To the best of the authors' knowledge, mesh optimization studies have been limited to problems with straight boundaries. A typical problem having a curved boundary is shown in Fig. 5. An optimization study of the arch beam problem has been conducted [17] using CST, linear and parabolic isoparametric elements. An additional complication arises when trying to optimize models having curved boundaries; care must be taken to ensure that nodal repositioning does not change the nature of the problem being analyzed. For instance, if CST elements are used to model the arch beam, mesh optimization will cause the elements to pack more closely in the region $30° \leq \theta \geq 90°$. As Fig. 5 indicates, such movement changes the nature of the straight-line approximation to the curved boundary and hence a different problem is being analyzed. One is left with the options of requiring all boundary nodes to be fixed or of allowing the boundary nodes to move along the circular arc but adding enough elements so that the geometric changes are negligible.

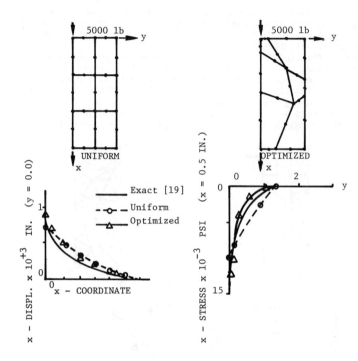

Fig. 4 Eight-noded quadrilateral optimization

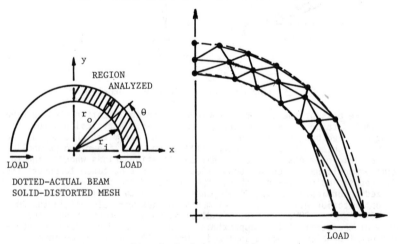

Fig. 5 Arch beam problem

In concluding the mesh optimization review, several unresolved problem areas should be mentioned: (a) current optimization procedures are so costly as to be prohibitive for realistic engineering problems, (b) optimization guidelines are cumbersome and difficult to apply to new problems, (c) optimization procedures are currently limited to linear solid mechanics applications; applications in heat transfer, fluid flow, etc., remain to be examined, (d) grid optimization with isoparametric elements is awkward unless element geometry is limited to the linear mode, and (e) problems involving curved boundaries [17] are awkward to optimize unless all boundary nodes are restrained from repositioning.

MESH REFINEMENT

Literature Review and Theory

Since uniform mesh refinement nearly always introduces new nodes and elements in regions where mesh enrichment is unnecessary, successful techniques for identifying regions where mesh refinement will be more productive can dramatically reduce the computer costs associated with finite element analysis. It is somewhat surprising that the technical literature related to grid refinement strategies apparently only dates back to 1974. Somervaile and Kabaila [20] devised a local enrichment procedure in which the finite element solution was locally refined and its behavior at the edge of the refined zone was suitably restricted by introducing the appropriate constraints via the use of Lagrange multipliers in the variational statement. This approach has obvious disadvantages in regards to compatibility with existing software.

Selective mesh enrichment requires that one develop a criterion for predicting regions or elements which will benefit from mesh refinement and that one formulate a refinement procedure that introduces more degrees of freedom into the model without violating interelement compatibility, without changing points of load applications, etc. For applications in solid mechanics, the refinement criterion should, in general, have the following characteristics: (a) it should be independent of the finite element type, shape, and displacement basis; (b) it should be problem-independent and viable regardless of the initial mesh [21]; (c) the calculations required must not be so overburdensome as to destroy the economic advantage of selective enrichment; and (d) it should, hopefully, lend itself to automatic selection of regions or elements that need refinement, rather than relying on judgments based on past experiences.

Similarly, the actual refinement procedure, wherein additional nodes and elements are introduced into the model, should also meet most of the above requirements. In addition, interelement compatibility must be maintained and the refinement sequence should ensure monotonic convergence of the solution energy associated with successive refinements [22].

Killian [21] examined several refinement criteria and finally employed the strain energy distribution as a measure that could be examined to identify potential candidates for mesh enrichment. Elements having "above-average" strain energy values were refined, the thinking being that an even distribution of strain energy would indicate a sort of optimal contribution of each element to the response under load. While this criterion was effective for some applications, in a number of problems uniform refinement led to results of equal or better accuracy.

Melosh and Killian [22] later determined that a more effective criterion was one based on the change in strain energy produced by introducing an additional node within an existing element. After estimating the

change in strain energy caused by introducing an additional node within
each element, elements are selected for refinement by choosing to
introduce those nodes whose strain energy changes are above the average.
The results obtained using this criterion were more encouraging than those
based on the strain energy distribution [21]. However, the approach used,
in calculating the change in strain energy produced by introducing a new
node is very element-dependent and hence precludes its use in general
purpose programs.

The actual refinement procedure used by Killian and Melosh [21, 22]
was the same as that used by Carey [23]. The examples considered were
restricted to use of the three-noded. linear displacement triangle (CST).
After deciding which elements would benefit from mesh enrichment, nodes
are added at the midsides of the element, which essentially creates four
elements to replace the original triangle (see Fig. 6). Depending on
whether or not adjacent elements have also been refined, one or two of the
added nodes must be constrained to maintain compatibility at element
interfaces. Note that this subdivision strategy ensures monotonic convergence of the strain energy and ensures that any refined mesh cannot involve
an element geometry that is more extreme than the initial mesh [22].
Carey [23] has shown the appropriate matrix operations required to obtain
the proper stiffness of such constrained elements. In addition, Carey has
suggested other criteria for locating refinement zones and solves an
elastostatic potential problem by simply refining in those regions where
the solution is most rapidly changing.

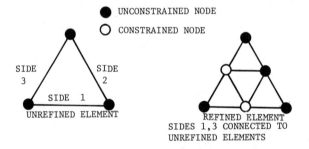

Fig. 6   Subdivision of triangular elements

More recently, Melosh and Marcal [24] have generalized the adaptive
mesh refinement approach [22] to include all types of linear, discrete
elements, i.e., plate elements, shell elements, etc. The energy measure
employed by Melosh and Marcal is based on the total potential energy of
the continuum, which may be expressed as

$$\Pi = \frac{1}{2} \{u\}^T [K] \{u\} - \{u\}^T \{F\} \qquad (8)$$

The effect on the potential of introducing an additional degree of freedom,
u, can be written as

$$\frac{\partial \Pi}{\partial u} = \frac{1}{2} \{u\}^T \frac{\partial [K]}{\partial u} \{u\} \qquad (9)$$

assuming that (U), (F) define an equilibrium state. Assuming that u only affects element j with stiffness [K_j], an element energy differential can be calculated from

$$\frac{\partial \Pi}{\partial u} = \frac{1}{2} \left\{ U \right\}^T \frac{\partial [K_j]}{\partial u} \left\{ U \right\} \tag{10}$$

which is required to vanish in a mesh which yields the exact solution [24]. In order to avoid element dependent logic, a backward finite difference measure of the energy differential is used for each element

$$\frac{\Delta \Pi}{\Delta u} = \frac{1}{2} \left\{ U_c \right\}^T [K_j] \left\{ U_c \right\} - \frac{1}{2} \left\{ U_r \right\}^T [K_j] \left\{ U_r \right\} \tag{11}$$

where (U$_c$), and U$_r$. are vectors of nodal displacements for the current and reduced displacement fields, respectively. The reduced degrees of freedom are defined so as to include only generalized constant strain states (constant strain for membranes, constant curvature for plates, etc.).

The strain energy is obtained by integrating the strain energy density over the volume of the element; hence the difference between the energy integrals for the current and reduced displacements may be interpreted as a sensitivity measure of the effect of higher energy participation on the solution [24]. The difference of the integrands is defined as the specific energy difference (SED) which, in practice, is obtained by taking the difference between the specific strain energy at a chosen point and the specific strain energy at the element centroid.

Finite element theory requires that [24]:

1. Absolute value of the SED must approach zero as element size shrinks to zero.
2. If mesh refinement leaves the SED unchanged in all regions, the exact solution is available.

Clearly, this proposed measure for determining regions that will benefit from mesh refinement requires very little computational effort and is applicable to broad classes of problems in solid mechanics. Computer costs associated with generating SED information is negligible in comparison to analysis costs. Melosh and Marcal [24] have considered membrane, plate, and shell applications involving the use of SED contours.

Mesh Enrichment Examples

In general, after performing an initial analysis with a coarse grid, SED contours are plotted and additional elements are placed in regions where larger values of SED exist. The direction and spacing of the contours may also indicate what type of refinement is appropriate and whether additional refinement will be productive or nonproductive. The two examples given in this section illustrate the use of SED contours in mesh refinement decisions. The mesh enrichment examples and figures are taken directly from the paper by Melosh and Marcal [24].

The first problem is that of a square membrane subjected to a pair of diagonal corner loads. Because of symmetry, only one-quarter of the plate is analyzed, as shown in Fig. 7. The initial finite element model consists of four parabolic isoparametric elements [18]. The SEDs were evaluated at the nine Gauss points associated with each element; the contours (straight-line plots) are shown in Fig. 8.

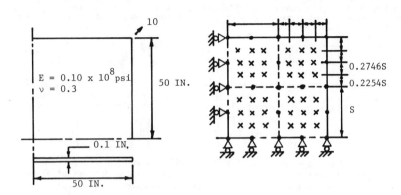

a. Corner-loaded membrane   b. Initial finite element model

Fig. 7 Point-loaded membrane and initial model

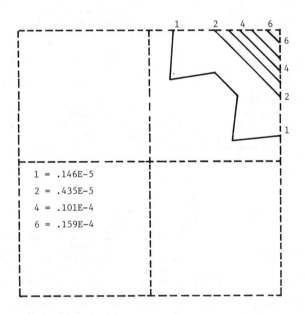

Fig. 8 SED contours for membrane

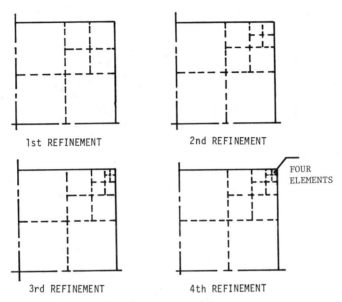

1st REFINEMENT   2nd REFINEMENT

FOUR
ELEMENTS

3rd REFINEMENT   4th REFINEMENT

Fig. 9 Sequence of refined membrane meshes

The cluster of SED$ in the corner element indicate that this element
is a prime candidate for subdivision. Subsequent analyses and examinations
prompt the sequence of refined meshes shown in Fig. 9. Obviously, in
order to maintain displacement compatibility, the midside nodes of the
smaller squares must be constrained to move as dictated by the nodal
movements of the larger adjacent squares. Figure 10 illustrates the
change in strain energy as a function of the number of degrees of freedom
used in the model. Note the monotonic convergence of the strain energy
and that a uniform mesh (1200 dof) of simplex elements exhibits approximately the same strain energy as a selectively subdivided mesh of quadri-
laterals having one-tenth the number of degrees of freedom. The simplex
solutions have higher energy values than the rectangular solutions because
relatively few degrees of freedom lie in the loaded corner of the quadrilateral meshes. Because of the nature of the stress distribution in the
corner-loaded membrane, investigators [8-10, 21, 22, 24] have frequently
examined this problem from optimization and refinement standpoint.

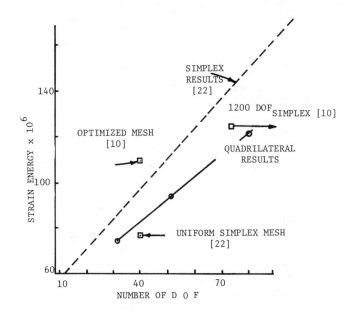

Fig. 10 Membrane strain energy results

The second example illustrates how SED contours can indicate what type of refinement is most appropriate. A cantilevered pipework modeled by shell elements [12], founded on bicubic shape functions and Koiter-Sanders shell theory, is shown in Fig. 11. Straight piping sections were modeled as simple beam elements. The piping system is loaded with a tip-load.

The SED contours at the lower end of the bend are nearly parallel to the pipe axis; hence improvements in the lower end can be achieved more economically by simply adding more elements around the periphery rather than refining along the axis and around the periphery. In the upper region the contours are nearly perpendicular to the axis, indicating that mesh refinement should take the form of additional elements along the pipe axis. Also, since the SED contours in the upper region are three times larger than in the lower portion, more elements should be used in the upper region.

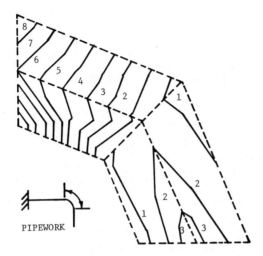

Fig. 11   SED contours for pipe bend

The mesh enrichment examples presented herein may be somewhat misleading in that the SED patterns are very simple to interpret for refinement decisions. For some problems, the SED contours are so irregular as
to defy even a qualitative evaluation, at least by an inexperienced user.
Some example problems given in a recent MARC newsletter [25] have SED
contours that are much more difficult to use for enrichment decisions.

In concluding the mesh enrichment review, it should be noted that
adaptive mesh refinement strategies can have very significant economic
implications, especially for three-dimensional analysis. Additional work
is, of course, needed to automate the selection and refinement procedure
so as to eliminate manual examination of SED contours and manual selection
of refinement procedures.

While mesh refinement procedures appear to be economically more viable
than optimization techniques, additional research is needed to: (a) automate the use of the SED criterion and the refinement process or to develop
even better criteria; (b) consider nonlinear applications in solid mechanics and to consider linear and nonlinear applications in other disciplines,
and (c) couple refinement and cost estimates to allow the user to obtain
the "best" solution for a range of computational costs [26]. In addition,
very little effort has been directed toward the combined use of optimization and enrichment theory. That is, after using enrichment theory to
decide which elements are to be subdivided, perhaps optimization algorithms
or guidelines should be used to decide exactly how such elements should be
divided so as to achieve maximum accuracy. As a final objective, one
would like to couple generation, refinement, optimization, and cost and
error estimates so as to obtain a sequence of solutions that yield the
most accurate "answers" for a prespecified cost. Using a rigorous mathematical approach rather than an energy-based engineering approach, Babuska
and his associates [26-29] have considered error estimates and self-adap-

tive mesh refinement procedures for certain classes of problems having
singularities.

AVAILABLE PROGRAMS

To the best of the authors' knowledge, there are no commercial programs
available to perform finite element mesh optimization. At the moment,
mesh optimization capabilities are limited to a few special purpose programs created by researchers in this field.
    Capabilities associated with mesh enrichment theory are also very
limited. Plotting of SED contours has been implemented as a standard output option for the MARC general purpose finite element program which is
available on several time-sharing systems such as CDC CYBERNET, McDonnell
Douglas Automation Services, etc. Once the SED contours have been plotted,
the user must still examine the contours and make judgments related to
the proper mesh refinement. Further information regarding the availability of MARC can be obtained by writing to Marc Analysis Research Corporation, 260 Sheridan Avenue, Suite 314, Palo Alto, Calif. 94306.

CONCLUSIONS

The technical literature related to mesh optimization and refinement has
been reviewed, and several unpublished examples of mesh optimization have
been presented. Although considerable effort has been devoted to mesh
optimization algorithms and to guidelines for manually optimizing the grid
without using formal optimization procedures, current mathematical procedures are clearly too expensive to be applied to realistic problems and
optimization guidelines leave much to be desired [17]. Most investigators
have considered problems with straight boundaries and have employed
straight-sided elements; the current trend toward the increasing use of
isoparametric elements dictates that more general optimization problems
be considered both in solid mechanics applications as well as other fields
of interest.
    Adaptive mesh refinement developments are much more encouraging in
regards to implementation as a standard option on commercial software. In
particular, the use of SED contours to determine regions that will, or will
not, benefit from mesh enrichment seems economically viable and has been
implemented in one general purpose finite element program. Additional
work related to automating the refinement process is needed and additional
research may lead to even better refinement criteria. At the moment, nonlinear applications in solid mechanics, and linear and nonlinear applications in other areas, remain to be considered.

ACKNOWLEDGMENTS

The authors would like to acknowledge the help of Dr. Robert Hayduk of
NASA Langley Research Center, who generously supplied several of the
references. In addition, the assistance of Dr. Ahmed Noor of George
Washington University, who furnished several references that were unknown
to the authors, is gratefully acknowledged.
    The authors would also like to express their appreciation to Drs.
Robert Melosh and Pedro Marcal for their permission to use the figures
associated with the mesh enrichment examples.

REFERENCES

1 Carroll, W. E., "On Optimum Idealizations in Discrete Element Analysis," Ph.D. Thesis, Virginia Polytechnic Institute and State University, Blacksburg, 1971.

2 Marcal, P. V., and McNeice, G. M., "Optimization of Finite Element Grids Based on Minimum Potential Energy," ONR Tech. Rept. N00014-0007/7, June 1971. Also Journal of Engineering for Industry, Feb. 1973, pp. 186-190.

3 Ebner, A., "Guidelines for Finite Element Idealization," Proc. ASCE Struct. Engr. Conv., New Orleans, 1975.

4 Carroll, W. E.,and Barker, R. M., "A Theorem for Optimum Finite Element Idealizations," Int. Journal of Solids and Structures, Vol. 9, 1973, pp. 883-95.

5 Oliveira, E. R. Arantes, "Optimization of Finite Element Solutions," Proc. of 3rd Conf. on Matrix Methods in Struct. Mech., Dayton, Ohio, Oct. 1971.

6 Taylor, R. L., and Iding, R., "Application of Extended Variational Principles to Finite Element Analysis," Conference on Variational Methods in Engineering, Southampton University, England, 1972, pp. 2/54-2/67.

7 Turcke, D. J., and McNeice, G. M., "A Variational Approach to Grid Optimization in the Finite Element Method," Conf. on Variational Methods in Engineering, Southampton University, England, 1972, pp. 4/114-4/130.

8 Turcke, D. J., and McNeice, G. M., "Procedure for Selecting Near Optimum Finite Element Grids for Improved Stress Analysis," Proc. 2nd Int. Conf. on Pressure Vessels and Piping Technology, ASME, San Antonio, Texas, 1973.

9 Turcke, D. J., and McNeice, G. M., "Application of Grid Selection Procedures for Improved Finite Element Stress Analysis," Int. Conf. on Vehicle Structural Mechanics, SAE, Detroit, 1974, pp. 205-16.

10 Turcke, D. J., and McNeice, G. M., "Guidelines for Selecting Finite Element Grids Based on an Optimization Study," Int. Journal of Computers and Structures, Vol. 4, 1974, pp. 449-519.

11 Fletcher, R., and Reeves, C. M., "Function Minimization by Conjugate Gradients," Computer Journal, Vol. 7, 1964, pp. 149-54.

12 Rosenbrock, H. H., "An Automatic Method of Finding the Greatest or Least Value of a Function," Computer Journal, Vol. 3, 1960, pp. 75-184.

13 Carroll, W. E., "Ramifications of Optimum Idealization Geometry in Discrete Element Analysis," Proc. World Congress on Finite Elements Struct. Mechanics, Bournemouth, England, 1975.

14 Carroll, W. E., "Inclusive Criteria for Optimum Grid Generation in the Discrete Analysis Technique," Computers & Structures, Vol. 6, 1976, pp. 333-37.

15 Carroll, W. E., "On the Reformulation of the Finite Element Method," presented at the International Symposium on Innovative Numerical Analysis in Applied Engineering Science, Versailles (France), May 1977.

16 Carroll, W. E., "Application of Near Optimum Mesh Generation Technique to Conforming and Nonconforming Finite Element Solution," Symposium on Applications of Computer Methods in Engineering, University of Southern California, Aug. 1977.

17 Stango, R. J., "Optimum Grid Selection for Finite Element Analyses," Masters Thesis, Dept. of Mechanical Engineering, University of Bridgeport, Bridgeport, Conn., May 1977.
18 Zienkiewicz, O. C., The Finite Element Method in Engineering Science, McGraw-Hill, New York, 1971.
19 Timoshenko, S., and Goodier, J. N., Theory of Elasticity, 2nd ed., McGraw-Hill, New York, 1951, pp. 85-91.
20 Somervailee, I. J., and Kabaila, A. P., "Mesh Grading Techniques for Compatible and Equilibrium Elements," Proc. Int. Conf. on Finite Element Methods in Engineering, Clarendon Press, Sydney, Aug. 1974, pp. 257-71.
21 Killian, D. E., "Selective Refinement of a Finite Element Mesh for Improved Accuracy," Masters Thesis in Engineering Mechanics, Virginia Polytechnic Institute and State University, Blacksburg, Virginia, April 1975.
22 Melosh, R. J., and Killian, D. E., "Finite Element Analysis to Attain a Prescribed Accuracy," 2nd Nat. Symposium on Computerized Structural Analysis, George Washington University, Washington, D.C., 1976.
23 Carey, G. F., "A Mesh-Refinement Scheme for Finite Element Computations," Computer Methods in Applied Mechanics, Vol. 7, 1976, pp. 93-105.
24 Melosh, R. J., and Marcal, P. V., "An Energy Basis for Mesh Refinement of Structural Continua," Int. Journal of Numerical Methods in Engineering, Vol. 11, 1977, pp. 1083-91.
25 MARC Analysis Research Corporation Quarterly Newsletter, Second Quarter 1977, MARC Analysis Research Corporation, Providence, R.I.
26 Babuska, I., and Rheinboldt, W. C., "Computational Aspects of Finite Element Analysis," Proc. Software Conference, Madison, 1977, Academic Press, New York.
27 Babuska, I., and Rheinboldt, W. C., "A-Posteriori Error Estimates for the Finite Element Method," University of Maryland, Computer Science Report Series, TR-81, Sept. 1977.
28 Babuska, I., and Rheinboldt, W. C., "Error Estimates for Adaptive Finite Element Computations," University of Maryland, Institute for Physical Science and Technology, Tech. Note BN-854, May 1977.
29 Babuska, I., Rheinboldt, W. C., and Mesztenyi, C., "Self-Adaptive Refinements in the Finite Element Method," University of Maryland, Computer Science Report Series, TR-375, May 1975.

Mixed Methods Analysis

Ahmed K. Noor

George Washington University Center

NASA Langley Research Center

INTRODUCTION

Mixed or multifield formulations are defined here to be those formulations wherein the fundamental unknowns belong to more than one field.
In structural and solid mechanics problems the fundamental unknowns
include force (or stress) and kinematic variables (e.g., strains and/or
displacements). The use of mixed formulations dates back to the precomputer era. With the advent of digital computers, the mixed method
has been further developed and applied to several static stress analysis,
eigenvalue and nonlinear problems. Also, applications to nonstructural
problems are multiplying rapidly. A number of computer programs have
been developed which are based on the mixed method of analysis. The
extensive literature now available on the mixed method makes a state-of-the
art summary highly desirable for engineers and researchers working on the
subject. The present chapter attempts to summarize the status of and recent
developments in the mixed method of analysis and its application to
structural and solid mechanics problems. Since the subject is very
broad, discussion is focused on a number of aspects which are of interest
to the author, and which have not been grouped together in one publication before. These aspects include:

1. Different levels of mixing the variables
2. Mixed variational principles
3. Analysis procedures based on the mixed method
4. Assets and liabilities of the mixed method
5. Future directions of research

Also, an extensive list of references and a survey of some of the computer programs based on the mixed method are included.
    The references are grouped into nine sections. References in the
first section deal with precomputer applications of the mixed method and
with other topics related to the mixed method. References in subsequent
sections deal with the aspects and applications of the mixed method
identified by the section headings. The references in each section are
arranged alphabetically.

Early Applications of the Mixed Method

Precomputer applications of the mixed method were motivated by the reduction in the number of algebraic equations which can be achieved by using certain versions of the mixed method. Among these applications are:

1. Linear analysis of frameworks
2. Linear analysis of shallow shells
3. Nonlinear analysis of plates

     Gvozdev [1.2] proposed a method of analyzing complex struc-tural frameworks based on removing supports at certain points of the framework and inserting them at others. The governing algebraic equations of the system (canonical equations) express the vanishing of displacements at the first set of points and the absence of reactions at the latter points. Each equation contains the unknown forces and displacements simultaneously. Some of the structural systems for which this method proved to be useful have been identified in Ref. [1.2]. For example, the analysis of continuous beams with unequal spans can be reduced, through the use of this mixed method, to the analysis of beams with equal spans.
     Rebinovich [1.9] presented a mixed method for solving linear problems of symmetric structural frameworks subjected to arbitrary loadings. The method is based on decomposing the loading into symmetric and antisymmetric systems. The symmetric system is analyzed by the method of displacements, and the antisymmetric system is analyzed by the method of forces, thereby achieving a total reduction in the number of simultaneous equations to be solved (see Fig. 1).

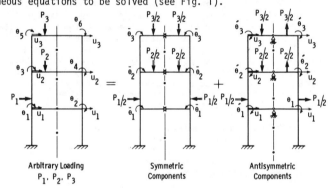

	Arbitrary Loading P_1, P_2, P_3	Symmetric Components	Antisymmetric Components
Force redundants	9 (normal forces, shearing forces and bending moments at center line)	6 (normal forces and bending moments at center line)	3 (shearing forces at center line)
Kinematic redundants	9 (3 u's, 6 θ's)	3 ($\bar{\theta}_1$, $\bar{\theta}_2$ and $\bar{\theta}_3$)	6 (3 u's and 3 θ's)
Appropriate method of analysis	Either force or displacement	Displacement	Force

Fig. 1   Mixed method of analysis of symmetric frameworks

Vlasov's equations of the linear bending theory of shallow shells [1.15] and von Karman's equations of the geometrically nonlinear theory of plates ⌊1.14] belong to the class of mixed formulations. In both cases the fundamental unknowns were chosen to be the Airy stress function and the transverse displacement component. Several approximate solutions were presented using these equations (see, for example, Ref. [1.11, 15].

DIFFERENT LEVELS OF MIXING THE VARIABLES

Mixing of the stress and kinematic variables can be done at either one of two levels (or both):

1. On the element level
2. On the system level

Mixed Variables on the Element Level

The variables can be mixed on the infinitesimal element level by specifying that:

1. the fundamental unknowns in the governing differential equations include both stress and kinematic variables, or
2. the primary fields (subject to variation) in the variational principle include stress and kinematic (e.g., strain and/or displacement) fields resulting in a mixed (multifield) variational principle. These variational principles are discussed in the next section.

Several formats are possible for the mixed differential equations, varying in number and mathematical complexity. For example, the linear bending problem of shallow shells can be formulated in a number of different ways ranging from two fourth-order partial differential equations in a stress function and transverse displacement component (see, e.g., Ref. [1.15]) to thirteen first-order partial differential equations in thirteen shell generalized displacements and stress resultants [5.4]. Both sets of equations are given in Appendix I. Although the first-order equation formulation involves more simultaneous differential equations (and more fundamental unknowns) than other formulations, it offers the following major advantages:

1. The governing differential equations have a very simple mathematical structure and reflect clearly the statement of the problem. For example, in static problems the governing equations consist of the equilibrium equations and constitutive relations (expressed in terms of forces and displacement gradients). Any simplifications (e.g., neglecting shear deformation) can be easily identified in the differential equations (see Appendix I).
2. The governing equations contain no derivatives of the material characteristics of the structure.
3. The statement of the boundary conditions involves linear combinations of the fundamental unknowns and not their derivatives (i.e., the boundary conditions are of the Dirichlet type), which results in simplifying the discretization and improving the accuracy of the solution.
4. Since all the unknown forces and displacements of the structure are taken as fundamental unknowns, once the problem is solved, all the

quantities of interest are readily available. In view of this, first-
order equation formulations have often been referred to as integrated
formulations.
   5. If the fundamental unknowns in the governing differential
equations are replaced by their increments, the governing equations
can be used to study the inelastic response of the structure.

   For certain classes of structural mechanics problems where the response can be represented by ordinary differential equations (e.g., beams,
arches, and shells of revolution), the aforementioned advantages have
been recognized and the mixed first-order equation formulation has been
widely used in conjunction with numerical integration techniques, matrix
progression or transfer matrices, and the method of initial functions.
This will be further discussed in subsequent sections.

Mixed Variables on the System Level

Mixing of the variables on the system level occurs when the structure
is divided into components (or substructures), some of which are analyzed
by the displacement method and others by the force method. The system
equations thus obtained contain both forces and displacements as unknowns.
Structures in which certain elements or substructures are considerably
stiffer than others are best suited for this mixed method. The stiff
structure segments are analyzed by the displacement method, and the
flexible substructures are analyzed by the force method [3.11-3.13].
   It may be noted that the early works of Gvozdev [1.2] and Rabinovitch
[1.9] on the analysis of structural frameworks belong to the category of
mixed variables on the system level.

MIXED VARIATIONAL PRINCIPLES

Classical Mixed Principles

The first mixed variational principle in which stresses and displacements
are varied independently was presented by Hellinger in 1914 [2.5] for
finite elasticity problems. Hellinger's variational principle does not
account for boundary conditions. For linear elasticity problems, Prange
[2.16] modified Hellinger's principle by including the boundary conditions.
Reissner, apparently unaware of Hellinger's work, presented in 1950 [2.18]
a variational theorem for linear elasticity with independent displacement
and stress fields which includes the boundary conditions. Extension of
this theorem to include finite elasticity was presented in 1953 [2.19].
In 1954 Hu presented a three-field mixed variational theorem which includes
independent displacement, stress, and strain fields [2.7]. A similar
theorem was presented independently by Washizu [1.16]. Historical
accounts of mixed variational principles are given in Refs. [1.10] and
[2.11], and a generalized version of Hellinger's principle in more modern
notation is given in Ref. [1.12].
   For elasticity problems the interrelationships among the mixed and
other variational principles (e.g., minimum potential energy and minimum
complementary energt) are discussed in Refs. [2.3] and [2.24]. A more
elegent approach to establishing the three-field Hu-Washizu principle
and the two-field Helling-Reissner principle is to start with the potential energy functional and successively relax conditions on the applicability of the minimum potential energy principle and effect satisfaction

of certain other conditions. This approach is discussed in Ref. [1.16] and is shown schematically in Fig. 2.

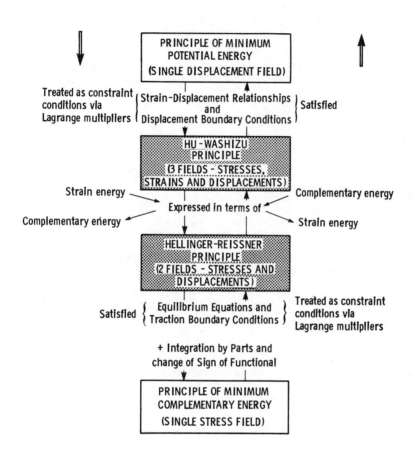

Fig. 2 Relations between mixed and other variational principles

Several extensions and applications of mixed variational principles have been reported in the literature. Among these, mention may be made of the applications to shells [2.2, 2.10, and 2.20]; plates [2.22]; continuum mechanics [2.21]; and initial value and dynamic problems [2.1, 2.17].

Mixed variational principles have proved to be useful for the analysis of incompressible (and nearly incompressible) solids [2.4, 2.8, and 2.23]   The incompressibility of the material implies the vanishing of the mean (or volumetric) strain. The use of analysis techniques based on the principle of minimum potential energy for such materials encounters computational difficulties and yields inaccurate solutions.

Mixed Variational Principles with Relaxed Continuity Requirements

In an effort to simplify the construction of approximate solutions to solid mechanics problems by means of finite element and finite difference techniques, generalized variational principles with discontinuous fields were proposed. A systematic derivation of a number of variational principles with discontinuous fields was given by Prager [2.14 and 2.15]. In the context of finite element applications the generalized principles allow the a priori relaxation of the constraints on interelement displacement continuity and/or traction reciprocity in a finite element assembly. The generalized principles are often referred to as hybrid formulations [1.1, 1.8].

A number of applications of mixed variational principles with discontinuous fields have been reported in the literature [2.9, 2.11, 4.39, and 4.40]. These will be further discussed in the next section. Applications to other variational principles with discontinuous fields (viz., modified potential energy and modified complementary energy) are given in Refs. [1.1 and 1.8] and are not considered here.

Incremental Variational Principles

For solving problems with combined geometrical and material non-linearities using the finite element method, it is convenient to use incremental methods. Mixed variational principles of the incremental type have been given in Refs. [2.6, 2.12, 2.25, and 2.26]. In Ref. [2.12], the effects of equilibrium imbalance and compatibility mismatch at the beginning of each loading increment are included in the variational principle.

ANALYSIS PROCEDURES BASED ON THE MIXED METHOD

Several analysis procedures and discretization techniques have been used in conjunction with mixed variational principles and mixed differential equations for the solution of solid and structural mechanics problems. Among these techniques, mention may be made of direct variational methods, finite element methods, finite differences, numerical integration, matrix progression, and the method of initial functions. All of these techniques lead to matrix equations which have force and kinematic variables as unknowns and a coefficient matrix which is

indefinite. Some aspects and applications of the aforementioned techniques are reviewed in the following subsections.

Direct Variational Methods

The use of direct (global) methods in conjunction with mixed variational principles allows the selection of independent approximation
functions for both stress and kinematic variables over the whole domain.
The approximation functions can be chosen to satisfy not only the
geometric but also the stress boundary conditions, thereby achieving
balanced accuracy for the stress and kinematic variables. The use of
direct methods with mixed variational principles predates the development
of mixed finite element models. Most of the reported applications of
these methods are based on the Hellinger-Reissner mixed variational
principle and modifications thereof. Among the reported applications
are large deflections and thermoelastic stress analysis of heated strips
[2.27], linear stress and vibration analysis of cantilevered skew plates
[2.28], post-buckling of rectangular plates [2.29], and dynamic response
of rapidly heated plates [2.30].

Mixed Finite Element Methods

In mixed finite element methods the unknowns (nodal parameters or
coefficients) in the final matrix equations consist of forces, strains,
and/or displacements. The coefficient matrix of the resulting system
of equations is indefinite.

Formulation of Finite Element Equations

Generally speaking, there are three approaches for formulating the
mixed finite element equations:

1. The direct method, in which the fundamental equations of motion
(or equilibrium), constitutive relations, and strain displacement
relations are combined directly for each element
2. The weighted residual approach, in which approximation functions for the stresses and displacements are substituted into the mixed
governing differential equations of the structure and an attempt is made
to minimize a weighted integral of the residuals over the region of a
finite element, according to some criterion
3. The variational approach, based on the use of mixed (multifield)
variational principles

The first approach is useful for simple structural elements such as
truss and beam elements, especially in the presence of geometric and
material nonlinearities. However, it becomes difficult to apply to
more complex elements (e.g., shells). Some of the early applications
of mixed finite elements used the direct method [3.1-3.8].
References [3.9] and [3.10] report on the application of the direct
method to the nonlinear static and dynamic analysis of pin-jointed
space trusses.
The weighted-residual approach has broader scope than either of the
direct or variational approaches. It does not require the existence of

a variational principle. The weighting functions may be chosen in a
variety of ways, and each choice corresponds to a different criterion
in the method of weighted residuals. Most of the reported applications
have used either Galerkin or least-square weighted-residual criteria
[4.59-4.62]. For a number of structural mechanics problems the Galerkin
criterion of the method of weighted residuals yields results which
are identical with those obtained by variational approaches. It may
be mentioned that the least-square weighted-residual criterion involves
more computatinal effort than the other criteria. However, it has the
advantage that the resulting algebraic equations are always symmetric
and positive definite. Therefore, iterative methods may be successfully
used for their solution.

Applications of Variational-Based Mixed Finite Elements

The variational approach to formulating the mixed finite element
equations is by far the most commonly used to date among the three
approaches. It has been applied to a large number of structural and
solid mechanics problems. Almost all the reported applications are
based on the Hellinger-Reissner mixed variational principle or modifications thereof. The first application of a variational approach to
develop mixed finite elements is due to Herrmann [4.29 and 4.30], who
developed two triangular elements for the linear static bending analysis
of thin plates. The first element is based on a linear variation for
the transverse displacement w and constant distributions for the
three stress couples $M_{\alpha\beta}$ (α, β = 1, 2). The second element is based
on linear variation for each of w and $M_{\alpha\beta}$. Since the publication
of Ref. [4.29], several mixed finite elements have been developed for
the analysis of plates and shells. Among the various applications of
these models, mention may be made of static, vibration, and stability
analysis of plates [4.2, 4.3, 4.13, 4.18, 4.19, 4.35, 4.36, 4.40,
4.47, 4.51, and 4.57], linear analysis of cylindrical and shallow
shells [4.4, 4.5, 4.6, 4.17, 4.21, 4.32, 4.48, 4.49, 4.53, 4.55, and
4.58], and analysis of shells of revolution [4.10, 4.15, 4.22, 4.25,
and 4.26]. In Ref. [4.43], mixed shear-flexible finite elements were
applied to the stress and free vibration analysis of laminated composite plates and shells. Other linear problems analyzed by mixed finite
elements include plane stress [4.20], arches [4.24], Saint-Venant torsion
[4.42], plane problems with sharp cracks [4.46], and incompressible
solids [4.11].
     Mixed finite elements have also been applied to a number of non-
linear problems including elastoplastic analysis of plates [4.8, 4.9],
large deflection and large amplitude free vibrations of plates
[4.23, 4.38, and 4.50], geometrically nonlinear analysis of shells
of revolution [4.16 and 4.56], geometrically nonlinear analysis of
cylindrical and shallow shells [4.23, 4.45, 4.48, and 4.54], limit
analysis of plates [4.14, and geometrically nonlinear analysis of
arches [4.44].
     Applications of mixed finite elements to transient response problems
of three-dimensional solids and shells of revolution are given in
Refs. [4.12] and [4.16]. In the first reference both geometric and
material nonlinearities are included.
     References [2.13] and [4.33] give detailed accounts of the various
applications of mixed finite elements including those with relaxed

continuity requirements.

Mathematical Aspects of Finite Elements

The mathematical aspects of mixed finite elements have recently
attracted the attention of many investigators. Convergence properties
and a priori error estimates have been developed for a number of
variational-based and weighted-residual mixed elements [4.63-4.85].
However, most of the mathematical studies go through the extra step of
decomposing the higher-order differential operators (e.g., Laplace or
biharmonic operators) into lower-order ones, instead of using from the
start the "natural" lower-order operators associated with the fundamental equations of structural and solid mechanics.

Computational Aspects of Mixed Finite Elements

The efficiency of mixed finite elements and their effectiveness in
solving structural mechanics problems depend, among other things, on:

    1. The algorithm used for generating the element characteristic
arrays
    2. The technique for assembly and solution of the resulting
algebraic equations

For mixed models with a large number of degrees of freedom (e.g.,
shear-flexible shell elements with thirteen degrees of freedom at each
node), the element characteristic arrays need not be formed in full.
Rather, the submatrices representing nodal contributions are formed
and stored on disk files. Only a few of these submatrices need to
reside in central memory arrays at any one time during the assembly
process. For the convenience of the assembly process, each of the submatrices is stored as a separate record in the disk files. Large-size
problems can be handled by using the hypermatrix (or block matrix)
storage scheme [4.43]. This procedure is suitable for computers
with a random-access backing store such as a disk or drum.
    The global (structure) matrices are obtained by assembling the
nodal contributions from different elements. This is accomplished by
submatrix additions. An address (or pointer) matrix is used to identify
the location of nonzero submatrices in the global matrix (hypermatrix).
A zero entry in the address matrix denotes a zero submatrix which is
neither generated nor stored.
    The hypermatrix storage scheme combines the following advantages for
handling the large system of equations of the mixed method:

    1. Independence of the central memory requirements on the problem
type and size
    2. A controllable ratio between central processing unit (CPU)
time and data transfer (I/O) time
    3. High modularity of both program and data

The difficulties associated with the nondefinite character of the
resulting algebraic equations are overcome by assembling the force
parameters first, followed by the kinematic parameters (corresponding to

generating the constitutive equations for the whole structure followed
by the equilibrium equations). Gaussian elimination technique is then
used for the solution of the equations,and no reordering or pivoting will
be needed. However, the number of arithmetic operations and the storage
requirements in the solution process can be significantly larger than
those resulting from assembling the force and kinematic parameters at
each node. To remedy this drawback a nested dissection scheme is used.
The nested dissection scheme is an ordering strategy for the node numbers
which is closely related to multilevel substructuring (see Ref. [4.45]).
    The questions of numerical accuracy, stability,and conditioning of
the indefinite equations of the mixed method have not been adequately
studied. In particular, the effect of the nested dissection ordering
strategy on the numerical accuracy of solutions requires more
investigation. Reference [4.44] shows that for the case of curved
beams, appropriate nondimensionalization of the fundamental unknowns of
the mixed formulation can lead to considerable reduction in the condition
number of the resulting algebraic equations.

Advantages of Mixed Finite Elements

If the mixed finite element models are contrasted with displacement
of stress models, the following major advantages can be identified:

    1. Simplicity of element formulation
        a. Because the Euler-Lagrange equations of the mixed func-
           tionals are the more basic equations of structural
           mechanics with lower-order derivatives, the continuity
           requirements on the assumed fields are of lower order
           than for the conventional variational principles (viz.,
           principles of minimum potential energy and minimum
           complementary energy). This is particularly signifi-
           cant for thin plates and shells where only C^0
           continuity is required for the shape functions.
        b. The development of mixed models involves considerably
           fewer arithmetic operations than that of the displace-
           ment models based on the same polynomial approximation
           (see Refs. [4.43 and 4.45]). The element development
           can be further simplified by using group-theoretic
           methods in conjunction with computerized symbolic
           manipulation (see Ref. [4.43]). Moreover, for a number
           of linear problems (e.g., shear-flexible shallow
           shells), analytic expressions can be easily obtained
           for the generalized stiffness, load,and mass matrices
           of isoparametric elements, which is a unique feature
           of the mixed formulation.
    2. Balanced accuracy for stress and kinematic variables
    3. Insensitivity of the performance to variations in geometric and
material characteristics of the structure. Three examples can be cited
where the performance of mixed models was shown to be considerably less
sensitive to variations in the geometric and material characteristics of
the structure than that of displacement models [2.13]. The first is the
case of nearly incompressible materials where the mean (or volumetric)
strain is close to zero. The second example is the application of
shear-flexible plate (or shell) elements to analyze thin plates
(or shells) with negligible shear deformation. The third problem is

the use of shell elements, which do not include the rigid body modes explicitly, to analyze very thin shells with negligible extensional energy. For all three problems the displacement models encounter computational difficulties.

    4. Nonlinear algebraic equations of a lower order than those of the displacement formulation. For geometrically nonlinear problems, the resulting finite element equations of the mixed formulation contain bilinear and quadratic terms in the force and kinematic parameters. By contrast, the finite element equations of the displacement models are cubic in the nodal displacements.

Mixed Finite Difference Schemes

The finite difference method is one of the oldest numerical methods of solution of linear and nonlinear structural and solid mechanics problems. In the usual application of the mixed finite difference method, the derivatives in the governing differential equations are replaced by difference quotient expressions at each mesh point, yielding a set of simultaneous algebraic equations.

    An alternate approach for obtaining the finite difference equations consists of replacing the derivatives in the functional of any of the mixed variational principles by their difference quotient expressions and applying the stationary conditions to the discretized functional. Only few applications of this approach have been reported in the literature (see, for example, Refs. [5.3] and [5.19]). This is to be contrasted with its wide application for the derivation of the finite difference equations of the displacement models.

    The makeup of a mixed finite difference scheme involves the selection of the following four components:

    1. Fundamental unknowns of the problem
    2. Form of the governing differential equations or the functional of the variational principle used
    3. Mesh topology in particular, the control points for the different fundamental unknowns
    4. Difference-quotient expressions, or computational molecules, to be used at the interior as well as at the boundaries of the domain

    Within each of the categories of the component parts there is a variety of alternatives to choose from. The accuracy and computational efficiency of the finite difference scheme depends on the proper choice of the four components.

Improvement of Accuracy of Mixed Finite Difference Schemes

The discretization error of the finite difference solution can be reduced by reducing the size of the finite difference grid. In addition, several other alternatives exist which do not lead to substantial increases in the number of equations to be solved. Among these alternatives are:

    1. Employing higher-order difference formulas achieved by increasing the number of mesh points used to establish the approximate

expressions for the derivatives
    2. Using higher-order difference formulas at the boundaries
    3. Introducing a graded network in regions of rapid change
    4. Using difference-quotient expressions which include the
derivatives of the function in addition to the values of the function
at more than just the point under consideration (multilocal or
Hermitian difference methods)
    5. Using modified finite difference schemes wherein the odd-order
derivatives of each of the fundamental unknowns are defined at points
lying midway between the control points of the same function and its
even-order derivatives

    Modified finite difference schemes can be obtained by using sets of
interlacing grids for the different fundamental unknowns. Such schemes
provide effective discretization procedures for solid mechanics problems.
An example of the interlacing grids for isotropic shallow shells is shown
in Fig. 3, and a historical account of the development of modified
finite difference schemes is given in Ref. [1.5].

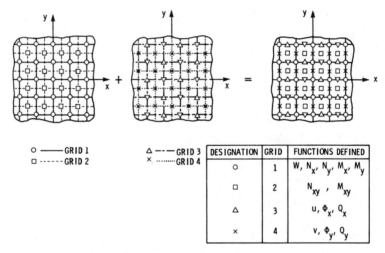

o ——— GRID 1	
□ ------ GRID 2	

△ —·— GRID 3	DESIGNATION	GRID	FUNCTIONS DEFINED
×· ········ GRID 4	o	1	W, N_x, N_y, M_x, M_y
	□	2	N_{xy}, M_{xy}
	△	3	u, Φ_x, Q_x
	×	4	v, Φ_y, Q_y

Fig. 3   Interlacing grids and control points of different fundamental
           unknowns used in modified finite differences. Isotropic
           shallow shells (see governing equations in Appendix I)

Mixed First-Order Equation Difference Schemes

Early applications of the mixed finite difference method were based
on the use of higher-order differential equations. Among these applications, mention may be made of the two fourth-order differential
equations in the transverse displacement and an Airy stress function
for the analysis of shallow shells [1.4, 5.17, and 5.18]. Budiansky
and Radkowski [5.11] presented a mixed finite difference scheme

for the analysis of shells of revolution based on the use of four
second-order equations in the three displacement components and the
meridional moment.

More recently, mixed finite difference schemes based on a first-
order equation formulation have attracted increasing attention. The
feasibility and practicality of using these difference schemes in the
solution of a broad spectrum of solid mechanics problems was demonstrated
by the present author and his colleagues in Refs. [5.9] and [5.11].

The work of Utku and Norris [1.13] can be considered as the
first attempt to apply the finite difference discretization to a large
number of simultaneous partial differential equations. In the cited
work, shell problems were formulated in terms of nineteen governing
equations with the field variables including generalized displacements,
strains, and stress resultants. However, the resulting algebraic
equations were manipulated to eliminate both the stress resultants
and strains.

Mileykovsky [5.4] presented a mixed finite difference model
based on the use of thirteen first-order partial differential equations
for the analysis of doubly curved shallow shells. References [5.2, 5.14,
5.15, and 5.16] show applications of mixed difference models to the solution of two-dimensional and three-dimensional dynamic problems of
isotropic solids.

In all the cited references, however, conventional lower-order finite
difference approximations were used, and consequently, the number of
simultaneous algebraic equations required for any reasonable accuracy
becomes quite large. More recently, mixed modified finite difference
models have been used by the author and his coworkers in a number of
applications including stress and free-vibration analysis of rotationally symmetric shells [5.11, 5.12, and 1.5], arbitrary cylindrical
shells [5.5, 5.7, and 5.8], Saint-Venant torsion of nonhomogeneous
anisotropic bars [5.6], laminated cylinders [5.9 and 5.13], thick
plates [5.10], and generalized plane stress and skew anisotropic
plates [5.11].

The importance of the proper choice of the fundamental unknowns,
selection of their points of definition, and the form of the governing
equations of the mixed models is emphasized in Refs. [5.9 and 5.11].
This is especially true in nonlinear problems where a total Lagrangian
formulation is used.

Mixed Multilocal (Hermitian) Difference Schemes

When using multilocal difference methods, difference expressions are
used which include the values of the derivatives appearing in the governing differential equations at more than one point in addition to the
values of the function. For the derivation of these multilocal expressions, Taylor's series expansion of the fundamental unknowns and of
their derivatives appearing in the governing differential equations,
at a suitably chosen set of neighboring points, is combined in such
a manner that all terms below a certain degree in the difference interval cancel out. This approach is referred to as Taylor's cancellation
method.

Multilocal differences lead to algebraic equations with a smaller
bandwidth than those of ordinary differences having the same order of
discretization error. Reported applications of mixed multilocal difference schemes include plate vibrations [5.21], stress analysis

of plates and cylindrical shells [5.22, 5.23, and 5.24], and stress
analysis of general shells [5.20]. References [5.25] and [5.26]
demonstrate the advantages of combining the multilocal schemes with
modified differences (based on using interlacing grids) for the stress
and free-vibration analysis of arbitrary cylindrical shells.

Dynamic Relaxation Technique

The essence of the dynamic relaxation technique is to replace the
static equilibrium equations of the discretized structure by the dynamic
equations of damped oscillations and then to apply an explicit central difference scheme for their integration. If the mass matrix is diagonal
(as is commonly the case when finite differences are used for the
spatial discretization), the equations are uncoupled. If a suitable
damping coefficient is introduced in the dynamic equations, the oscillations die out rapidly and a satisfactory steady-state (static)
solution to the problem is obtained in few steps.
    In most of the reported applications of the dynamic relaxation
technique, mixed finite difference schemes were used for the spatial
discretization. However, the applicability of the method is not dependent on the use of finite differences. The method has been used to
analyze a variety of problems including portal frames [5.28], pressure
vessels [5.31], and plates having geometric and material nonlinearities
[5.27, 5.29, 5.30, and 5.33].

Mixed Methods Based on Replacing the Boundary-Value
Problem by a Set of Initial-Value Problems

A variety of numerical solution techniques have been developed for
solving a broad class of boundary-value problems in structural mechanics
by converting these problems into sets of initial-value problems. Among
the techniques included in this category are:

1. The various numerical integration procedures
2. Matrix progression or transfer matrices
3. The method of initial functions

    The first step in the application of these techniques is to reduce
the governing differential equations of the two-point boundary value
problem to first-order differential equations. The fundamental unknowns
in these equations are chosen to be the force and kinematic parameters
which appear in the statement of the boundary conditions. Since all of
the aforementioned techniques use the mixed first-order ordinary differential equation formulation, they are limited to solving problems
which only require one-dimensional discretization. The class of structures which can be analyzed by these techniques includes one-dimensional
structures (e.g., beams and arches) as well as two- and three-dimensional
structures whose configuration and boundary conditions admit the use of
semianalytic techniques so that the governing equations can be reduced
to ordinary differential equations (e.g., shells of revolution with
arbitrary boundary conditions and cylindrical panels with simply
supported curved edges).
    Problems which cannot be reduced to a system of ordinary differ-
ential equations may sometimes be solved by combining one of the

aforementioned techniques with other numerical or approximate techniques
(e.g., finite differences) thereby reducing the governing equations to
coupled sets of ordinary differential equations (see, for example,
Refs. [6.13] and [6.27]).

The details of the application of the numerical integration procedures, the matrix progression technique, and the method of initial
functions to structural mechanics problems are not discussed here.
The interested reader is referred to the survey papers [6.9] and [6.22],
the two monographs [6.23] and [6.24], and to the other papers in the
list (Refs. [6.1-6.31]).

APPLICATIONS TO STRUCTURAL REANALYSIS
AND NONSTRUCTURAL PROBLEMS

Structural Reanalysis

The structure of the equations of the mixed method makes them well
suited for use with reanalysis techniques in automated optimum design
systems.

References [7.1] and [7.2] report on the application of the reanalysis technique, based on the Taylor series expansion of response
variables in terms of design variables to pin-jointed trusses. The
design variables were taken to be the cross-sectional areas of the members in Ref. [7.2] and the nodal coordinates in Ref. [7.1]. In both
cases, a two-term (first-order) truncated Taylor series provided highly
accurate approximations to the stresses and displacements, even when the
changes in design variables were as large as 50 percent.

Reference [4.43] discusses the potential for using mixed isoparametric shell elements with reanalysis techniques. However, no numerical
studies are presented.

Nonstructural Problems

In recent years increasing attention has been devoted to the application of the mixed, multiplied finite elements to nonstructural problems.
Among the successful applications, mention is made of potential flow
problems [8.2], Navier-Stokes equations [8.4], transient flow of
viscous imcompressible fluids [8.6], steady fluid and metal flow [8.5],
hydrocapillary vibrations [8.3], and transonic flutter [8.1].

In most of the cited references the method of weighted residuals
with a Galerkin or a least-square criterion was used for formulating
the finite element equations.

COMPUTER PROGRAMS BASED ON MIXED METHOD

Although considerable literature has been devoted to applications of
the mixed method to various structural and solid mechanics problems, most
of the programs developed for obtaining the reported solutions are research oriented and do not have the special facilities of general purpose
user-oriented programs. In this section a list of a number of programs
based on the mixed method is given. The information presented
herein is based on answers to questionnaires sent to several program

developers and organizations. The assistance of these individuals and organizations is gratefully acknowledged.

The general capabilities of the programs are summarized in Table 1. Also, abstracts of all the programs included in Table 1 are given in Appendix II.

Table 1   Survey of Computer Programs

Capability		Crack Analysis	DYGENIS	FARSS	FASOR	FESAPM	FORMAT	HYBOS	MIX	NAST	ROT B	STARS	WULFF
1. Types of Structures Analyzed													
Pin-jointed trusses		•					•			•			
Framed structures							•						
Plane membranes		•		•			•		•				
Membranes in space							•		•				
Shear panels							•						
Plates			•				•		•				
Thin shells			•			•			•				
Thick shells			•			•							
Shells of revolution					•					•	•	•	
Axisymmetric solids					•					•			
Three-dimensional solids													•
Crack-tip		•											
2. Range of Applications and Phenomena													
Linear elastostatics		•	•	•	•	•	•	•	•	•	•	•	•
Nonlinear statics	a) Large displacements, small strains	•		•	•	•			•	•		•	
	b) Large strains and plasticity										+	x	
Linear dynamics	a) Free vibrations	•	•	•	•	•	•					•	
	b) Transient response		•				•			•		Δ	
Nonlinear dynamics	a) Nonlinear vibrations											xx	
	b) Transient response									•		Δ	•
	c) Large strains and plasticity										+		•
Linear bifurcation buckling			•		•		•		•			•	

+ Nonlinear elasticity   x Small strains and plasticity
Δ Experimental version   xx Axisymmetric

Table 1   (Cont'd)

Capability	Crack Analysis	DYGENIS	FARSS	FASOR	FESAPM	FORMAT	HYBOS	MIX	NAST	ROT B	STARS	WULFF
3. Flexibility to handle varied loadings and boundary conditions												
Concentrated loads	•	•	•		•	•	•	•	•		•	
Line loads	•	•	•	•		•	•			•	•	
Surface loads	•	•	•	•	•	x	•	•		•	•	x
Initial stress, strain or velocities		•	•			•					•	•
Thermal loading		•	•			•	•				•	
Prescribed displacements	•	•	•	•	•	•	•					
Contact forces						•						
Frictional forces							•				•	
Elastic foundation						•	•				•	
4. Discretization Technique												
Finite elements — Full spatial discretization	•	•			•	•		•	•			•
Finite elements — Semianalytic	+		•								•	
Matrix progression or transfer matrices						xx			xx			
Numerical integration				•			•				•	Δ
5. Other Capabilities												
Substructuring	+		•			•					•	
Repeated use of identical substructures with different loads			•			•						
Automatic mesh, coordinate or load generation	++	++	•		•	•					++	•
Restart capability		•	•	•	•	•	•		•		•	•
Automatic renumbering of nodes, elements or equations			•	•	•	•						
6. Program Operational on												
CDC	•		•	•	•	•	•		•		•	•
IBM						•	•	•			•	
UNIVAC	•		•			•	•				•	
GE						•						
TELEFUNKEN			•							•	•	
ICL										•	•	

x Uniform pressure loading   + For crack tip element   xx Used for developing
Δ For temporal integration   ++ Semi-automatic   elemental matrices

Reference [9.5] describes a general purpose computer program which
can be used for mixed finite element analysis and for combined displace-
ment/force methods of analysis (wherein the force and kinematic variables
are mixed on the system level). The characteristics of this program are
not included in Table 1.

ASSETS AND LIABILITIES OF MIXED METHOD

The studies made of the different aspects of the mixed method have
identified the following two major advantages over single-field methods
(e.g., displacement or force methods):

1. Simplicity. This includes simplicity of:
    a. Formulation. This is particularly true when first-order
       differential equations or functionals containing all the
       fields of interest are used.
    b. Discretization,which follows from the simplicity of the
       form of the governing differential equations or the func-
       tional in the mixed variational principles. This makes
       the development of a mixed finite element (or the generation
       of mixed finite difference equations) more straight-
       forward than that of the displacement or stress formulations.
       As mentioned previously, mixed isoparametric elements have
       the unique feature that analytic expressions can be easily
       obtained for the linear "generalized" stiffness, load, and
       mass matrices. Moreover, the development of mixed models
       involves considerably fewer arithmetic operations than the
       displacement models based on the same polynomial
       approximation.
    c. Treatment of boundary, discontinuity, and interface
       conditions.
    d. The form of the governing equations, which
       provides flexibility for easily improving or modifying
       the discretization technique. For instance, in the case
       of finite elements, isoparametric, curved, and higher-order
       elements can be used; and in the case of finite differences,
       the use of any of the following improved techniques, or
       their combination, becomes feasible:
        i)   Interlacing grids with the different fundamental
             unknowns defined at different points (modified
             finite differences).
        ii) Variable and nonorthogonal grids.
        iii) Use of higher-order difference quotient expressions
             in the interior or at the boundary.
        iv) Use of multilocal (or Hermitian) difference method.
    e. The effort involved in the computer implementation (coding,
       debugging, and verifications), in view of the above-mentioned
       characteristics (a to c above), has been found to be signifi-
       cantly reduced.
2. Accuracy. This is especially true for stress predictions, and
in the presence of steep gradients or singularities. Also, since both
stress and displacement parameters are chosen as the fundamental unknowns,
all the quantities of interest are readily available upon solving the
problem. In the case of finite difference discretization of the first-
order equation formulation, the following two points are noteworthy:

    a. The derivatives of the elastic characteristics of the medium
         are absent, and therefore, no numerical approximation for
         such derivatives is needed.
    b. The statement of the boundary, discontinuity, and interface
         conditions involves linear combinations of the fundamental
         unknowns, but not their derivatives (Dirichlet type
         conditions).

While there are a number of advantages in using mixed finite differences and mixed finite elements, three major difficulties arise:

    1. The first results from the increase in the number of degrees of freedom used in the mixed method. This results in a substantial increase in the size of the elemental matrices and the number of simultaneous equations as compared with the stiffness method.
    2. The second difficulty is due to the nondefiniteness of the matrix of resulting algebraic equations. Since these equations are not positive definite, some efficient algorithms used with the displacement models cannot be applied.
    3. The third difficulty results from the use of mixed variational principles. Since these principles are stationary and not extremum principles, a bound on the numerical solution cannot be obtained.

The first two difficulties can be greatly alleviated (or possibly nullified) by using the computational procedure described in the section on computational aspects of mixed finite elements.
The third difficulty is not a practical one although bounds on the solution can be a nice feature to have in a numerical procedure.

FUTURE DIRECTIONS FOR RESEARCH

Several different aspects of the mixed method appear to have high potential for research.

Use of Reduction Methods in Conjunction with the Mixed Formulation for Nonlinear Analysis

In reduction methods, an attempt is made to reduce the total number of degrees of freedom of the discretized problem without sacrificing the accuracy. A possible approach for applying reduction methods in conjunction with the mixed formulation is to use finite elements (or finite differences) for the initial discretization, resulting in a large system of nonlinear algebraic equations with the unknowns being stress and kinematic parameters. The vector of these unknowns is then expressed as a linear combination of a small number of basis vectors. A Rayleigh-Ritz (or Galerkin) technique is used to approximate the finite element (or finite difference) equations by a reduced system of nonlinear algebraic equations. The basis vectors can be chosen to be those commonly used in the static perturbation technique; namely, a nonlinear solution and a number of its path derivatives for static problems (or a nonlinear solution and a number of its time derivatives for dynamic problems). The effectiveness of this set of basis vectors for nonlinear static analysis has been demonstrated in Refs. [1.6] and [1.7] where a displacement formulation was used.

Mixed Method in Structural Reanalysis

The high potential of using the mixed method with reanalysis techniques in the optimum design of complex structures has already been
recognized [4.43]. However, computational algorithms need to be
developed to realize this potential for the case when the design
variables include configuration parameters (such as nodal coordinates).

Application of Mixed Method to Nonlinear
Dynamic Analysis of Structures

The use of explicit temporal integration schemes in conjunction with
the mixed method appear to have high potential for the dynamic analysis
of structures with combined geometric and material nonlinearities. The
fundamental unknowns consist of stresses, displacements, and velocity
components. The governing equations consist of the three separate sets
of equations:

1. Constitutive relations
2. Equations of motion
3. Relations between velocity and displacement components

The effectiveness of using this approach for the dynamic analysis of
truss structures with combined geometric and material nonlinearities has
been demonstrated [3.10]. Also, preliminary results by the
author and his coworkers show that when the finite element method is
used for the spatial discretization, the aforementioned equations can
be uncoupled by lumping both the masses and flexibilities of the
individual elements. This can be accomplished by using the procedure
presented in Ref. [1.3] for lumping the masses in the displacement
formulation.

Implementation of Mixed Method in General
Purpose Finite Element Codes

In spite of the documented advantages of the mixed method, it has
not been widely used in general purpose finite element systems as yet.
In order to achieve this, the following developments are needed:

1. Automatic treatment of the interfaces between elements of
different types and dimensionality
2. Reduction in the number of equations required for the analysis
3. Identification of stress boundary conditions to be used in
various situations
4. A study of the numerical accuracy, stability,and conditioning
of the indefinite equations of the mixed method

CONCLUDING REMARKS

The status of and recent developments in the mixed method of analysis and
its application to structural and solid mechanics problems have been
summarized. A number of aspects of the mixed method are considered
herein including: different levels of mixing the variables; mixed

variational principles; analysis procedures based on the mixed method; and computational aspects. The major advantages and drawbacks of the mixed method of analysis are outlined and a number of aspects of the mixed method which have high potential for research are identified.

REFERENCES

General

1.1 Atluri, S. N., and Murakawa, H., "On Hybrid Finite Element Models in Nonlinear Solid Mechanics," in Finite Elements in Nonlinear Mechanics, ed. P. G. Bergan et al., Tapir Press, Norwegian Institute of Technology, Trondheim, Vol. 1, 1978, pp. 3-41.

1.2 Gvozdev, A. A., "General Method of Analysis of Complex Statically Indeterminate Systems," Moskovski Institut Inzhenerno Zhelezno-Dorozhni Transport, 1927 (Russian).

1.3 Hinton, E., Rock, T., and Zienkiewicz, O. C., "A Note on Mass Lumping and Related Processes in the Finite Element Method," Earthquake Engineering and Structural Dynamics, Vol. 4, 1976, pp. 245-49.

1.4 Noor, A. K., and Veletsos, A. S., "A Study of Doubly-Curved Shallow Shells," University of Illinois, SRS Report No. 274, Nov. 1963.

1.5 Noor, A. K., and Schnobrich, W. C., "On Improved Finite-Difference Discretization Procedures," Variational Methods in Engineering, ed. C. A. Brebbia and H. Tottenham, Southampton University Press, Vol. 2, 1973, pp. 12/1-50.

1.6 Noor, A. K., and Peters, J. M., "Reduced Basis Technique for Nonlinear Analysis of Structures," Proceedings of the AIAA/ASME/ASCE/AHS 20th Structures, Structural Dynamics and Materials Conference, St. Louis, Mo., April 4-6, 1979, pp. 116-26.

1.7 Noor, A. K., Andersen, C. M., and Peters, J. M., "Global-Local Approach for Nonlinear Shell Analysis," Proceedings of the Seventh ASCE Conference on Electronic Computation, Washington University, St. Louis, Mo., Aug. 6-8, 1979.

1.8 Pian, T. H. H., "Hybrid Models," Numerical and Computer Methods in Structural Mechanics, ed. S. J. Fenves et al., Academic Press, New York, 1971, pp. 59-78.

1.9 Rabinovich, I. M., Method of Analysis of Frames, Vols. 1, 2 and 3 , Gosstroiizdat, Moscow, 1931-37   (Russian).

1.10 Reissner, E., "Variational Methods and Boundary Conditions in Shell Theory,"   Studies in Optimization, Proceedings of the Symposium on Optimization, Vol. 1, Society of Industrial and Applied Mathematics, Philadelphia, Pa., 1970, pp. 78-94.

1.11 Timoshenko, S., and Woinowsky-Krieger, S., Theory of Plates and Shells, McGraw-Hill, New York, 1959.

1.12 Truesdell, C., and Toupin, R., "The Classical Field Theories," Encyclopedia of Physics, ed. S. Flugge, Vol. 3/1, Springer, Berlin, 1960.

1.13 Utku, S., and Norris, C. H., "Utilization of Digital Computers in the Analysis of Thin Shells," Paper No. 27, Symposium on the Use of Computers in Civil Engineering, Lisbon, Portugal, Oct. 1962.

1.14 Von Karman, Th., "Festigkeitsprobleme im Maschinenbau," Encyklopadie der Mathematischen Wissenschaften, Vol. 4, 1910, pp. 348-51 (German).

        1.15 Vlasov, V. Z., "General Theory of Shells and Its Application to
Engineering," Moscow-Leningrad, 1949 (Russian), NASA Technical Translation,
NASA TT-F-99 (1964).
        1.16 Washizu, K., Variational Methods in Elasticity and Plasticity,
2nd ed., Pergamon Press, Oxford, 1975.

                            Mixed Variational Principles and
                               Direct Variational Methods

Mixed Variational Principles

        2.1 Barr, A. D. S., "An Extension of the Hu-Washizu Variational
Principle in Linear Elasticity for Dynamic Problems," Journal of Applied
Mechanics, Vol. 33, No. 2, June 1966, p. 465.
        2.2 Elias, Z. M., "Mixed Variational Principles for Shells," in
Variational Methods in Engineering, ed. C. A. Brebbia and H. Tottenham,
Southampton University Press, 1973, pp. 3/33-45.
        2.3 Fraeijs de Veubeke, B. M., "Displacement and Equilibrium Models
in the Finite Element Method," Stress Analysis, ed. O. C. Zienkiewicz
and G. S. Holister, Wiley, London, 1965, pp. 145-97.
        2.4 Herrmann, L. R., "Elasticity Equations for Incompressible and
Nearly Incompressible Materials by a Variational Theorem," AIAA Journal,
Vol. 3, 1965, pp. 1896-1900.
        2.5 Hellinger, E., "Der Allgemeine Ansatz der Mechanik der Kontinua,"
Encyclopadie der Mathematischen Wissenschaften, Vol. 4, Part 4, 1914,
pp. 602-94.
        2.6 Horrigmoe, G., and Bergan, P. G., "Incremental Variational
Principles and Finite Element Models for Nonlinear Problems," Computer
Methods in Applied Mechanics and Engineering, Vol. 7, No. 2, 1976,
pp. 201-17.
        2.7 Hu, Hai-Chang, "On Some Variational Principles in the Theory of
Elasticity and Theory of Plasticity," Scientia Sinica, Vol. 4, 1955,
pp. 33-54.
        2.8 Key, S. W., "A Variational Principle for Incompressible and
Nearly Incompressible Anisotropic Elasticity," International Journal of
Solids and Structures, Vol. 5, 1969, pp. 824-26.
        2.9 Lee, K. N., and Nemat-Nasser, S., "Mixed Variational Principles,
Finite Elements, and Finite Elasticity," Computational Methods in
Nonlinear Mechanics, ed. J. T. Oden et al., The Texas Institute for
Computational Mechanics, Austin, Texas, 1974, pp. 637-49.
        2.10 Naghdi, P. M., "On a Variational Theory in Elasticity and Its
Application to Shell Theory," Journal of Applied Mechanics, Vol. 31,
1964, pp. 647-53.
        2.11 Nemat-Nasser, S., "General Variational Principles in Nonlinear
and Linear Elasticity with Applications," Mechanics Today, Vol. 1, Per-
gamon Press, 1972, pp. 241-61.
        2.12 Pian, T. H. H., "Variational Principles for Incremental Finite
Element Methods," Journal of the Franklin Institute, Vol. 302, Nos. 5
and 6, Nov./Dec. 1976, pp. 473-88.
        2.13 Pian, T. H. H., and Tong, P., "Reissner's Principle in Finite
Element Formulations," to appear in Mechanics Today, Vol. 6, Pergamon
Press.

2.14 Prager, W., "Variational Principles of Linear Elastostatics for Discontinuous Displacements, Strains, and Stresses," Recent Progress in Applied Mechanics, the Folke-Odqvist Volume, ed. B. Broberg, J. Hult, and F. Niordson, Stockholm, 1967, pp. 463-74.

2.15 Prager, W., "Variational Principles for Elastic Plates with Relaxed Continuity Requirements," International Journal of Solids and Structures, Vol. 4, 1968, pp. 837-44.

2.16 Prange, D., "Die Theorie des Balkens in der Technischen Elastizitätslehre," Zeitschrift für Architektur und Ingenieurwesen, Vol. 65, No. 24, 1919, pp. 83-96 and 121-150.

2.17 Reddy, J. N., "A Note on Mixed Variational Principles for Initial Value Problems," Quarterly Journal of Mechanics and Applied Mathematics, Vol. 28, Part 1, February 1975, pp. 123-32.

2.18 Reissner, E., "On a Variational Theorem in Elasticity," Journal of Mathematics and Physics, Vol. 29, 1950, pp. 90-95.

2.19 Reissner, E., "On a Variational Theorem for Finite Element Deformations," Journal of Mathematics and Physics, Vol. 32, Nos. 2-3, July-Oct. 1953, pp. 129-35.

2.20 Reissner, E., "On the Form of Variationally Derived Shell Equations," Journal of Applied Mechanics, ASME, Vol. 31, June 1964, pp. 233-38.

2.21 Sandhu, R. S., and Pister, K. S., "Variational Principles for Boundary Value and Initial-Boundary Value Problems in Continuum Mechanics," International Journal of Solids and Structures, Vol. 7, 1971, pp. 639-54.

2.22 Sandhu, R. S., and Pister, K. S., "Variational Principles for Plate Bending - A Unified Approach," Variational Methods in Engineering, ed. C. A. Brebbia and H. Tottenham, Southampton University Press, Vol. 1, 1973, pp. 2/68-80.

2.23 Taylor, R. L., Pister, K. S., and Herrmann, L. R., "On a Variational Theorem for Incompressible and Nearly-Incompressible Orthotropic Elasticity," International Journal of Solids and Structures, Vol. 4, 1968, pp. 875-83.

2.24 Tonti, E., "Variational Principles in Elastostatics," Meccanica, Vol. 2, Dec. 1967, pp. 201-8.

2.25 Wunderlich, W., "Incremental Formulation of the Generalized Variational Approach in Structural Mechanics," Variational Methods in Engineering, ed. C. A. Brebbia and H. Tottenham, Southampton University Press, 1973, pp. 7/109-23.

2.26 Wunderlich, W., "Incremental Formulations for Geometrically Nonlinear Problems," Formulations and Computational Algorithms in Finite Element Analysis: U.S.-Germany Symposium, ed. K. J. Bathe, J. T. Oden, and W. Wunderlich, M.I.T. Press, Cambridge, Mass. 1977, pp. 193-240.

Direct Variational Methods

2.27 Chen, M. M., and Foss, K. A., "On Some Solutions for Large Deflections of Heated Strips and Plates, " Proceedings of the Fourth Midwestern Conference on Solid Mechanics, Austin, Texas, Sept. 1959, University of Texas Press, pp. 207-32.

2.28 Plass, H. J., Jr., Gaines, H. H., and Newsom, C. D., "Application of Reissner's Variational Principle to Cantilever Plate Deflection and Vibration Problems," Journal of Applied Mechanics, Vol. 29, March 1962, pp. 127-35.

2.29 Mayers, J., and Nelson, E., "Elastic and Maximum Strength
Analyses of Post-Buckled Rectangular Plates Based upon Modified Versions
of Reissner's Variational Principle," USAAVLABS Technical Report 69-64,
U.S. Army Aviation Material Laboratories, Fort Eustis, Virginia, July
1970; also AIAA Paper 68-171, New York, Jan. 1968.
  2.30 Stroud, R. C., and Mayers, J., "Dynamic Response of Rapidly
Heated Plate Elements," AIAA Journal, Vol. 9, No. 1, Jan. 1971, pp. 76-83.
  2.31 Wunderlich, W., "A Method for the Analysis of Thick Elastic
Shells and Comparisons between Various Approximations for the Shells,"
Proceedings of the International Colloquium on Progress of Shell Structures
in the Last Ten Years and Its Future Development, Madrid, Sept.-Oct.
1969, Vol. 4.

Analysis of Pin-Jointed Trusses and
Framed and Skin Type Structures

  3.1 Klein, B., "A Simple Method of Matric Structural Analysis,"
Journal of the Aeronautical Sciences, Vol. 24, No. 1, Jan. 1957, pp. 39-46.
  3.2 Klein, B., "A Simple Method of Matric Structural Analysis:
Part II - Effects of Taper and a Consideration of Curvature," Journal of
the Aeronautical Sciences, Vol. 24, No. 11, Nov. 1957, pp. 813-20.
  3.3 Klein, B., "A Simple Method of Matric Structural Analysis,
Part III - Analysis of Flexible Frames and Stiffened Cylindrical Shells,"
Journal of the Aeronautical Sciences, Vol. 25, No. 6, June 1958,
pp. 385-94.
  3.4 Klein, B., "A Simple Method of Matric Structural Analysis:
Part IV - Nonlinear Problems," Journal of the Aerospace Sciences,
Vol. 26, No. 6, June 1959, pp. 351-59.
  3.5 Klein, B., and Chirico, M., "New Methods in Matric Structural
Analysis," Proceedings of the Second Conference on Electronic Computation,
held in Pittsburgh, Pa., Sept. 8-10, 1960, pp. 213-23.
  3.6 Klein, B., "A Simple Method of Matric Structural Analysis:
Part V - Structures Containing Plate Elements of Arbitrary Shape and
Thickness," Journal of the Aerospace Sciences, Vol. 27, No. 11, Nov.
1960, pp. 859-66.
  3.7 Klein, B., "Application of a New Matric Method to Vibration
Analysis of Structures," Journal of the Aerospace Sciences, Vol. 29,
March 1962, pp. 350-51.
  3.8 Klein, B., "Use of Special Coordinates to Simplify Matric
Structural Analysis," Journal of the Aerospace Sciences, Vol. 29, No. 9,
1962, p. 1127.
  3.9 Noor, A. K., "Nonlinear Analysis of Space Trusses," Journal
of the Structural Division, ASCE, Vol. 100, No. ST3, March 1974,
pp. 533-46.
  3.10 Noor, A. K., and Peters, J. M., "Nonlinear Dynamic Analysis of
Space Trusses," to appear in Computer Methods in Applied Mechanics and
Engineering.
  3.11 Wiberg, N. E., "Diacoptics and Codiacoptics - Two Dual Mixed
Methods for Analyzing Elastic Structures," Report 67:8, Chalmers
University of Technology, Göteborg, 1967.
  3.12 Wiberg, N. E., "Matrix Structural Analysis with Mixed
Variables," International Journal for Numerical Methods in Engineering,
Vol. 8, 1974, pp. 167-94.

3.13 Wiberg, N. E., "System Analysis in Structural Mechanics by Use of Mixed Force and Displacement Variables," Dissertation No. 105, Chalmers University of Technology, Göteborg, 1970.

Mixed Finite Elements

Variational Based

4.1 Abbas, S. F., "Dynamic Analysis of Shallow Shells Using Finite Element Mixed Models," Ph.D. Thesis, University of Toronto, Canada, 1975.

4.2 Allman, D. J., "Finite Element Analysis of Plate Buckling Using a Mixed Variational Principle," Proceedings of the Third Conference on Matrix Methods in Structural Mechanics, held at Wright-Patterson Air Force Base, Ohio, Oct. 1971, Report AFFDL TR-71-160, pp. 683-705.

4.3 Altman, W., and Venancio-Filho, F., "Stability of Plates Using a Mixed Finite Element Formulation," Computers and Structures, Vol. 4, No. 2, March 1974, pp. 437-43.

4.4 Altman, W., and Iguti, F., "A Thin Cylindrical Shell Finite Element Based on a Mixed Formulation," Computers and Structures, Vol. 6, No. 2, 1976, pp. 149-55.

4.5 Altman, W., and Bismarck-Nasr, M. N., "Vibration of Thin Cylindrical Shells Based on a Mixed Finite Element Formulation," Computers and Structures, Vol. 8, 1978, pp. 217-21.

4.6 Ando, Y., Yagawa, G., Kikuchi, F., Iida, K., and Kawai, T., "On the Application of Mixed Finite Element Methods to the Stress Concentration Problems of Cylindrical Shells with a Circular Cutout or a Crack," Bulletin of the Japan Society of Mechanical Engineers, Vol. 15, 1972, pp. 647-56.

4.7 Astafev, V. I., "Application of Mixed Finite Element Technique to the Solution of Plate Bending Problems," Moskovskii Gosudarstvennyi Universitet, Institut Mekhaniki, Nauchnye Trudy, No. 37, 1975, pp. 9-14 (Russian).

4.8 Backlund, J., "Mixed Finite Element Analysis of Plates in Bending, Small Deflection Theory of Elastic and Elasto-Plastic Plates," Department of Structural Mechanics, Chalmers University of Technology, Göteborg, 1971.

4.9 Backlund, J., "Mixed Finite Element Analysis of Elasto-Plastic Plates in Bending," Archiwum Mechaniki Stowsowanej, Vol. 24, No. 3, 1972, pp. 319-35.

4.10 Barony, S. Y., and Tottenham, H., "The Analysis of Rotational Shells Using a Curved Ring Element and the Mixed Variational Formulation," International Journal for Numerical Methods in Engineering, Vol. 10, 1976, pp. 861-72.

4.11 Bercovier, M., "Finite Elements for Incompressible or Nearly-Incompressible Materials," Proceedings of the ADINA Conference, Massachusetts Institute of Technology, Cambridge, Mass., Aug. 1977, pp. 384-400.

4.12 Biffle, J. H., and Key, S. W., "Finite Element Formulations for Transient Dynamic Problems in Solids Using Explicit Time Integration," Computer Methods in Applied Mechanics and Engineering, Vol. 12, 1977, pp. 323-36.

4.13 Bron, J., and Dhatt, G., "Mixed Quadrilateral Elements for Bending," AIAA Journal, Vol. 10, No. 10, Oct. 1972, pp. 1359-61.

4.14 Casciaro, R., and DiCarlo, A., "Mixed Finite Element Models in Limit Analysis," Proceedings of the International Conference on Computational Methods in Nonlinear Mechanics, University of Texas, Austin, Sept. 23-25, 1974, pp. 171-81.

4.15 Chan, A. S. L., and Trbojevic, V. M., "Thin Shell Finite Element by the Mixed Method Formulation - Part 1," Computer Methods in Applied Mechanics and Engineering, Vol. 9, 1976, pp. 337-67.

4.16 Chan, A. S. L., and Trbojevic, V. M., "Thin Shell Finite Element by the Mixed Method Formulation - Parts 2 and 3," Computer Methods in Applied Mechanics and Engineering, Vol. 10, 1977, pp. 75-103.

4.17 Connor, J., and Will, D., "A Mixed Finite Element Shallow Shell Formulation," in Recent Advances in Matrix Methods of Structural Analysis and Design, ed. R. H. Gallagher, Y. Yamada, and J. T. Oden, The University of Alabama Press, 1971, pp. 105-37.

4.18 Connor, J., "Mixed Models for Plates," Proceedings of Seminar on Finite Element Techniques in Structural Mechanics, University of Southampton, ed. H. Tottenham and C. Brebbia, Stress Analysis Publishers, Southhampton, England, 1970, pp. 125-51.

4.19 Cook, R. D., "Eigenvalue Problems with a Mixed Plate Element," AIAA Journal, Vol. 7, No. 5, 1969, pp. 982-83.

4.20 Dunham, R. S., and Pister, K. S., "A Finite Element Application of the Hellinger-Reissner Variational Theorem," Proceedings of the Second Conference on Matrix Methods in Structural Mechanics, Wright-Patterson Air Force Base, Ohio, 1968, pp. 471-87.

4.21 Eatock-Taylor, W. R., "Discrete Element Analysis of Shells," Ph.D. Thesis, Stanford University, California, Aug. 1968.

4.22 Elias, Z. M., "Mixed Finite Element Method for Axisymmetric Shells," International Journal for Numerical Methods in Engineering, Vol. 4, No. 2, 1972, pp. 261-77.

4.23 Gass, N., and Tabarrok, B., "Large Deformation Analysis of Plates and Cylindrical Shells by a Mixed Finite Element Method," International Journal for Numerical Methods in Engineering, Vol. 10, 1976, pp. 731-46.

4.24 Gellert, M., and Laursen, M. E., "Formulation and Convergence of a Mixed Finite Element Method Applied to Elastic Arches of Arbitrary Geometry and Loading," Computer Methods in Applied Mechanics and Engineering, Vol. 7, 1976, pp. 285-302.

4.25 Gould, P. L., and Sen, S. K., "Refined Mixed Method Finite Elements for Shells of Revolution," Proceedings of the Third Conference on Matrix Methods in Structural Mechanics, held at Wright-Patterson Air Force Base, Ohio, Oct. 1971, Report AFFDL TR-71-160, pp. 397-422.

4.26 Gould, P. L., "Condensation for Mixed Dynamic FE Analysis of Rotational Shells," in Trends in Computerized Structural Analysis and Synthesis, ed. A. K. Noor and H. G. McComb, Jr., Pergamon Press, 1978, pp. 251-53.

4.27 Harbord, R., "Computation of Shells with Finite Displacements: Mixed Finite Elements," Institut für Statik, Technische Universität Braunschweig, West Germany, Report No. REPT-72-7, 1973 (German).

4.28 Harbord, R., Kroplin, B., and Schroder, R., "Shell Elements in Mixed Representation - Theory, Criticism, Examples," Ingenieur-Archiv, Vol. 47, No. 4, 1978, pp. 207-22 (German).

4.29 Herrmann, L. R., "A Bending Analysis for Plates," Proceedings of the First Conference on Matrix Methods in Structural Mechanics, Wright-Patterson Air Force Base, Ohio, 1965, pp. 577-604.

4.30 Herrmann, L. R., "Finite Element Bending Analysis for Plates," Journal of the Engineering Mechanics Division, ASCE, Vol. 93, No. EM5, Oct. 1967, pp. 13-26.

4.31 Herrmann, L. R., and Campbell, D. M., "A Finite Element Analysis for Thin Shells," AIAA Journal, Vol. 6, No. 10, Oct. 1968, pp. 1842-47.

4.32 Herrmann, L. R., and Mason, W. E., "Mixed Formulations for Finite Element Shell Analysis," Conference on Computer-Oriented Analysis of Shell Structures, Report No. AFFDL TR-71-79, June 1971, pp. 290-336.

4.33 Horrigmoe, G., "Nonlinear Finite Element Models in Solid Mechanics," Division of Structural Mechanics, The Norwegian Institute of Technology, The University of Trondheim, Norway, Report No. 76-2, Aug. 1976.

4.34 Kawamata, S., Magara, E., and Kunita, J., "Analysis of Cable Nets in Mixed Formulation," Theory and Practice in Finite Element Structural Analysis, ed. Y. Yamada and R. G. Gallagher, Proceedings of the 1973 Tokyo Seminar on Finite Element Analysis, pp. 157-75.

4.35 Kikuchi, T., and Ando, Y., "Rectangular Finite Element for Plate Bending Analysis Based on Hellinger-Reissner's Variational Principle," Journal of Nuclear Science and Technology, Vol. 9, 1972, pp. 28-35.

4.36 Lee, S. W., and Pian, T. H. H., "Improvement of Plate and Shell Finite Elements by Mixed Formulations," AIAA Journal, Vol. 16, 1978, pp. 29-34.

4.37 Malkus, D. S., and Hughes, T. J. R., "Mixed Finite Element Methods - Reduced and Selective Integration Techniques - A Unification of Concepts," Computer Methods in Applied Mechanics and Engineering, Vol. 15, July 1978, pp. 63-81.

4.38 Miyoshi, T., "A Mixed Finite Element Method for the Solution of the von Karman Equations," Numerical Mathematics, Vol. 26, 1976, pp. 255-69.

4.39 Nemat-Nasser, S., and Lee, K. N., "Application of General Variational Methods with Discontinuous Fields to Bending, Buckling, and Vibration of Beams," Computer Methods in Applied Mechanics and Engineering, Vol. 2, 1973, pp. 33-41.

4.40 Nemat-Nasser, S., and Lee, K. N., "Finite Element Formulations for Elastic Plates by General Variational Statements with Discontinuous Fields," in Developments in Mechanics, Vol. 7, Proceedings of the Thirteenth Midwestern Mechanics Conference, 1973, pp. 979-95.

4.41 Newsom, C. D., "Finite Element Formulation of Mixed and Stress Variational Principles for Structural Dynamic Analysis," Ph.D. Thesis, The University of Texas, Austin, 1972.

4.42 Noor, A. K., and Andersen, C. M., "Mixed Isoparametric Elements for Saint-Venant Torsion," Computer Methods in Applied Mechanics and Engineering, Vol. 6, 1975, pp. 195-218.

4.43 Noor, A. K., and Andersen, C. M., "Mixed Isoparametric Finite Element Models of Laminated Composite Shells," Computer Methods in Applied Mechanics and Engineering, Vol. 11, 1977, pp. 255-80.

4.44 Noor, A. K., Greene, W. H., and Hartley, S. J., "Nonlinear Finite Element Analysis of Curved Beams," Computer Methods in Applied Mechanics and Engineering, Vol. 12, 1977, pp. 289-307.

4.45 Noor, A. K., and Hartley, S. J., "Nonlinear Shell Analysis via Mixed Isoparametric Elements," Computers and Structures, Vol. 7, No. 5, Oct. 1977, pp. 615-26.

4.46 Olson, M. D., and Mirza, F. A., "A Mixed Finite Element Method for Calculating Stress Intensity Factors," Numerical Methods in Fracture Mechanics, ed. A. R. Luxmore, and D. R. J. Owen, University College of Swansea, 1978, pp. 798-803.

4.47 Poceski, A., "A Mixed Finite Element Method for Bending of Plates," International Journal for Numerical Methods in Engineering, Vol. 9, 1975, pp. 3-15.

4.48 Prato, C. A., "A Mixed Finite Element for Thin Shell Analysis," Sc.D. Dissertation, Massachusetts Institute of Technology, 1968.

4.49 Prato, C. A., "Shell Finite Element Method via Reissner's Principle," International Journal of Solids and Structures, Vol. 5, 1969, pp. 1119-33.

4.50 Reddy, J. N., and Stricklin, J. D., "Large Deflection and Large Amplitude Free Vibrations of Thin Rectangular Plates Using Mixed Isoparametric Elements," Proceedings of Symposium on Applications of Computer Methods in Engineering, Los Angeles, California, Aug. 23-26, 1977, Vol. 2, University of Southern California, Los Angeles, 1978, pp. 1323-35.

4.51 Sander, G., and Carnoy, E., "Equilibrium and Mixed Formulations in Stability Analysis Plate Bending Finite Element Derivation Using Variational Principle," Proceedings of the International Conference on Finite Elements in Nonlinear Solid and Structural Mechanics, Aug. 29-Sept. 1, 1977, Geilo, Norway, Vol. 1, pp. 87-108.

4.52 Scharnhorst, T., and Pian, T. H. H., "Finite Element Analysis of Rubber-Like Materials by a Mixed Model," International Journal for Numerical Methods in Engineering, Vol. 12, 1978, pp. 665-76.

4.53 Sodhi, D. S., "Mixed Finite Element Method for Vibration Analysis of Shallow Shells," Proceedings of the Fourth Canadian Congress of Applied Mechanics, EC. Polytech., Montreal, Canada, May 28-June 1, 1973, pp. 527-28.

4.54 Tahiani, C., "Analysis of Geometrically Nonlinear Thin Shells by Mixed Elements," D.Sc. Thesis, Laval University, Quebec, Canada, Aug. 1971 (French).

4.55 Talaslidis, D., and Wunderlich, W., "Static and Dynamic Analysis of Kirchhoff Shells Based on a Mixed Finite Element Formulation," Trends in Computerized Structural Analysis and Synthesis, ed. A. K. Noor and H. G. McComb, Jr., Pergamon Press, 1978, pp. 239-49.

4.56 Tottenham, H., and Barony, S. Y., "Mixed Finite Element Formulation for Geometrically Nonlinear Analysis of Shells of Revolution," International Journal for Numerical Methods in Engineering, Vol. 12, 1978, pp. 195-201.

4.57 Visser, W., "A Refined Mixed-Type Plate Bending Element," AIAA Journal, Vol. 7, No. 9, Sept. 1969, pp. 1801-3.

4.58 Visser, W., "The Application of a Curved Mixed-Type Shell Element," IUTAM Symposium on High Speed Computing of Elastic Structures, Liege, Belgium, Aug. 1970, Vol. 1, pp. 321-56.

Weighted Residual

4.59 Chatterjee, A., and Setlur, A. V., "A Mixed Finite Element Formulation for Plate Problems," International Journal for Numerical Methods in Engineering, Vol. 4, 1972, pp. 67-84.

4.60 Rossow, M. P., "The Least-Squares Variational Principle for Finite Element Applications," Journal of Applied Mechanics, Dec. 1975, pp. 900-901.

4.61 Salaam, U., and Sandhu, R. S., "A Finite Element Galerkin Formulation and Its Numerical Performance," International Journal for Numerical Methods in Engineering, Vol. 10, 1976, pp. 1077-95.

4.62 Zienkiewicz, O. C., Owen, D. R. J., and Lee, K. N., "Least Square Finite Element for Elasto-Static Problems - Use of 'Reduced' Integration," International Journal for Numerical Methods in Engineering, Vol. 8, 1974, pp. 341-58.

Mathematical Aspects

4.63 Babuska, I., Oden, J. T., and Lee, J. K., "Mixed-Hybrid Finite Element Approximations of Second-Order Elliptic Boundary-Value Problems," Computer Methods in Applied Mechanics and Engineering, Vol. 11, 1977, pp. 175-206.

4.64 Bhandari, D. R., and Oden, J. T., "General Mixed Finite Element Methods of Nonlinear Continua," Zeitschrift für Angewandte Mathematik und Mechanik, Vol. 53, 1973, pp. 441-51.

4.65 Brezzi, F., Johnson, C., and Mercier, B., "Analysis of a Mixed Finite Element Method for Elasto-Plastic Plates," Mathematics of Computation, Vol. 31, No. 140, Oct. 1977, pp. 809-17.

4.66 Ciarlet, P. G., and Raviart, P. A., "A Mixed Finite Element Method for the Biharmonic Equation," Mathematical Aspects of Finite Elements in Partial Differential Equations, ed. C. de Boor, Academic Press, New York, 1974, pp. 125-45.

4.67 Johnson, C., "On the Convergence of a Mixed Finite Element Method for Plate Bending Problems," Numerische Mathematik, Vol. 21, 1973, pp. 43-62.

4.68 Kikuchi, F., and Ando, Y., "On the Convergence of a Mixed Finite Element Scheme for Plate Bending," Nuclear Engineering Design, Vol. 24, No. 3, 1973, pp. 357-73.

4.69 Mercier, B., "Numerical Solution of the Biharmonic Problem by Mixed Finite Element of Class C^0," Report Laboratorio di Analisi Numerical Del C.N.R., Pavia, 1973.

4.70 Mirza, F. A., "Convergence of Mixed Methods in Continuum Mechanics and Finite Element Analysis," Ph.D. Thesis, University of British Columbia, Canada, 1977.

4.71 Miyoshi, T., "Finite Element Method of Mixed Type and Its Convergence in Linear Shell Problems," Kumamoto Journal of Science (Mathematics), Vol. 10, 1973, pp. 35-8.

4.72 Oden, J. T., and Reddy, J. N., "Mixed Conjugate Finite Element Approximations of Linear Operators," Journal of Structural Mechanics, Vol. 1, No. 1, 1972, pp. 113-31.

4.73 Oden, J. T., "Generalized Conjugate Functions for Mixed Finite Element Approximations of Boundary-Value Problems," The Mathematical Foundations of the Finite Element Method with Applications to Partial Differential Equations, ed. A. K. Aziz, Academic Press, New York, 1972, pp. 629-69.

4.74 Oden, J. T., Goos, G., and Harminas, J., "Formulation and Application of Certain Primal and Mixed Finite Element Models of Finite Deformations of Elastic Bodies," Lecture Notes in Computer Science, Vol. 10, Computer Methods in Applied Sciences and Engineering, Part 1, Springer-Verlag, Berlin-Heidelberg, 1974, pp. 334-65.

4.75 Oden, J. T., "A Theory of Mixed Finite Element Approximations of Non-Self-Adjoint Boundary-Value Problems," Proceedings of the Seventh U.S. National Congress of Applied Mechanics, Boulder, Colorado, June 1974, pp. 39-51.

4.76 Oden, J. T., "Some Contributions to the Mathematical Theory of Mixed Finite Element Approximations," Theory and Practice in Finite Element Structural Analysis, ed. Y. Yamada and R. H. Gallagher, Proceedings of the 1973 Tokyo Seminar on Finite Element Analysis, The University of Tokyo Press, 1974, pp. 3-23.

4.77 Oden, J. T., and Lee, J. K., "Theory of Mixed and Hybrid Finite Element Approximations in Linear Elasticity," Lecture Notes in Mathematics, Proceedings of the IUTAM/IUM Symposium on Applications of Methods of Functional Analysis to Problems of Mechanics, Marseille, France, Sept. 1975, Springer-Verlag, Berlin, Vol. 503, 1976, pp. 90-109.

4.78 Oden, J. T., and Reddy, J. N., "Some Observations on Properties of Certain Mixed Finite Element Approximations," International Journal for Numerical Methods in Engineering, Vol. 9, No. 4, 1975, pp. 933-38.

4.79 Oden, J. T., and Reddy, J. N., "On Mixed Finite Element Approximations," SIAM Journal of Numerical Analysis, Vol. 13, No. 3, June 1976, pp. 393-404.

4.80 Reddy, J. N., "A Mathematical Theory of Complementary-Dual Variational Principles and Mixed Finite Element Approximations of Linear Boundary Value Problems in Continuum Mechanics," Ph.D. Dissertation, University of Alabama, Huntsville, 1973.

4.81 Reddy, J. N., and Oden, J. T., "Convergence of Mixed Finite-Element Approximations of a Class of Linear Boundary-Value Problems," Journal of Structural Mechanics, Vol. 2, No. 2, 1973, pp. 83-108.

4.82 Reddy, J. N., "Some Mathematical Properties of Certain Mixed Galerkin Approximations in Nonlinear Elasticity," Proceedings of the International Conference on Computational Methods in Nonlinear Mechanics, University of Texas, Austin, Sept. 23-25, 1974, pp. 627-35.

4.83 Reddy, J. N., and Oden, J. T., "Mixed Finite Element Approximations of Linear Boundary Value Problems," Quarterly of Applied Mathematics, Vol. 33, No. 3, 1975, pp. 255-80.

4.84 Sheu, M. G., "On Theories and Applications of Mixed Finite Element Methods for Linear Boundary-Value Problems," Computers and Mathematics with Applications, Vol. 4, No. 4, 1978, pp. 333-47.

4.85 Talaslidis, D., "On the Convergence of a Mixed Finite Element Approximation for Cylindrical Shells," to be published in Zeitschrift für Angewandte Mathematik und Mechanik, 1979.

Mixed Finite Difference Schemes

Ordinary Finite Differences

5.1 Budiansky, B., and Radkowski, P. P., "Numerical Analysis of Unsymmetrical Bending of Shells of Revolution," AIAA Journal, Vol. 1, 1963, pp. 1833-42.

5.2 Clifton, R. J., "A Difference Method for Plane Problems in Dynamic Elasticity," Quarterly of Applied Mathematics, Vol. 25, No. 1, 1967, pp. 97-116.

5.3 Kukishev, V. L., and Fridman, V. M., "A Variational Finite-Difference Method of the Theory of Elastic Vibrations Based on Reissner's Variational Principle," Akademia Nauk SSSR, Izvestiia, Mekhanika Tverdogo Tela, Sept.-Oct. 1976, pp. 112-19 (Russian).

5.4 Mileykovsky, I. E., "Fundamental Equations Method for the Computer Analysis of Shells," Sbornik Noviye Metodi Rashota Stroiter-lnikh Konstruktsi, Moscow, 1968, pp. 20-31 (Russian).

5.5 Noor, A. K., and Khandelwal, V. K., "Improved Finite Difference Variant for the Bending Analysis of Arbitrary Cylindrical Shells," UNICIV Report No. R-58, University of New South Wales, Australia, Dec. 1969.

5.6 Noor, A. K., and Robertson, K. J., "On a Mixed Formulation of Saint-Venant Torsion Problem of Nonhomogeneous Anisotropic Bars," UNICIV Report No. R-65, University of New South Wales, Australia, April 1971.

5.7 Noor, A. K., "Improved Mixed Finite Difference Scheme for Thermoelastic Stress Analysis of Noncircular Cylindrical Shell Roofs," Proceedings of the IASS Conference on Shell Structures and Climatic Influences, Calgary, Canada, July 3-6, 1972, pp. 335-45.

5.8 Noor, A. K., and Stephens, W. B., "Mixed Finite Difference Scheme for Free Vibration Analysis of Noncircular Cylinders," NASA TN D-7107, Feb. 1973.

5.9 Noor, A. K., "Mixed Finite Difference Scheme for a Class of Linear and Nonlinear Structural Mechanics Problems," in Developments in Mechanics, Vol. 7, Proceedings of the Thirteenth Midwestern Mechanics Conference, Pittsburgh, Pa., Aug. 1973, pp. 657-74.

5.10 Noor, A. K., "Mixed Finite Difference Scheme for Analysis of Simply Supported Thick Plates," Computers and Structures, Vol. 3, No. 5, Sept. 1973, pp. 967-82.

5.11 Noor, A. K., Stephens, W. B., and Fulton, R. E., "An Improved Numerical Process for the Solution of Solid Mechanics Problems," Computers and Structures, Vol. 3, No. 6, Nov. 1973, pp. 1397-1437.

5.12 Noor, A. K., and Stephens, W. B., "Comparison of Finite Difference Schemes for Analysis of Shells of Revolution," NASA TN D-7337, Dec. 1973.

5.13 Noor, A. K., and Rarig, P. L., "Three-Dimensional Solutions of Laminated Cylinders," Computer Methods in Applied Mechanics and Engineering, Vol. 3, No. 3, May 1974, pp. 319-34.

5.14 Rao, N. S. V. K., and Das, Y. C., "A Mixed Method in Elasticity," Paper 76-WA/APM-30, presented at the Winter Annual Meeting of the ASME, New York, Dec. 1976.

5.15 Recker, W. W., "A Numerical Solution of Three-Dimensional Problems in Dynamic Elasticity," Journal of Applied Mechanics, Vol. 37, 1970, pp. 116-22.

5.16 Recker, W. W., "A Numerical Solution of Axisymmetrical Problems in Elastodynamics," International Journal for Numerical Methods in Engineering, Vol. 3, 1971, pp. 361-77.

5.17 Shaishmelashvili, V. N., "On the Analysis of Interstorey Ceilings of the Type of a Thin Spherical Shell," Soobschchenya Akademii Nauk Gruzinskoi SSR, Vol. 10, No. 4, 1949 (Russian).

5.18 Shaishmelashvili, V. N., "Some Methods of Analysis of Shallow Shells," Trudi Instituta Stroitelnovo Dela, Akademii Nauk Gruzinskoi SSR, Vol. 5, 1955 (Russian).

5.19 Shatilov, V. P., "A Numerical Method of the Theory of Elastic Plates and Shells," Prikladnaia Mekhanika, Vol. 12, Oct. 1976, pp. 122-25 (Russian).

Multilocal Differences

5.20 Almannai, A., "A Two-Dimensional Multilocal Method for the
Solution of Shell Problems and Its Application to the Bending Theory of
General Shells," Ph.D. Dissertation, Institut für Konstruktiven Ingen-
ieubau, Ruhr-Universität Bochum, May 1976 (German).
5.21 Chang, A. T., "An Improved Finite Difference Method for Plate
Vibration," International Journal for Numerical Methods in Engineering,
Vol. 5, Nov.-Dec. 1972, pp. 289-96.
5.22 Giencki, E., "Simple 'Mixed' Method for Plate and Shell
Problems," Nuclear Engineering Design, Vol. 29, No. 1, 1974, pp. 141-55.
5.23 Nelson, N., "The Derivation of Improved Difference Equations
and Their Application to Solid Mechanics," Ph.D. Dissertation, Stevens
Institute of Technology, Hoboken, N.J., 1971.
5.24 Nelson, N., and Chang, A., "An Improved Finite Difference Method
Applied to Thin Shells," Journal of Engineering for Industry, ASME,
Nov. 1971, Vol. 93, No. 4, pp. 1030-36.
5.25 Noor, A. K., "Improved Multilocal Finite Difference Variant for
the Bending Analysis of Arbitrary Cylindrical Shells," University of
New South Wales, Australia, UNICIV Report No. R-63, March 1971.
5.26 Noor, A. K., "Noncircular Cylinder Vibration by Multilocal
Method," Journal of the Engineering Mechanics Division, ASCE, Vol. 99,
No. EM2, April 1973, pp. 389-407.

Dynamic Relaxation

5.27 Alwar, R. S., and Rao, N. R., "Large Elastic Deformations of
Clamped Skewed Plates by Dynamic Relaxation," Computers and Structures,
Vol. 4, No. 2, March 1974, pp. 381-98.
5.28 Day, A. S., "An Introduction to Dynamic Relaxation," The
Engineer, Vol. 219, 1965, pp. 218-21.
5.29 Day, A. S., "Analysis of Plates by Dynamic Relaxation with
Special Reference to Boundary Conditions," International Symposium on
the Use of Electrical Digital Computers in Structural Engineering,
University of Newcastle-upon-Tyne, Paper No. 10, 1966.
5.30 Frieze, P. A., Hobbs, R. E., and Dowling, P. J., "Application
of Dynamic Relaxation to the Large Deflection Elasto-Plastic Analysis
of Plates," Computers and Structures, Vol. 8, No. 2, April 1978,
pp. 301-10.
5.31 Otter, J. R. H., "Computations for Prestressed Concrete
Reactor Pressure Vessels Using Dynamic Relaxation," Nuclear Structural
Engineering, Vol. 1, 1968, pp. 61-75.
5.32 Rushton, K. R., "Dynamic Relaxation Solutions of Elastic Plate
Problems," Journal of Strain Analysis, Vol. 3, No. 1, 1968, pp. 23-32.
5.33 Rushton, K. R., "Dynamic Relaxation Solutions for the Large
Deflection of Plates with Specified Boundary Stresses," Journal of
Strain Analysis, Vol. 4, 1969, pp. 75-80.
5.34 Rushton, K. R., "The Dynamic Relaxation Method Used for Stress
Analysis,"   Recent Advances in Stress Analysis, 1968, pp. 41-46.

Mixed Methods Based on Transforming the Boundary
Value to an Initial-Value Problem

Numerical Integration

6.1 Cohen, G. A., "Computer Analysis of Asymmetric Deformation of Orthotropic Shells of Revolution," AIAA Journal, Vol. 2, 1964, pp. 932-34.

6.2 Cohen, G. A., "Computer Analysis of Asymmetric Free Vibrations of Ring-Stiffened Orthotropic Shells of Revolution," AIAA Journal, Vol. 3, No. 12, Dec. 1965, pp. 2305-12.

6.3 Cohen, G. A., "Analysis of Multicircuit Shells of Revolution by the Field Method," Computer Methods in Applied Mechanics and Engineering, Vol. 8, 1976, pp. 301-18.

6.4 Goldberg, J. E., Bogdanoff, J. L., and Helms, H. E., "Lateral Buckling of Rimmed Rotating Disks," Proceedings of the Third U.S. National Congress of Applied Mechanics, Providence, 1958, pp. 253-57.

6.5 Goldberg, J. E., and Bogdanoff, J. L., "Static and Dynamic Analysis of Nonuniform Conical Shells under Symmetrical and Unsymmetrical Conditions," Proceedings of the Sixth Symposium on Ballistic Missile and Aerospace Technology, Los Angeles, Vol. 1, Academic Press, New York, 1961, pp. 219-38.

6.6 Goldberg, J. E., Bogdanoff, J. L., and Alspaugh, D. W., "Stress in Spherical Domes under Arbitrary Loading Including Thermal and Shrinkage Effects," Proceedings of the International Association for Shell Structures Symposium on Non-Classical Shell Problems, Warsaw, 1963, North Holland Publishing Company, Amsterdam, pp. 116-35.

6.7 Goldberg, J. E., Bogdanoff, J. L., and Alspaugh, D. W., "Modes and Frequencies of Pressurized Conical Shells," Journal of Aircraft, AIAA, Vol. 1, No. 6, 1964, pp. 372-74.

6.8 Goldberg, J. E., and Setlur, A. V., "Analysis of Noncircular Cylindrical Shells," Proceedings of the IASS Symposium on Shell Structures, Budapest, 1965.

6.9 Goldberg, J. E., "Computer Analysis of Shells," Proceedings of the Symposium on the Theory of Shells, University of Houston, Texas, 1967, pp. 5-22.

6.10 Goldberg, J. E., Bogdanoff, J. L., and Glauz, W. D., "Lateral and Torsional Buckling of Thin-Walled Beams," Memoires of the International Association for Bridge and Structural Engineering, Vol. 24, 1964, pp. 92-100.

6.11 Kalnins, A., "Analysis of Shells of Revolution Subjected to Symmetrical and Nonsymmetrical Loads," Journal of Applied Mechanics, Vol. 33, 1964, pp. 467-76.

6.12 Kalnins, A., "Static, Free Vibration and Stability Analysis of Thin Elastic Shells of Revolution," Technical Report AFFDL TR-68-144, Air Force Flight Dynamics Laboratory, Wright-Patterson Air Force Base, Ohio, March 1969.

6.13 Kalnins, A., "Analysis of Curved Thin-Walled Shells of Revolution," AIAA Journal, Vol. 6, No. 4, April 1968, pp. 584-88.

Matrix Progression and Transfer Matrices

6.14 Aass, A., "Matrix Progression Method," Der Bauingenieur, Vol. 39, No. 8, 1964, pp. 306-11.

6.15 Bahar, L. Y., "Transfer Matrix Approach to Layered Systems," Journal of the Engineering Mechanics Division, ASCE, Vol. 98, No. EM5, Oct. 1972, pp. 1159-72.

6.16 Bahar, L. Y., "A Transfer Matrix Approach to Elastodynamics of Layered Media," Journal of the Acoustical Society of America, Vol. 57, No. 3, March 1975, pp. 606-9.

6.17 Bahar, L. Y., and Sinha, A. K., "Matrix Exponential Approach to Dynamic Response," Computers and Structures, Vol. 5, No. 2/3, June 1975, pp. 159-65.

6.18 Bahar, L. Y., "Transfer Matrix Approach to Layered Systems with Axial Symmetry," Advances in Engineering Science, Vol. 2, NASA CP-2001, Proceedings of the Thirteenth Annual Meeting of the Society of Engineering Science, Hampton, Virginia, Nov. 1-3, 1976, pp. 721-29.

6.19 Bahar, L. Y., and Hetnarski, R. B., "Transfer Matrix Approach to Thermoelasticity," Developments in Mechanics, Vol. 8, Proceedings of the Fifteenth Midwestern Mechanics Conference, University of Illinois at Chicago Circle, Chicago, Illinois, March 23-25, 1977, pp. 161-63.

6.20 Henderson, J. P., and McDaniel, T. J., "The Analysis of Curved Multispan Structures," Journal of Sound and Vibration, Vol. 18, No. 2, 1971, pp. 203-19.

6.21 Jenkins, R. S., and Tottenham, H., "The Solution of Shell Problems by the Matrix Progression Method," Proceedings of the World Conference on Shell Structures, San Francisco, Oct. 1-4, 1962, published by the National Academy of Sciences, No. 1187, 1964, pp. 563-80.

6.22 Lin, Y. K., and Donaldson, B. K., "A Brief Survey of Transfer Matrix Techniques with Special Reference to the Analysis of Aircraft Panels," Journal of Sound and Vibration, Vol. 10, No. 1, 1969, pp. 103-43.

6.23 Pestel, E. C., and Leckie, F. A., Matrix Methods in Elasto Mechanics, McGraw-Hill, New York, 1963.

6.24 Pilkey, W. D., and Chang, P. Y., Modern Formulas for Statics and Dynamics, McGraw-Hill, New York, 1978.

6.25 Raizer, V. D., "A Matrix-Operator Method for the Analysis of Shallow Shells," Sbornik Noviye Metodi Rashota Stroitelnikh Konstruktsi, Moscow, 1968, pp. 62-77 (Russian).

6.26 Tottenham, H., "The Matrix Progression Method in Structural Analysis," Structural Problems in Nuclear Reactor Engineering, Pergamon Press, London, 1962, pp. 189-210.

6.27 Tottenham, H., and Kanchi, M. B., "Foundations of the Generalized Matrix Progression Method and Its Application to the Problems of Structural Mechanics," Institution of Engineers (India-J.), Vol. 49, Sept. 1968, pp. 115-35.

6.28 Wunderlich, W., "Calculation of Transfer Matrices Applied to the Bending Theory of Shells of Revolution," International Symposium on the Use of Computers in Structural Engineering, Newcastle-upon-Tyne, 1966.

Method of Initial Functions

6.29 Das, Y. C., and Setlur, A. V., "Method of Initial Functions in Two-Dimensional Elastodynamic Problems," Journal of Applied Mechanics, Vol. 37, No. 1, March 1970, pp. 137-40.

6.30 Vlasov, V. Z., "Method of Initial Functions in Problems of Theory of Thick Plates and Shells," Proceedings of the Ninth International Congress of Applied Mechanics, Vol. 6, University of Brussels, 1957, pp. 321-30.

6.31 Vlasov, V. Z., "Application of the Method of Initial Functions to Some Problems of Bending of Rectangular Plates," Inzhenerniye Sbornik, Vol. 30, 1960, pp. 78-84 (Russian).

Structural Reanalysis

7.1 Noor, A. K., "Multiple Configuration Analysis Via Mixed Method," Journal of the Structural Division, ASCE, Vol. 100, No. ST9, Sept. 1974, pp. 1991-97.
7.2 Noor, A. K., and Lowder, H. E., "Structural Reanalysis Via a Mixed Method," Computers and Structures, Vol. 5, No. 1, April 1975, pp. 9-12.

Nonstructural Applications

8.1 Fix, G. F., and Gunzburger, M. D., "On Least Squares Approximations to Indefinite Problems of the Mixed Type," International Journal for Numerical Methods in Engineering, Vol. 12, 1978, pp. 453-69.
8.2 Meissner, U., "A Mixed Finite Element Model for Use in Potential Flow Problems," International Journal for Numerical Methods in Engineering, Vol. 6, No. 4, 1973, pp. 467-73.
8.3 Morand, H., and Ohayon, R., "Variational Formulations of the Hydrocapillary Vibration Problems," Colloque International sur la Stabilisation des Vehicules Spatiaux et les Problemes Technologiques et Dynamiques Posés par les Liquides, European Space Agency and Centre National d'Etudes Spatiales, Toulouse, France, Oct. 10-12, 1977, pp. 105-19 (French).
8.4 Taylor, C., and Hood, P., "A Numerical Solution of the Navier-Stokes Equations Using the Finite Element Technique," Computers and Fluids, Vol. 1, No. 1, 1973, pp. 73-100.
8.5 Yamada, Y., Ito, K., Yokouchi, Y., Tamano, T., and Ohtsubo, T., "Finite Element Analysis of Steady Fluid and Metal Flow," Finite Elements in Fluids, ed. R. H. Gallagher, J. T. Oden, C. Taylor, and O. C. Zienkiewicz, Vol. 1, 1975, pp. 73-94.
8.6 Zienkiewicz, O. C., and Taylor, C., "Weighted Residual Processes in Finite Element Method with Particular Reference to Some Transient and Coupled Problems," Lectures on Finite Element Methods in Continuum Mechanics, ed. J. T. Oden and E. R. A. Oliveira, University of Alabama Press, Huntsville, Alabama, 1973, pp. 415-58.

Computer Programs

9.1 Cohen, G. A., "FASOR - A Second Generation Shell of Revolution Code," Trends in Computerized Structural Analysis and Synthesis, ed. A. K. Noor and H. G. McComb, Jr., Pergamon Press, 1978, pp. 301-9.
9.2 Biffle, J. H., and Gubbels, M. H., "WULFF - A Set of Computer Programs for the Large Displacement Dynamic Response of Three-Dimensional Solids," Report SAND 76-0096, Sandia Laboratories, Albuquerque, New Mexico, Aug. 1976.

9.3 Pickard, J., "FORMAT-FORTRAN Matrix Abstraction Technique -
Vol. V, Supplement II, Engineering User and Technical Report -
Extended," AFFDL TR-66-207, Wright Patterson Air Force Base, Ohio,
April 1973.
9.4 User's Manual, "Automated Structural Design Computer Program,"
DAC-33447, McDonnell Douglas, 1970.
9.5 Wiberg, N. E., and Tagnfors, H., "FEMWT - A General Purpose
Computer Program for Solving Problems by Finite Element Methods,"
Publication 72:2, Division of Structural Mechanics, Chalmers University
of Technology, Göteborg, Sweden, 1972.

APPENDIX I

GOVERNING DIFFERENTIAL EQUATIONS OF THE
LINEAR BENDING THEORY OF SHALLOW SHELLS

Two forms of the mixed governing differential equations of the linear
bending theory of isotropic shallow shells are given in this appendix.
The first is in terms of two fourth-order partial differential equations
in the transverse displacement w and an Airy stress function ϕ. The
second format is in terms of thirteen first-order partial differential
equations in the shell stress resultants and generalized displacements.

Equations in Terms of a Stress Function ϕ and the Transverse Displacement w

$$- \frac{1}{Eh} \nabla^2 \nabla^2 \phi + \nabla_k^2 w + \frac{1}{Eh} \left[\int \frac{\partial^2 p_y}{\partial x^2} \, dy - \int \frac{\partial^2 p_x}{\partial y^2} \, dx + \nu \left(\frac{\partial p_y}{\partial y} + \frac{\partial p_x}{\partial x} \right) \right] = 0$$

and $\hspace{10cm}$ (A.1)

$$D \nabla^2 \nabla^2 w + \nabla_k^2 \phi - k_x \int p_x \, dx - k_y \int p_y \, dy - p_z = 0$$

where

$$\nabla^2 = \frac{\partial^2}{\partial x^2} + \frac{\partial^2}{\partial y^2}$$

$$\nabla_k^2 = k_y \frac{\partial^2}{\partial x^2} - 2 k_{xy} \frac{\partial^2}{\partial x \partial y} + k_x \frac{\partial^2}{\partial y^2}$$

p_x, p_y, p_z are the components of the external loads in the x, y, and z
directions, respectively; k_x and k_y are the curvatures of the normal
sections along the coordinate lines x and y of the surface; k_{xy} is the
twist of the surface; E and ν are Young's modulus and Poisson's ratio
of the material; h is the shell thickness; and D is the bending rigidity
of the shell.

Thirteen First-Order Equation Formulation

The governing differential equations of this formulation can be
written in a symmetric matrix format as follows:

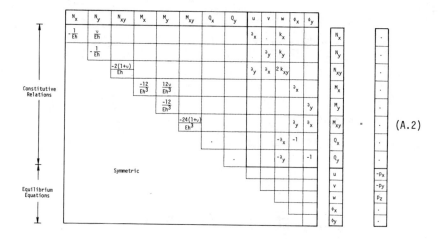

$$(A.2)$$

where $\partial_x \equiv \dfrac{\partial}{\partial x}$, $\partial_y \equiv \dfrac{\partial}{\partial y}$; the N, M, and Q are stress resultants; u, v, and w are displacement components in the coordinate directions; and ϕ_x, and ϕ_y are rotation components of the shell surface. The sign convention for these quantities is given in Fig. 4. Note that a shear deformation theory can be obtained from these equations by replacing the zeros on the diagonals of the seventh and eighth equations by the transverse shear flexibility.

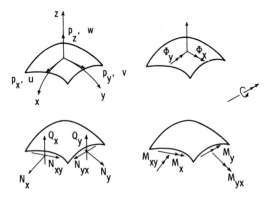

Fig. 4   Sign convention for forces and displacements

APPENDIX II

PROGRAM ABSTRACTS

CRACK ANALYSIS

Descriptive Program Title: K-Value Analysis for Two-Dimensional Elastic
    In-Plane Problems
Program Description: CRACK ANALYSIS is a finite element program for cal-
    culating the stress intensity factors for two-dimensional elastic
    problems. The element library consists of rod (bar) elements,
    triangular and quadrilateral membrane elements, and crack-tip
    elements.
Dates of First Release and Most Recent Update: June 1972, February 1976
Program Operational on: CDC 6000 and UNIVAC 1108
Developer: Kiyoshi Ando
          Ship Strength Research Laboratory
          Nagasaki Technical Institute
          Mitsubishi Heavy Industries, Ltd.
          5-717-1, Fukabori, Nagasaki
          Nagasaki 851-03
          Japan
Available From: Ship Strength Research Laboratory
                5-717-1, Fukabori, Nagasaki
                Nagasaki 851-03
                Japan

DYGENIS

Descriptive Program Title: Dynamic and Geometrically Nonlinear Analysis
    of Shells Using Mixed Finite Elements
Program Description: DYGENIS is a finite element program for the linear
    static, free vibration, bifurcation buckling, and geometrically non-
    linear analysis of thick shells (with transverse shear deformation
    included) and thin shells (with negligible shear deformation).
Dates of First Release and Most Recent Update: 1975, 1976
Program Operational on: AEG - Telefunken TR440
Developer: Lehrstuhl IV
          The Institute of Structural Engineering
          Ruhr-Universität Bochum
          Bochum, West Germany
Available From: Professor W. Wunderlich
                Ruhr-Universität Bochum
                Lehrstuhl für Konstruktiven Ingenieurbau IV
                Postfach 10 21 48
                D-4630 Bochum
                West Germany

FARSS

Descriptive Program Title: Fourier Analysis of Rotationally Symmetric
    Solids
Program Description: FARSS is a finite element program for the linear
    thermoelastic stress and dynamic analysis of axisymmetric shells and
    solids. It can be used for two-dimensional plane strain and plane
    stress problems. The material can be isotropic or orthotropic. For
    isotropic materials, incompressibility and near incompressibility
    can be included. Time-dependent mechanical and thermal loads as well
    as applied boundary displacements are allowed. Temperature-dependent
    material properties are allowed in the static version only.
        The semianalytic finite element method is used for the spatial
    discretization. Isoparametric quadrilateral finite elements with
    linear and quadratic interpolation functions for the displacement
    components and mean pressure are used. The Wilson-Theta and
    Newmark-Beta methods are used for temporal integration.
Date First Released and Most Recent Update: 1973, 1976
Program Operational on: UNIVAC 1100 series, CDC 6000 series
Developers: N. A. Cyr
             G. H. Ferguson
             R. D. Teter

             Lockheed Missiles and Space Company
             Department 81-12, Bldg. 154
             111 Lockheed Way
             Sunnyvale, California 94086
Available From: Developers

FASOR

Descriptive Program Title: Field Analysis of Shells of Revolution
Program Description: FASOR is an integrated, user-oriented system for
    linear stress, free vibration, bifurcation buckling, and large
    displacement elastic analysis of laminated shells of revolution
    with discrete rings and distributed stiffeners. Both transverse
    shear deformation and material anisotropy are included.
        The fundamental unknowns are chosen to be the effective axial,
    radial and circumferential stress resultants, bending and twisting
    moments (all acting on normal sections perpendicular to the shell
    meridian), as well as the corresponding displacements, normal
    element rotation, and circumferential transverse shear strain.
    The program uses the field method for the spatial discretization
    and treats branched shells with multiple circuits.
Date of First Release and Most Recent Update: 1972, 1979
Program Operational on: CDC 6000 and CYBER series
Developer: G. A. Cohen
             Structures Research Associates
             465 Forest Avenue
             Laguna Beach, California 92651
Available From: Developer

FESAPM

Descriptive Program Title: Finite Element Structural Analysis Program
for Shells Using Mixed Elements
Program Description: FESAPM is a finite element program for the linear
stress, free vibration,and geometrically nonlinear large displace-
ment analysis of elastic shells. Transverse shear deformation,
bending-extensional coupling,and material anisotropy are included.
Isoparametric triangular and quadrilateral shallow shell elements
with quadratic interpolation functions are used. The program can
handle very large-size problems through the use of the hypermatrix
storage scheme.
Date Program was Made Available: 1976
Program Operational on: CDC 6000 and CYBER series
Developer: A. K. Noor
MS-246
GWU-NASA Langley Research Center
Hampton, Virginia 23665
Available From: Developer

FORMAT

Descriptive Program Title: FORTRAN Matrix Abstraction Technique
Program Description: FORMAT is a finite element program for the linear
static, free vibration, transient response, bifurcation buckling,
and geometrically nonlinear large displacement analysis of structures.
It has a wide variety of elements including bars, beams, shear
panels, planar membranes, spatial membranes, and plate elements.
Cholesky decomposition, with optional reordering for minimum wave-
front, is used for the solution of algebraic equations.
Dates of First Release and Most Recent Update: March 1967, April 1973
Program Operational on: CDC, IBM, UNIVAC, GE
Developer: J. Pickard et al.
Douglas Aircraft Company
3855 Lakewood Boulevard
Long Beach, California 90846
Available From: Aerospace Structures Information and Analysis Center
AFFDL/FBR/ASIAC
Wright-Patterson Air Force Base, Ohio 45433

HYBOS

Descriptive Program Title: Hybrid Analysis of Shells
Program Description: HYBOS is a program system for the thermoelastic
stress analysis of hybrid shell of revolution and solid of revolution structures subjected to arbitrary mechanical and thermal
loads. Numerical integration is used for the spatial discretization.
Date Program was Made Available: 1972
Program Operational on: CDC 6000 series, IBM 370, UNIVAC 1100 series
and DEC 20

Developer: Z. Zudans
            Franklin Research Center
            20th and Race Streets
            Philadelphia, Pennsylvania 19103
Available From: Developer

MIX

Program Description: MIX is a set of finite element programs for the
    linear and large deflection nonlinear static analysis of thin
    shallow shells. Triangular elements having three and six nodes
    are used. The nodal parameters consist of the three displacements,
    three membrane stress resultants,and three bending stress result-
    ants at each node.
Date Program was Made Available: 1971
Program Operational on: IBM
Developer: C. Tahiani
            Department of Civil Engineering
            Royal Military College
            Kingston, Ontario K7L 2W3
            Canada
Available From: Developer

NAST

Descriptive Program Title: Nonlinear Analysis of Space Trusses
Program Description: NAST refers to a set of two programs for the
    static and dynamic analysis of pin-jointed space trusses with
    combined geometric (large deflection) and material nonlinearities.
    The fundamental unknowns consist of member forces and nodal
    displacements.
        For transient response problems nodal velocities are also
    taken as fundamental unknowns and an explicit, central difference
    scheme is used for the temporal integration. The material non-
    linearity is assumed in the form of Ramberg-Osgood nonlinear
    strain-stress relation.
Dates of First Release and Most Recent Update: 1973, 1978
Program Operational on: CDC 6000 and CYBER series
Developer: A. K. Noor
            MS-246
            GWU-NASA Langley Research Center
            Hampton, Virginia 23665
Available From: Developer

ROT B

Descriptive Program Title: Linear Analysis of Shells of Revolution
Program Description: ROT B is a finite element program for the linear
    static analysis of shells of revolution. The nodal parameters
    consist of displacements, rotations, membrane stress resultants,
    and bending stress resultants. The "generalized" stiffness matrix
    is developed through the use of the transfer matrix method.
Dates of First Release and Most Recent Update: 1966, 1976

Program Operational on: ICL, Telefunken TR440
Developer: W. Wunderlich
          Ruhr-Universität Bochum
          Lehrstuhl für Konstruktiven Ingenieurbau
          Postfach 10 21 48
          D-4630 Bochum
          West Germany
Available From: Developer

STARS

Descriptive Program Title: Shell Theory Automated for Revolved
    Structures
Program Description: STARS is a computer program for the analysis of
    shells of revolution. The program handles linear static, free
    vibration, and bifurcation buckling analysis as well as axisym-
    metric nonlinear vibration and post-buckling analyses. Both large
    deflections and plasticity are included. Linear and nonlinear
    transient response predictions are available in an experimental
    version of the program.
        Numerical integration is used for the spatial discretization.
Dates of First Release and Most Recent Update: 1968, 1974
Program Operational on: IBM, UNIVAC, CDC, Telefunken, ICL, DATA-SAAB
Developer: V. Svalbonas
          Koppers Company
          P.O. Box 312
          York, Pennsylvania 17405
Available From: Developer

WULFF

Descriptive Program Title: A Set of Computer Programs for the Large
    Displacement Dynamic Response of Three-Dimensional Solids
Program Description: WULFF is a set of computer programs which calculate
    the large displacement dynamic response of three-dimensional solids.
    The fundamental unknowns consist of stress, velocity, and displace-
    ment components. The spatial discretization is made using trilinear
    isoparametric eight-noded brick elements. The temporal integration
    is carried out using the central-difference explicit scheme.
Date Program was Made Available: September 1, 1978
Program Operational on: CDC 6000 series and 7600
Developer: J. H. Biffle and M. H. Gubbels
          Sandia Laboratories
          Albuquerque, New Mexico 87115
Available From: Developers

Damping Models and their Use in Computer Programs

Frederick C. Nelson

Robert Greif

Tufts University

INTRODUCTION

The purpose of this review is to survey and assess the ways in which
damping has been incorporated into general purpose shock and vibration
computer programs. The authors believe that a review of this topic will
be useful because they have encountered confusion over the various types
of damping models which are available, and confusion over the compromises
which must be made between physical reality and mathematical convenience
in the choice of a damping model.
  The review begins with a summary of damping forces followed by a
discussion of damping in multi-degree-of-freedom systems. The final part
of this review reports the results of a survey aimed at establishing
which damping models are available in various computer programs and the
relative success of these programs in solving problems of damped response
of discrete, multi-degree-of-freedom models.

THE NATURE OF DAMPING FORCES

Oscillatory mechanical systems have a reservoir of inertial energy, a
reservoir of elastic energy, and a means of dissipating energy. The
forces associated with inertia and elasticity can be calculated by formulas from theoretical mechanics; no recourse is necessary to experiment or
experience. This is not the case for damping forces. In this sense,
damping is irrational and requires the analyst to adopt a hypothesis
before calculating the damping force or the energy dissipated per cycle.
Also, the motivation for the hypothesis about damping can vary: the
motivation can be primarily physical, as in the cases of viscous, hysteretic, or Coulomb damping, or primarily to achieve a simple mathematical
formulation,as in the cases of proportional damping, equivalent viscous
modal damping, or complex stiffness. The challenge for each particular
problem is to strike the appropriate balance between physical reality
and mathematical tractability.

Since there is confusion over the various types of damping hypotheses and their associated terminology, a description of the more common choices will be given first. For clarity, the discussion will be limited to a damped, single-degree-of-freedom oscillator; additional discussion can be found in Refs. [1, 2, and 3]. Multi-degree-of-freedom systems are treated in subsequent parts of this review.

Viscous Damping

In linear viscous damping, energy is dissipated by laminar fluid friction. An example is energy dissipation due to flow of a Newtonian fluid between a tightly fitting piston and cylinder, i.e., the classical dashpot. The viscous damping force is proportional to the relative velocity and acts in the opposite direction. For sinusoidal motion, this behavior may be expressed as

$$\underline{F} = - c\underline{\dot{X}} \tag{1}$$

where
  $\underline{F}$ is the damping phasor[1]
  $\underline{\dot{X}}$ is the relative velocity phasor
  c is the damping coefficient

Introducing the damping ratio, β, defined as

$$\beta = \frac{c}{c_{cr}} = \frac{c}{2m\omega}$$

where
  c_{cr} is the critical damping ratio
  m is the mass
  ω is the undamped natural (circular) frequency

Eq. (1) becomes

$$\underline{F} = -2m\omega\beta\underline{\dot{X}} \tag{2}$$

Linear viscous damping is mathematically convenient and when laminar fluid flow is present, physically reasonable. Its use for the damping of metals or plastics is based more on its mathematical convenience than its physical reality.

---

[1]A physical quantity varying with frequency Ω can be represented as $x(t) = \mathrm{Re}[\underline{X}e^{i\Omega t}]$ where $\underline{X}$ is a complex quantity referred to as the phasor associated with $x(t)$.

The energy dissipation per cycle (D) associated with linear viscous damping can be shown to be

$$D = c \, \Omega \, \pi \, X^2 \qquad (3)$$

where
   X is the magnitude of the displacement phasor, $\underline{X}$
   Ω is the forcing frequency
Equation (3) implies that for viscous damping $D \propto \Omega$.
   Fluids can provide damping through the unbalanced pressure forces due to flow separation as well as through the viscous forces which act on the surface of a structure. A discussion of fluid damping due to pressure drag is not considered in this review even though such damping is very important in problems of flow-induced vibration. A treatment of this topic is provided in Ref. [4].

Hysteretic Damping

Hysteretic damping is sometimes referred to as material damping. The energy dissipation is due to various forms of internal friction as well as small-scale thermal and electrical effects. Details can be found in Refs. [5, 6].
   On the macroscopic scale, the hysteretic damping force for sinusoidal motion is usually represented by a force which is proportional to the displacement and in antiphase with the velocity. In phasor notation one may then write

$$F \propto - i \, \underline{X}$$

where i is $\sqrt{-1}$. If the constant of proportionality is taken as ηk, where k is the oscillator stiffness and η is defined as the loss factor, we may rewrite this as

$$\underline{F} = - i k \eta \underline{X} \qquad (4)$$

This suggests that the damping force may be combined with the spring force to give

$$\underline{F}_c = -k\underline{X} -ik\eta\underline{X} = -k(1+i\eta)\underline{X} = -\underline{k}\underline{X}$$

and that the loss factor η may be interpreted as a measure of the imaginary part of the complex stiffness $\underline{k}$. For sinusoidal response with $\Omega > 0$, Eq. (4) may be written

$$\underline{F} = - \frac{k\eta}{\Omega} \, \underline{\dot{X}} \qquad (5)$$

Comparing Eq. (5) to Eq. (1) we may define the equivalent viscous damping
coefficient as

$$c_{eq} = \frac{k\eta}{\Omega} \tag{6}$$

Comparing Eq. (5) to Eq. (2) we may write a relation between loss factor
and damping ratio

$$\eta = 2(\frac{\Omega}{\omega})\beta \tag{7}$$

where ω^2 = k/m. Note that at resonance ($\Omega=\omega$), Eq. (7) gives η = 2β.
    The energy dissipated per cycle associated with this formulation of
hysteretic damping is

$$D = k\eta\pi X^2 \tag{8}$$

and implies that D is independent of Ω. It was this experimental obser-
vation that led Kimball and Lovell to suggest the hysteretic damping
hypothesis in 1927 [7].
    Because of the difference in frequency dependence of the damping
force for viscous damping and that for hysteretic damping, the single-
degree-of-freedom, steady-state response curves are different. Most
notable among these differences are the following.
    1. For viscous damping, the resonant frequency (i.e., frequency
associated with peak displacement response) decreases with increasing β;
for hysteretic damping, the resonant frequency is the same for all η.
    2. For viscous damping, the static displacement (i.e., the dis-
placement as $\Omega\to0$) is the same for all β; for hysteretic damping, the
static displacement decreases with increasing η.
There are also differences in the absolute transmissibility curves for
oscillators with viscous or hysteretic damping, see Ref. [8] for details.
    It is helpful to distinguish between hysteretic damping as described
above and energy dissipation due to the generation of elastic-plastic
hysteresis loops. Elastic-plastic hysteresis is essentially a nonlinear
phenomenon,and we choose to exclude it from the present discussion which
is focused principally on linear damping mechanisms. A recent study of
the effects of elastic-plastic hysteresis on the steady-state response
of single- and multi-degree-of-freedom systems is given in Ref. [9].
    The use of the complex stiffness model for hysteretic damping for
free vibration or multiple-frequency forcing (such as force pulses) is
open to question [2, 10]. In such cases, linear rheological models can
be used [11]; a viscous model of hysteretic damping can be postulated
[12]; or a nonlinear model can be adopted [13]. However, the problem
of how best to model hysteretic damping for nonsinusoidal motion is
a persistant one. A recent attempt is given in Ref. [14]. It has been
suggested that the problem is more theoretical than practical and, in
this sense, is moot [15]. However, one's attitude on this depends on
one's taste in such matters.

It is of the upmost importance to recognize that the physical mechanism for hysteretic damping and the mathematical model of this mechanism
are distinct concepts. For example, the complex stiffness model is a
convenient, but not unique, way of representing hysteretic damping during
sinusoidal motion; Ref. [13] presents three alternatives to this
model. Similarly, for the nonsinusoidal case, extreme care must be used
in the choice of a mathematical model if the response is to be both
realistic and realizable.

Coulomb Damping

The energy dissipation in this case is due to dry friction between sliding surfaces. The normal force (N) and frictional force (F) between the
sliding surfaces are related by Coulomb's law,

$$F = \mu N$$

The direction of F is opposite to the relative velocity. The damping
force is thus a nonlinear function of the velocity and may be represented
mathematically by means of the signum function,[1]

$$F(t) = - \mu N \, sgn[\dot{x}(t)] \tag{9}$$

It can be shown that for sinusoidal response

$$c_{eq} = \frac{4\mu N}{\pi \Omega X} \tag{10}$$

and

$$D = 4\mu N X \tag{11}$$

This and other forms of nonlinear damping forces (in particular,
$F \propto (\dot{x})^n$) are discussed in Refs. [8, 16]. Techniques for computer
solution of single- and multiple-degree-of-freedom systems with
Coulomb damping are given in Ref. [17].
　　The damping provided by the joints of a built-up structure is often
called structural damping so as to distinguish it from material damping
and fluid damping. Coulomb damping is used to represent structural
damping due to relative slip at riveted or bolted joints. However, care
must be used since the dependence of D on μ for a fully slipped joint,
Eq. (18), is not the same as that for a partially slipped joint [18].
Also, joints can dissipate energy by mechanisms other than dry friction;
for example, by the "gas pumping" that results as adjacent surfaces

---

[1] $sgn(\dot{x}) = + 1$ for $\dot{x} > 0$; $sgn(\dot{x}) = - 1$ for $\dot{x} < 0$:
$sgn(\dot{x}) = 0$ for $\dot{x} = 0$

between fasteners move toward and away from one another; for details
see Ref. [18].

Structural damping is the least understood of the above three
phenomena. This is unfortunate for the design engineer since structural
damping usually dominates material and fluid damping. The damping of a
built-up structure is largely a function of how it is joined together
rather than the material of which it is made or the fluid by which it is
surrounded. Recognition of this simple fact can save much redesigning at
the vibration-testing phase of a project.

The above three damping hypotheses are based on physical conceptions
of the damping process. The choice of one hypothesis over another often
makes a negligible difference in the dynamic response of a system
[19]. For this reason, damping hypotheses have been introduced which
emphasize mathematical convenience more than physical processes,and we
shall discuss these next.

Proportional Damping

Proportional damping is sometimes called Rayleigh damping. For a single-
degree-of-freedom system the damping force is assumed to be a linear
function of the mass and stiffness, i.e.,

$$F(t) = - (a_0 m + a_1 k)\dot{x}(t) \tag{12}$$

where $\dot{x}(t)$ is the velocity. Note that if $a_0 = 0$ and $a_1 = n/\Omega$, this
becomes equivalent to the complex stiffness model of hysteretic damping.

This can be derived by assuming a dissipation function which is
quadratic in velocity:

$$R = \frac{1}{2} a_0 m\dot{x}^2 + \frac{1}{2} a_1 k\dot{x}^2$$
$$= \frac{1}{2} m\dot{x}^2 [a_0 + a_1 \omega^2] \tag{13}$$

The damping force is given by $F = -dR/d\dot{x}$. The dissipation function was
first introduced by Rayleigh [20]; the term "proportional" is probably
derived from the proportionality between R and the system kinetic energy.

Proportional damping is popular in multi-degree-of-freedom systems
because it leads to a damping matrix which is diagonalized by the same
transformation which diagonalizes the mass and stiffness matrices. This
is discussed in a later part of this review.

Equivalent Viscous Modal Damping

Modal analysis is a common method of solving multi-degree-of-freedom
systems. For damped systems this method requires that the governing
equations of motion be written in an uncoupled form for each mode. The
simplest way of accomplishing this is to replace the physical damping
process by equivalent viscous dampers, one for each normal mode of the
system.

Of course, one needs a rationale for selecting an equivalent viscous damping ratio for each mode. This can be as simple as choosing them from experience or as involved as measuring the frequency dependence of the damping of a particular mode shape and then choosing the equivalent viscous damping to match the actual damping at the natural frequency of that mode.

Guidance on representative values of equivalent viscous modal damping ratios is not easy to find in the literature. For the case of nuclear reactor structures, Ref. [21] is helpful and, for high-rise buildings, Ref. [22] can be consulted. Reference [23] and Chapter 8 of Ref. [4] contain lists of damping values for nuclear and nonnuclear steel and concrete structures. The effectiveness of viscoelastic materials in augmenting the damping of a variety of structures is discussed in Refs.[24,25].

Complex Stiffness

Using Eq. (4) for the damping force, the equation of motion of a single-degree-of-freedom system subjected to harmonic forcing can be written

$$m\underline{\ddot{X}} + ikn\underline{X} + k\underline{X} = \underline{F} \tag{14}$$

where ($\_$) denotes the complex phasor. Clearly, Eq. (14) can be written

$$m\underline{\ddot{X}} + k(1 + i\eta)\ \underline{X} = \underline{F} \tag{15}$$

or

$$m\underline{\ddot{X}} + \underline{k}\ \underline{X} = \underline{F}$$

where $\underline{k}$ is the complex stiffness. The physical solution to Eq. (15) is the real part of $\underline{X}e^{i\Omega t}$.

This method of representing the dynamic stiffness and damping is widely used for metals and polymers for example, see Refs. [1,26]. As mentioned above, this mathematical variant of hysteretic damping must be used with caution in the cases of free vibration and multi-frequency forcing, especially when the forcing function has a prominent zero frequency component.

In terms of viscoelastic materials, it is the complex modulus which is of interest. One writes

$$\underline{E} = E_1 + iE_2$$
$$\eta_M = E_2/E_1$$

where

E_1 is the storage modulus in direct stress

E_2 is the loss modulus in direct stress

n_M is the material loss factor in direct stress

These material properties are functions of temperature and frequency. For values of E_1 and n_M for some materials and their dependence on temperature and frequency, see Refs. [26, 27].

The hypothesis of a complex stiffness or modulus provides a very simple way of solving damped vibration problems analytically. Namely, first solve the undamped problem, e.g., for a single-degree-of-freedom sinusoidally forced oscillator,

$$x(t) = \frac{F \cos\Omega t}{k-m\Omega^2}$$

Then obtain the damped response by replacing k with $\underline{k} = k(1 + in)$ and take the real part:

$$x(t) = \text{Re}\left[\frac{Fe^{i\Omega t}}{\underline{k}-m\Omega^2}\right]$$

$$= \frac{F \cos(\Omega t + \phi)}{\sqrt{(k-m\Omega^2)^2 + (kn)^2}}$$

As is shown in [28], this method is equivalent to neglecting the imaginary part of the complex eigenvector associated with a damped system. In other words, one assumes that the eigenvector of the undamped mode is the same as that for the damped mode. The error introduced by this technique should be small unless the damping is large.

MATHEMATICAL ANALYSIS OF MULTI-DEGREE-OF-FREEDOM SYSTEMS

Modern problems in shock and vibration usually involve systems with many degrees of freedom and therefore require computer solution. For these problems, the concept of damping for a single degree-of-freedom, formulated in the previous section, must be expanded to the concept of a damping matrix. Quite often this damping matrix is not constructed directly from the material damping properties of the various components but is developed for mathematical convenience. In this section a mathematical analysis of the linear damping problem is given and in the next section a numerical example is worked out in detail.

The basic equation discussed in this section is

$$[m]\{\ddot{x}\} + [c]\{\dot{x}\} + [k]\{x\} = \{f(t)\} \tag{16}$$

in which [m], [c], and [k] denote the n x n mass, damping, and stiffness matrices, respectively, while {x} and {f(t)} are the n x 1 displacement and forcing function column matrices. Equation (16) represents n linear, coupled equations for the n degrees of freedom. In order to derive this equation, it is assumed that the analyst has modeled the original system to the accuracy desired. Typical modeling aids are the finite difference and finite element methods.

A common approach to the solution to this problem involves modal superposition using the eigenvalues and eigenvectors from the solution to the free vibration of the <u>undamped</u> system. The eigenproblem has the form

$$[k]\{\phi\} = \omega^2[m]\{\phi\} \tag{17}$$

Equation (17) may be transformed to the canonical form

$$[A]\{\psi\} = \omega^2\{\psi\} \tag{18}$$

where [A] is symmetric. An effective way of performing this transformation is the Cholesky decomposition. The eigenvalues, ω_i, can then be determined by any of a number of techniques, e.g., simultaneous iteration or the Householder-QR method. A discussion of these methods is given in Ref. [29]. The eigenvector $\{\phi\}_{(i)}$ associated with the ith mode is obtained by a transformation involving $\{\psi\}_{(i)}$. Due to the homogeneous nature of the eigenvalue problem, the elements of $\{\phi\}_{(i)}$ can only be determined to within an arbitrary multiplicative constant. For convenience of solution, a weighted modal matrix [ϕ] is constructed from the modal column matrices $\{\phi\}_{(i)}$ by dividing each column by the square root of the generalized mass for that mode M_i:

$$[\phi] = \left[\frac{1}{\sqrt{M_1}} \{\phi\}_{(1)} \;\middle|\; \frac{1}{\sqrt{M_2}} \{\phi\}_{(2)} \;\middle|\; \cdots \;\middle|\; \frac{1}{\sqrt{M_n}} \{\phi\}_{(n)} \right] \tag{19}$$

$$M_i = \{\phi\}_{(i)}^T [m]\{\phi\}_{(i)}$$

The orthogonality relationships then become

$$[\phi]^T[m][\phi] = [\ I\ ], \quad [\phi]^T[k][\phi] = \lceil \omega^2 \rfloor \tag{20}$$

The solution of the <u>damped</u> equations of motion by modal superposition is done by first transforming from the physical coordinates {x} to the coordinates {q} where

$$\{x\} = [\phi]\{q\} \tag{21}$$

Substitution into Eq. (16) and premultiplication by $[\phi]^T$ then yields

$$\{\ddot{q}\} + [\phi]^T[c][\phi]\{\dot{q}\} + \lceil\omega^2\rfloor\{q\} = [\phi]^T\{f(t)\} \tag{22}$$

The crucial step involves the diagonalization of the damping matrix $[\phi]^T[c][\phi]$. If this diagonalization cannot be done, there are other approximate and exact methods that may be used for the solution. These are discussed later.

Assuming that the diagonalization can be made by an orthogonality relationship of the form

$$[\phi]^T[c][\phi] = \lceil\tilde{c}\rfloor \tag{23}$$

then Eq. (22) becomes

$$\{\ddot{q}\} + \lceil\tilde{c}\rfloor\{\dot{q}\} + \lceil\omega^2\rfloor\{q\} = [\phi]^T\{f(t)\} \tag{24}$$

It is convenient at this stage to relate this equation to the standard form of the single-degree-of-freedom system [30]

$$\ddot{q} + 2\beta\omega\dot{q} + \omega^2 q = p(t) \tag{25}$$

in which β is the percent of critical damping (or damping ratio). The individual diagonal elements of $\lceil\tilde{c}\rfloor$ may then be written as

$$\tilde{c}_i = 2\beta_i\omega_i \qquad i = 1,2,\ldots,n \tag{26}$$

There has been a great deal of theoretical work done to ensure that uncoupled equations of this form are indeed obtained. Using the results of Eq. (20) it is obvious that uncoupling can be obtained if the damping matrix is proportional to the stiffness and/or mass matrix

$$[c] = a_0[m] + a_1[k] \tag{27}$$

This particular form of damping is the matrix form of proportional damping or Rayleigh damping discussed in the first section. Following the previous uncoupling procedure, Eq. (24) becomes

$$\{\ddot{q}\} + (a_0[\,I\,] + a_1\lceil\omega^2\rfloor)\{\dot{q}\} + \lceil\omega^2\rfloor\{q\} = [\phi]^T\{f(t)\} \tag{28}$$

Comparing this to an equivalent uncoupled case gives

$$\{\ddot{q}\} + 2 \lceil \beta\omega \rfloor \{\dot{q}\} + \lceil \omega^2 \rfloor \{q\} = [\phi]^T f(t) \qquad (29)$$

It is found by equating the $\{\dot{q}\}$ coefficients that

$$2\lceil \beta\omega \rfloor = a_0 [\ I\ ] + a_1 \lceil \omega^2 \rfloor \qquad (30)$$

Thus, for any mode i, the damping ratio may be written

$$\beta_i = \frac{a_0}{2\omega_i} + \frac{a_1\omega_i}{2} \qquad i = 1,\ldots,n \qquad (31)$$

When the damping matrix of Eq. (27) is proportional to the mass matrix ($a_1 = 0$), it follows from Eq. (31) that the damping ratio is inversely proportional to the frequency so that the higher modes will have very little damping. If the damping matrix is proportional to the stiffness matrix ($a_0 = 0$), the damping ratio grows linearly with frequency. These variations in the damping ratio are depicted in Fig. 1. Since the use of the Rayleigh damping matrix involves only two arbitrary constants, a_0 and a_1, the damping ratio β_i can only be specified in two modes; values of β_i for other modes are then fixed by Eq. (31). The modes used to calculate a_0 and a_1 are usually determined from the physics of the problem. For example, choosing the first two modes for this purpose tends to damp out the effects of the high-frequency components. A technique that is quite common in practice is to calculate a_0 and a_1 based on the lowest and highest modes that are expected to be of importance to the solution of the problem. The remaining modes between these extreme modes will then have reasonable values of damping.

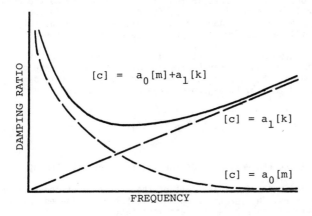

Fig. 1 Damping variation with frequency for Rayleigh damping

A relationship for [c] that is more general than Eq. (27), but which retains the crucial orthogonality condition, was derived by Caughey in 1960 [31]. A convenient form of this Caughey series is given in Ref. [32].

$$[c] = [m] \sum_{b=0}^{n-1} a_b ([m]^{-1}[k])^b \qquad (32)$$

$$= a_0[m] + a_1[k] + \ldots$$

Using the orthogonality relationship from Eq. (23) gives

$$\lceil c \rfloor = \left[\sum_{b=0}^{n=1} a_b \omega^{2b} \right] \qquad (33)$$

From Eq. (26) it then follows that

$$\beta_i = \frac{1}{2} \left(\frac{a_0}{\omega_i} + a_1\omega_i + a_2\omega_i^3 + \ldots + a_{n-1}\omega_i^{2n-3} \right) \quad i = 1,2,\ldots n \qquad (34)$$

It is interesting to note that the first two terms of this series correspond to the special case of Rayleigh damping, Eq. (31). The damping ratios in all the modes can now be controlled, with the constants a_i appropriately determined from the solution of the simultaneous equations dictated by Eq. (34). This may lead to numerical difficulties at high frequency because of the large numerical values of the natural frequency terms. An alternative method that eliminates some of these numerical problems is discussed in [32]. It should be noted that the damping ratio is often specified in only the first k modes that are the most important in the solution. The constants in Eq. (34) corresponding to the remaining terms are then set equal to zero. The damping ratios in these modes $i = k + 1,\ldots n$ are not zero and are still calculated from Eq. (34). Once again, this will tend to damp out the effects of the high-frequency components.

As was pointed out for a single-degree-of-freedom system, the complex model of hysteretic damping can be thought of as a special case of proportional damping. The complex stiffness model of hysteretic damping may also be extended to a multi-degree-of-freedom system. Let

$$[\underline{k}] = [k]_R + in[k]_I \qquad (35)$$

where
$[k]_R$ contains the real part of the stiffness of all elements of the system
$[k]_I$ contains the imaginary part of the stiffness of those elements which have hysteretic damping. It has been assumed that all these elements have the same loss factor.

For sinusoidal forcing, Eq. (16) may be written

$$[m]\{\underline{\ddot{X}}\} + [k]_R\{\underline{X}\} + in[k]_I\{\underline{X}\} = \{\underline{F}\} \tag{36}$$

where $\ddot{X}$ is the acceleration phasor, i.e., $\{\ddot{x}\} = \{\ddot{x}\} e^{i\Omega t}$; Eq. (21) now becomes $\{\underline{X}\} = [\phi]\{Q\}$ where $[\phi]$ is the (real) modal matrix of the undamped eigenvalue problem. Under this transformation, one finds as before

$$[\phi]^T[m][\phi] = \lceil M \rfloor, \text{ the modal masses}$$
$$[\phi]^T[k]_R[\phi] = \lceil K \rfloor, \text{ the modal stiffnesses} \tag{37}$$

so that Eq. (36) becomes

$$\lceil M \rfloor\{\ddot{Q}\} + \lceil K \rfloor\{Q\} + in[\phi]^T[k]_I[\phi]\{Q\} = [\phi]^T\{\underline{F}\} \tag{38}$$

By analogy with the single-degree-of-freedom case, one may then define a global loss factor for each mode i as

$$n_{g,i} = n \frac{\{\phi_i\}^T[k]_I\{\phi_i\}}{\{\phi_i\}^T[k]_R\{\phi_1\}}$$

If $\{Q\}$ and $\{F\}$ are separated into their real and imaginary parts, the equations of motion become

$$\begin{bmatrix} \lceil K \rfloor - \Omega^2 \lceil M \rfloor & -n[\phi]^T[k]_I[\phi] \\ n[\phi]^T[k]_I[\phi] & \lceil K \rfloor - \Omega^2 \lceil M \rfloor \end{bmatrix} \begin{Bmatrix} \{Q\}_R \\ \{Q\}_I \end{Bmatrix} = \begin{Bmatrix} [\phi]^T\{F\}_R \\ [\phi]^T\{F\}_I \end{Bmatrix} \tag{39}$$

The $2n \times 2n$ matrix in Eq. (39) is skew-symmetric and sparse so solution can be fairly efficient. In Ref. [33] Lalanne and his colleagues present a perturbation method for solving Eq. (39) which permits the use of frequency-dependent material properties.

If the damping matrix can not be diagonalized by the aforementioned methods, it is termed nonproportional and the transformed equations of motion (22) remain coupled. Because of the desirability of using modal superposition based on the vibration characteristics of the undamped system, a number of engineering approximations have been developed. The simplest approach is to perform the transformation of Eq. (23) and neglect the off-diagonal terms

$$\lceil \tilde{c} \rfloor = [\phi]^T[c][\phi] \tag{40}$$

It is of interest to consider the physical meaning of neglecting these
off-diagonal terms. A term on the diagonal represents the damping
force of a mode due to motion in that mode. A term off the diagonal is
associated with the damping force on a mode due to motion in another mode,
in effect coupling the modes. The usual case of small damping involves
dominant terms along the diagonal and small terms off the diagonal.
Therefore, by neglecting these off-diagonal terms it is implied that the
damping is small enough to make the coupling a second-order effect.
Recently, the results of Thomson, Calkins, and Caravani [19] have indicated
that this technique is accurate enough for engineering purposes for the
solution of lumped-mass systems subject to sinusoidal forcing functions.
A criterion in terms of damping ratio and frequency separation which will
ensure that the diagonalization process does not cause excessive errors in
the dynamic response of a system has been given by Warburton and Soni
[34]. Although this criterion is formulated from a study based on
harmonic excitation, the numerical results indicate that the level of
errors for random and aperiodic excitation is similar.
   Another technique that has been successful in dealing with nonproportional damping matrices involves comparing the steady-state sinusoidal response of the actual system containing the nonproportional
damping matrix to the response of the system with an assumed diagonal
damping matrix. Typically,this comparison is made at the various peak
amplitudes of the response. The equivalent modal damping ratio can then
be found by interative solution of the resulting simultaneous algebraic
equations as discussed by Tsai [35]. Although this technique is
apparently more accurate than the preceding method [19], of simply ignor-
ing the off-diagonal terms in the transformed damping matrix, it does
have some obvious limitations. First of all, it is necessary to solve
the coupled problem which may be a time-consuming task. Secondly, there
is the question of which location in the system to use for matching the
coupled and modal solutions. Tsai [35] suggests the location that is
most sensitive to the damping value; for ground motion input to an
idealized building, it is suggested that the top mass be used for comparison purposes. Finally, it would appear that the method is most efficient
for natural frequencies that are widely spaced.
   Another method that is useful for nonproportional problems is the
strain energy weighted modal rule first proposed by Biggs [36]. Although
partly derived on intuitive grounds, the method is related to the neglect
of the off-diagonal terms in Eq. (40). The equivalent modal damping ratio
in the ith mode, β_i, is expressed in terms of the damping ratio for each
element of the system with a weighting factor in the form of the maximum
elastic strain energy of each element j in the ith mode of vibration
$(SE)_{j_{max}}^{(i)}$. For a system in which all the damping is of a hysteretic type,
the equivalent modal damping ratio may be conveniently written in terms
of the loss factor for each element n_j,

$$\beta_i = \frac{\sum_j (n_j/2)(SE)_{j_{max}}^{(i)}}{\sum_j (SE)_{j_{max}}^{(i)}} \qquad (41)$$

It is interesting to note that if all the elements have a constant loss factor, η_j = constant, then the modal damping ratio β_j is a constant for all the modes of vibration. In Ref. [37], dealing with a soil-structure interaction problem, this strain energy weighted technique is extended to include the effects of hysteretic and viscous damping elements acting simultaneously.

The previous paragraphs describe approximate methods for uncoupling the equations of motion when the damping matrix is nonproportional. These methods are based upon the real eigenvalue problem, Eq. (17), associated with the undamped equations of motion, These methods should be reasonably accurate if the damping is light. However, it is also possible to derive an exact method for uncoupling when the damping matrix is nonproportional. This technique is based upon the complex eigenvalue problem associated with the damped equations of motion of Eq. (16),

$$(\lambda^2[m] + \lambda[c] + [k])\{\theta\} = \{0\} \tag{42}$$

which, in general, leads to complex eigenvalues and eigenvectors. As shown in Ref. [28], orthogonality relations exist between the eigenvalues and eigenvectors of Eq. (42) so that a modal superposition solution of Eq. (16) can be done for an arbitrary forcing function. Since Eq. (42) is not in a standard eigenvalue form, efficient numerical techniques have not been developed. However, the complex eigenvalue problem can be reduced to standard eigenvalue form as follows. One adds to Eq. (16) the trivial equation $[m]\{\dot{x}\} - [m]\{\dot{x}\} = 0$ (see Ref. [38]) and partitions these to form

$$[A]\{\dot{y}\} + [B]\{y\} = \{F(t)\} \tag{43}$$

where

$$[A] = \begin{bmatrix} [0] & [m] \\ [m] & [c] \end{bmatrix} \quad ; \quad [B] = \begin{bmatrix} -[m] & [0] \\ [0] & [k] \end{bmatrix}$$

$$\{y\} = \begin{Bmatrix} \{\dot{x}\} \\ \{x\} \end{Bmatrix} \quad ; \quad \{F(t)\} = \begin{Bmatrix} \{0\} \\ \{f(t)\} \end{Bmatrix} \tag{44}$$

The standard eigenvalue problem is obtained by setting $\{f(t)\} = 0$ and introducing $\{y\} = \{\psi\} \exp\lambda t$; that is,

$$\lambda[A]\{\psi\} + [B]\{\psi\} = \{0\} \tag{45}$$

If rigid body modes have been removed, [B] possesses an inverse and we may write

$$- [B]^{-1}[A]\{\psi\} = \frac{1}{\lambda}\{\psi\}$$

or

$$\begin{bmatrix} [0] & [I] \\ -[k]^{-1}[m] & -[k]^{-1}[c] \end{bmatrix} \{\psi\} = \frac{1}{\lambda}\{\psi\}$$

which is in standard form. An alternate standard form can be obtained by transforming to Eq. (22) before the above procedure is applied. The matrices in Eq. (45) are symmetric but not positive-definite, and in general, the eigenvalues and eigenvectors,will be complex. There are 2n eigenvalues and eigenvectors, both of which occur in conjugate pairs. The relationship between these eigenvalues and eigenvectors and those of Eq. (42) are given in Ref. [39]. If a modal matrix is formed from the eigenvectors of Eq. (45), it provides a coordinate transformation of the form of Eq. (21) which uncouples the damped equation of motion [40]. It then follows that the equations of motion for a forced vibration problem may be solved by modal superposition techniques using the above damped eigenvalues. These procedures are given in detail in Chapter 9 of [41]. Although this uncoupling technique for nonproportional damping is exact, it is not often used since for lightly damped systems the additional accuracy of this exact procedure is small and difficult to justify. Another factor to be considered is the large uncertainty which is usually associated with damping values for structures and equipment. However, if the damping is heavy or if the damping varies widely in a system, the gains in accuracy may be worth the added complexity of the analysis. A practical example in which both small and large modal damping ratios exist is in the multi-degree-of-freedom modeling of a railroad vehicle, which includes car body, truck, and wheel-rail interaction effects [42]. The large values of damping are due mainly to the creep forces which are generated between the wheels and the rails due to the difference in the rates of strain in the contact region. An interesting phenomenon may occur when the forward velocity of the vehicle increases: some of the modal damping ratios decrease with velocity and eventually become negative (i.e., the real part of the eigenvalue λ becomes positive). When a damping ratio becomes negative, it defines a critical velocity for that mode; such a velocity can be interpreted as a boundary of linear stability.

Another method that can be used for the nonproportional damping problem is the method of characteristic phase lags, introduced by Fraeijs de Veubeke [43]. Consider Eq. (16) for sinusoidal forcing

$$[m]\{\ddot{x}\} + [c]\{\dot{x}\} + [k]\{x\} = \{f\} \cos\Omega t \tag{46}$$

and assume a solution of the form $\{x\} = \{\phi\} \cos(\Omega t - \theta)$.

This combination produces the eigenvalue problem

$$[([k] - [m]\Omega^2)\tan\theta - [c]\Omega]\{\phi\} = \{0\} \tag{47}$$

which has n eigenvalues θ_i (the characteristic phase lags) and n eigenvectors $\{\phi\}_i$. There is also a forcing vector $\{f\}_i$ associated with each $\{\phi\}_i$. For this reason the $\{\phi\}_i$ are called "forced modes." The eigenvectors have orthogonality properties which permit the equations of motion to be uncoupled. The eigenvectors $\{\phi\}_i$ depend on the forcing frequency and this fact complicates the use of this method. In Ref. [44], it is shown that if $[c] = i[h]$, this dependence of $\{\phi\}_i$ on Ω disappears, and furthermore, if $[h] = n[k]$, the damped forced modes become identical to the undamped normal modes.

So far, this discussion has been based on solution by modal superposition. However, an alternative and widely used method is direct numerical integration of the equations of motion. Recent reviews of the relative advantages and disadvantages of these two techniques are given by Belytschko [45] and Chopra [46]. One obvious advantage of direct numerical integration is that the full damping matrix [c] can be utilized, although in many practical problems a banded form of the damping matrix is desirable to control computer costs. The implicit and explicit integration methods used for step-by-step solution in the time domain are not hampered by the introduction of the damping terms. Although both modal superposition and direct numerical integration may be used to solve linear problems, for nonlinear problems the direct integration technique tends to be a more convenient and powerful tool since [k] and [c] may be altered at various stages of the numerical procedure. Among the general disadvantages of direct integration are that it essentially provides no information about the modal characteristics. Also for problems in which the contribution from the first few modes is predominate, the method tends to be relatively expensive to use if the time increment Δt is chosen small enough to accurately include the effect of all n equations. Recent investigators have adopted a strategy to circumvent this difficulty. This involves choosing an unconditionally stable integration algorithm which exhibits amplitude decay as a function of $\Delta t/T$ (where T is the period). This decay phenomenon may be viewed as a form of artifical damping which is added to any existing damping. If only the first N modes are important in the dynamic response, the $\Delta t/T$ ratio is set to accurately calculate the effects of these modes and the higher modes will then damp out, with the highest frequency modes damping out the quickest. Essentially, the higher mode response is filtered out of the solution, [47]. Several investigators have also pursued the possibility of direct integration of the coupled modal equations Eq. (22). If only the first N undamped modes are important in the dynamic response,

$$\{x\} = [\bar{\phi}]\{\bar{q}\} \quad (N<n) \tag{48}$$

a modal truncation is first performed where $[\bar{\phi}]$ retains the first N modal column vectors and $\bar{q}$ is an N x 1 vector. Although the resulting set of truncated equations in $\bar{q}$ is still coupled due to the nonproportional damping matrix, the equations often requires less time to integrate numerically than the full set of coupled equations of motion in terms of the original physical coordinates. A discussion of this truncation technique including accuracy and numerical integration time considerations is given in Ref. [48].

There are certain classes of problems for which the damping terms are functions of frequency, and it is not adequate to replace these terms by average values that are independent of frequency [10, 49]. For problems of this type it is useful to transform the equations to the frequency domain with a Fourier transform and then to incorporate the correct relationship between damping and frequency. After solution in the frequency domain, an inverse Fourier transform is used to return to the time domain. Until recently, this procedure was not computationally efficient even when using discrete Fourier transforms. However, the development of the fast Fourier transform (FFT), an accurate and efficient algorithm for computing discrete Fourier transforms, has radically changed this entire situation [50,51]. Many special purpose FFT programs have been written to facilitate this procedure and the technique appears to be competitive with direct numerical time integration for certain problems.

NUMERICAL EXAMPLE

In order to provide more insight into the physical applications of the previous theoretical discussion, the system shown in Fig. 2 will be investigated in detail. For identical masses of m lb-sec^2/ft and identical springs of stiffness k lb/ft, the following matrices can be derived

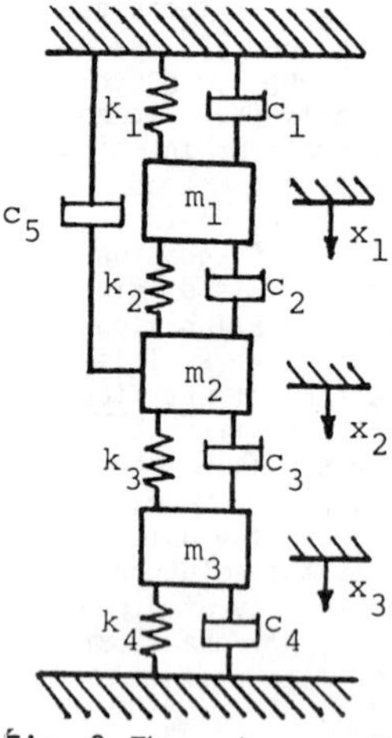

$$[m] = \begin{bmatrix} m_1 & & \\ & m_2 & \\ & & m_3 \end{bmatrix} = m \begin{bmatrix} 1 & & \\ & 1 & \\ & & 1 \end{bmatrix}$$

$$[k] = \begin{bmatrix} (k_1+k_2) & -k_2 & 0 \\ -k_2 & (k_2+k_3) & -k_3 \\ 0 & -k_3 & (k_3+k_4) \end{bmatrix} = k \begin{bmatrix} 2 & -1 & 0 \\ -1 & 2 & -1 \\ 0 & -1 & 2 \end{bmatrix}$$

$$[c] = \begin{bmatrix} (c_1+c_2) & -c_2 & 0 \\ -c_2 & (c_2+c_3+c_5) & -c_3 \\ 0 & -c_3 & (c_3+c_4) \end{bmatrix} \quad ; \quad \{x\} = \begin{Bmatrix} x_1 \\ x_2 \\ x_3 \end{Bmatrix}$$

(49)

Fig. 2 Three-degree-of-freedom-system

Using standard methods to solve Eq. (17), the undamped free vibration characteristics of the system are

$$\omega_1 = 0.76537\sqrt{k/m}, \quad \omega_2 = 1.41421\sqrt{k/m}, \quad \omega_3 = 1.84776\sqrt{k/m} \ \frac{rad}{sec} \tag{50}$$

$$\{\phi\}_{(1)} = \begin{Bmatrix} .7071 \\ 1.0 \\ .7071 \end{Bmatrix}, \quad \{\phi\}_{(2)} = \begin{Bmatrix} 1.0 \\ 0 \\ -1.0 \end{Bmatrix}, \quad \{\phi\}_{(3)} = \begin{Bmatrix} .7071 \\ -1.0 \\ .7071 \end{Bmatrix}$$

Following Eq. (19) the weighted modal matrix is formed

$$[\phi] = \begin{bmatrix} \frac{1}{\sqrt{2m}} \begin{Bmatrix} .7071 \\ 1.0 \\ .7071 \end{Bmatrix} & \frac{1}{\sqrt{2m}} \begin{Bmatrix} 1.0 \\ 0 \\ -1.0 \end{Bmatrix} & \frac{1}{\sqrt{2m}} \begin{Bmatrix} .7071 \\ -1.0 \\ .7071 \end{Bmatrix} \end{bmatrix} \tag{51}$$

Several calculations will now be done illustrating methods of controlling damping in specified modes and the resulting effects in other modes. Yeh [52] has presented several numerical calculations of damping ratios with application to nuclear reactor containment vessels. As an initial example, consider the case of proportional damping in the specialized form of $[c] = a_1[k]$. Then from Eq. (20) it follows that

$$[\phi]^T[c][\phi] = a_1 \ulcorner \omega^2 \lrcorner \tag{52}$$

Comparison to the equivalent uncoupled system of Eq. (29)

$$\{\ddot{q}\} + 2\ulcorner \beta\omega \lrcorner\{\dot{q}\} + \ulcorner \omega^2 \lrcorner\{q\} = [\phi]^T\{f(t)\} \tag{53}$$

leads to

$$2\ulcorner \beta\omega \lrcorner = a_1 \ulcorner \omega^2 \lrcorner$$

$$\beta_1 = \frac{a_1}{2} \omega_1 \ , \quad \beta_2 = \frac{a_1}{2} \omega_2, \quad \beta_3 = \frac{a_1}{2} \omega_3 \tag{54}$$

This shows quite clearly the increase in modal damping ratio with natural frequency as predicted by Eq. (31) (for $a_0 = 0$). Since there is one arbitrary constant involved, a_1, damping can be specified in just one mode with the remaining values dictated by Eq. (54). Picking this to be 5% in the first mode leads to

$$a_1 = .13066\sqrt{m/k}$$

$$\beta_1 = .05 \; , \; \beta_2 = .092 \; , \; \beta_3 = .121$$

$$[c] = \sqrt{km} \begin{bmatrix} .26132 & -.13066 & 0 \\ -.13066 & .26132 & -.13066 \\ 0 & -.13066 & .26132 \end{bmatrix} \quad (55)$$

Comparison of this damping matrix with Eq. (49) leads to the following values of the component damping coefficients $c_1 = c_2 = c_3 = c_4 = .13066\sqrt{km}$, $c_5 = 0$. If, instead of fixing the damping in the first mode, the constant a_1 is chosen to fix the damping ratio at 5% in the second mode, then the following values are found

$$a_1 = .07071\sqrt{m/k}$$

$$\beta_1 = .027 \quad , \quad \beta_2 = .05 \quad , \quad \beta_3 = .065$$

$$[c] = \sqrt{km} \begin{bmatrix} .14142 & -.07071 & 0 \\ -.07071 & .14142 & -.07071 \\ 0 & -.07071 & .14142 \end{bmatrix} \quad (56)$$

Consider the same system with the dissipative mechanism associated with material or hysteretic damping. Assuming that each element has the same loss factor η associated with it, the equivalent damping matrix extension of Eq. (6) that is proportional to the stiffness matrix may be written in the form

$$[c] = \frac{\eta}{\Omega} [k] \quad (57)$$

This leads to

$$2 \lceil \beta\omega \rfloor = \frac{\eta}{\Omega} \lceil \omega^2 \rfloor$$

$$\beta_1 = \frac{\eta}{2} \frac{\omega_1}{\Omega} \; , \quad \beta_2 = \frac{\eta}{2} \frac{\omega_2}{\Omega} \; , \quad \beta_3 = \frac{\eta}{2} \frac{\omega_3}{\Omega} \quad (58)$$

For small damping the frequency Ω may be approximated by the value of the natural frequency ω_i associated with the ith mode [10]. Thus

$$\beta_1 = \beta_2 = \beta_3 = \eta/2 \tag{59}$$

This shows that if the damping in the system is light, uniform, and hysteretic, the damping ratio is a constant for all the modes and is identical to the component damping ratio at resonance. If the damping ratio is specified as 5% in the first mode, it remains 5% in all the modes. These results for hysteretic damping may also be deduced from the strain energy damping rule expressed in Eq. (41).

For the case of Rayleigh or proportional damping, the damping matrix takes the form $[c] = a_0[m] + a_1[k]$. From Eq. (31) the relation between the damping ratio and the constants a_0, a_1 is

$$\beta_i = \frac{a_0}{2\omega_i} + \frac{a_1\omega_i}{2} \quad i = 1,2,3 \tag{60}$$

Assuming that the damping ratio is fixed at 5% in the first two modes, the constants a_0 and a_1 may be calculated from Eq. (60) as $a_0 = .04966\sqrt{k/m}$, $a_1 = .04588\sqrt{m/k}$. This leads to

$$\beta_1 = .05 \quad , \quad \beta_2 = .05 \quad , \quad \beta_3 = .056$$

$$[c] = \sqrt{km} \begin{bmatrix} .14142 & -.04588 & 0 \\ -.04588 & .14142 & -.04588 \\ 0 & -.04588 & .14142 \end{bmatrix} \tag{61}$$

It is interesting to note that the damping ratio in the third mode is quite close to the 5% value of the first two modes. Comparison of the damping matrices of Eq. (61) and Eq. (49) leads to $c_1 = c_4 = .09554\sqrt{km}$, $c_2 = c_3 = .04588\sqrt{km}$, $c_5 = .04966\sqrt{km}$. The damping matrices of Eq. (61) and Eq. (56) show a close comparison (particularly with respect to the dominant diagonal elements) even though in the latter case the damping was only fixed in the second mode. However, the damping ratios in the two cases differ importantly for the first mode. In addition, the damping component from m_2 to ground is zero from Eq. (56), while in the present proportional damping case it is found to have the value $c_5 = .04966\sqrt{km}$.

The damping ratio can be controlled in all three modes by using the Caughey series approach outlined in Eqs. (32-34). Fixing the damping ratio at 5% in each mode, the constants a_0, a_1, a_2 are calculated from the three simultaneous equations associated with

$$\beta_i = \frac{1}{2} \left(\frac{a_0}{\omega_i} + a_1\omega_i + a_2\omega_i^3 \right) \quad i = 1,2,3 \tag{62}$$

This produces $a_0 = .04335\sqrt{k/m}$, $a_1 = .05980\sqrt{m/k}$, $a_2 = -0.00538(m/k)^{3/2}$.
Reasonable comparison is expected for the approaches based on the Caughey
series and proportional damping since this latter method led to a damping
ratio in the third mode only 12% above the desired value of $\beta_3 = .05$.
The actual damping matrix may now be found from

$$[c] = [m] \sum_{b=0}^{2} a_b ([m]^{-1}[k])^b$$

$$[c] = \sqrt{km} \begin{bmatrix} .13605 & -.03828 & -.00538 \\ -.03828 & .13067 & -.03828 \\ -.00538 & -.03828 & .13605 \end{bmatrix} \qquad (63)$$

From comparison with Eq. (49), it is immediately apparent that the present
matrix is no longer tri-diagonal; there now exists a component connecting
m_1 to m_3 (see Fig. 1) with damping value $.00538\sqrt{km}$. For all the previous
calculations this component had zero damping coefficient. However, in
order to control damping in all three modes, a nonzero value for this
far-coupled term is now required. The rest of the damping constants are
$c_1 = c_4 = .09239\sqrt{km}$, $c_2 = c_3 = .03828\sqrt{km}$, $c_5 = .05411\sqrt{km}$. The diagonalization of the transformed damping matrix follows from Eq. (23)

$$[\phi]^T[c][\phi] = \sqrt{km} \begin{bmatrix} .0765 & & \\ & .1414 & \\ & & .1848 \end{bmatrix} \qquad (64)$$

From Eqs. (50) and (53) it follows that $\beta_1 = \beta_2 = \beta_3 = 5\%$.
    For nonproportional damping the transformed matrix is no longer
diagonal. Typically nonproportional damping occurs when the damping matrix
is composed directly from the individual damping values of the components.
For example, consider the previous case involving the matrix of Eq. (63),
but now arbitrarily double the value of the damping constant c_5 associated
with the component from m_2 to ground. The damping matrix is now slightly
different from that of Eq. (63) since the (2,2) element is altered, i.e.,

$$[c] = \sqrt{km} \begin{bmatrix} .13605 & -.03828 & -.00538 \\ -.03828 & .18478 & -.03828 \\ -.00538 & -.03828 & .13605 \end{bmatrix} \qquad (65)$$

The transformation of the damping matrix then leads to the nondiagonal form

$$[\phi]^T[c][\phi] = \sqrt{k/m} \begin{bmatrix} .1036 & 0 & -.0271 \\ 0 & .1414 & 0 \\ -.0271 & 0 & .2119 \end{bmatrix} \qquad (66)$$

To continue with a solution based on modal superposition, the usual assumption as expressed by Eq. (40) is to neglect the off-diagonal terms and define equivalent modal damping values based on the diagonal terms of Eq. (66). For many different types of forcing functions of practical importance this technique would produce adequate answers for dynamic response since the off-diagonal terms are much smaller than the diagonal terms. The damping ratios based on this approximation are β_1 = .068, β_2 = .05, β_3 = .057; the damping ratio in the second mode remains the same value as that found from the Caughey series approach leading to Eq. (64). This is expected on physical grounds since in the second mode of vibration the middle mass remains stationary. Therefore, increasing the damping of the dissipative element from m_2 to ground should have no influence on β_2. However, as expected, β_1 and β_3 are increased since extra damping has been added to the overall system. As a rigorous check on the damping ratios found by neglecting the off-diagonal terms of Eq. (66), the equations of motion including the full damping matrix of Eq. (65) can be solved using the complex mode approach outlined in Eqs. (42-44) . The solutions for the complex eigenvalue λ, and the damping ratios, are

$$\lambda_{1,2} = (-.0518 \pm i\ .7637)\sqrt{\frac{k}{m}}\ ,\ \beta_{1,2} = .068$$

$$\lambda_{3,4} = (-.0707 \pm i\ 1.4124)\sqrt{\frac{k}{m}}\ ,\ \beta_{3,4} = .050$$

$$\lambda_{5,6} = (-.1059 \pm i\ 1.8445)\sqrt{\frac{k}{m}}\ ,\ \beta_{5,6} = .057$$

The fact that the damping ratios remain the same shows the effectiveness of the aforementioned engineering approximation for lightly damped systems.

It is of interest to investigate the form [c]' of the approximate diagonalized damping matrix when it is transformed back to the original physical system. Letting $\lceil \tilde{c} \rfloor$ be this diagonalized form of Eq. (66), obtained by omitting the off-diagonal terms, it follows that

$$[c]' = ([\phi]^{-1})^T \lceil c \rfloor [\phi]^{-1}$$

$$[c]' = \sqrt{km} \begin{bmatrix} .1496 & -.0383 & .0082 \\ -.0383 & .1577 & -.0383 \\ .0082 & -.0383 & .1496 \end{bmatrix} \tag{67}$$

The damping matrices of Eq. (65) and Eq. (67) differ, as expected. In particular, from Eq. (67) it follows that the damper between m_1 and m_3 now has a negative value of damping coefficient. However, the damping matrix can be shown to be positive definite by a simple application of Sylvester's theorem [53].

COMPUTER PROGRAMS

The authors surveyed both users and developers of general purpose computer programs in shock and vibration via a mailed questionnaire to ascertain the types of damping models which are available and the success of these programs in predicting the damped response of discrete, multi-degree-of-freedom systems. The results of this survey are reported below with most of the remarks limited to the damping aspect of the programs. Further general information on these programs is available in Ref. [45].

A major caveat of the reported comments is the confusion generated by simple labels. Many programs with the same acronym appear to have both public and private versions; accordingly, the capabilities and user reactions may vary depending on the version involved. In addition, a number of special purpose programs were reported, but it was decided not to list all of these because of uncertainty about the limitations of program availabilities and capabilities.

Program ANSYS

Capability: Can accept discrete viscous, hysteretic,and Coulomb dampers as well as proportional damping matrices (and complex stiffness matrices). The program will compute equivalent modal damping parameters based on supplied material damping properties.
Method: The method of solution is direct integration,and both linear and nonlinear responses may be calculated.
Usage: It has been successfully used for damped response under conditions of free vibration, harmonic forcing, force transients, seismic excitation, and random input.
Availability: Available from Swanson Analysis Systems, Inc., Johnson Road, P.O. Box 65, Houston, PA 15342, (412)746-3304

Program ASKA II

Capability: Accepts either proportional damping matrices or equivalent viscous modal damping
Method: Modal superposition

Usage: Successful solutions have been obtained for free vibration,
    harmonic forcing, transient forcing, seismic excitation, and
    random excitation.
Availability: Institut für Statik and Dynamick, Pfaffenwaldring 27,
    Stuttgart, 80, W. Germany

Program ASTRE

Capability: Accepts a complex stiffness matrix. All viscoelastic
    finite elements must have the same loss factor.
Method: Modal superposition
Usage: Has been used successfully to determine the dynamic response of
    thick structures damped by viscoelastic layers and subjected to
    harmonic forcing
Availability: Laboratoire de Mécanique des Structures, Institut
    National des Sciences Appliquées de Lyon, 69621 Villeurbanne,
    France

Program DAMP

Capability: A damping matrix, as well as a stiffness and a mass
    matrix, must be supplied as input. The program then computes the
    complex eigenvalues and eigenvectors associated with these matrices.
Method: Vibration problems are solved by modal superposition.
Usage: Any structure can be analyzed provided the mass, stiffness, and
    damping matrices of the structure can be obtained. The program
    has been successfully used to solve practical problems via complex
    modal superposition.
Availability: COSMIC, Barrow Hall, University of Georgia, Athens, GA,
    30601.

Program KSHEL

Capability: This program is available in two versions, KSHEL 1D
    and KSHEL 3D   KSHEL 1D is used for harmonic forcing and incor-
    porates damping by means of a complex stiffness. KSHEL 3D
    accepts discrete viscous or hysteretic dampers and is used for
    free vibration or transient forcing functions.
Method: The damped transient analysis uses modal superposition based
    on the undamped modes. However, KSHEL 3D can also compute the
    complex eigenvalues and eigenvectors.
Usage: These programs have been successful in cases of free vibration,
    harmonic forcing, and general transient response. Their
    principal usage has been in shell dynamics.
Availability: These programs are available from Prof. A. Kalnins,
    Dept. of Mech. Engr., Lehigh University, Bethlehem, PA 18015.

Program MINI-ELAS

Capability: Uses equivalent viscous damping
Method: Modal superposition.
Usage: Has been successful with random input
Availability: Contact Dr. I. B. Alpay, Dept. of Civil Engr.,
    Duke University, Durham, NC 27706.

Program MARC

Capability: Will accept discrete viscous dashpots, proportional damp-
     ing, and equivalent modal viscous damping.
Method: Program provides the option of modal superposition or direct
     integration.
Usage: Many forms of structures have been successfully analyzed includ-
     ing stiffened and layered shells under transient loading. Will
     not accept random loading. Acceptable comparison with measured
     responses have been obtained for nonlinear systems.
Availability: This program is available on the CDC Cybernet Service
     or from MARC Analysis Research Corp, 314 Courthouse Plaza,
     Palo Alto, CA 94306.

Program NASTRAN

Capability: All damping formats may be used.
Method: Direct integration or modal superposition is available. If
     damped harmonic response is computed by modal superposition,
     equivalent viscous modal damping must be used. If damped harmonic
     response is computed by direct integration, discrete viscous
     damper, discrete hysteretic dampers, or a complex stiffness matrix
     may be used. The complex stiffness matrix allows each finite
     element to have a different loss factor. Transient response with
     damping may be solved by direct integration or modal superposition;
     Coulomb damping may be used in conjunction with direct integration.
     The program will also compute complex eigenvalues and eigenvectors.
     It will also accept a user-supplied damping matrix.
Usage: Success was reported for problems involving periodic and shock
     pulse excitations.
Availability: The public version is available from COSMIC.

Program SAMIS

Capability: Equivalent viscous modal damping and discrete viscous dampers
Method: Modal superposition. SAMIS can compute complex eigenvalues and
     eigenvectors.
Usage: Success was reported for a variety of practical problems.
Availability: COSMIC

Program SAPIV

Capability: Proportional damping, equivalent viscous modal damping, or
     nonproportional damping are permitted. Several users have modified
     SAPIV to accommodate the complex stiffness model of hysteretic
     damping.
Method: Modal superposition is used for proportional damping and equiv-
     alent viscous modal damping. Direct integration is used for non-
     proportional damping.
Usage: Success was reported for structures subjected to general force
     transients and seismic excitation.

Availability: National Information Service Earthquake Engineering/
     Computer Program Applications, Davis Hall, Univ. of California,
     Berkeley, CA 94720, (415)642-5113. Documentation is also available
     in the Software Series, Volume II; see Chapter 1 of this volume for
     dissemination information.

Program STARDYNE

Capability: Proportional damping, equivalent viscous modal damping,or
     discrete viscous dampers. The program can use the Biggs strain
     energy weighting method to compute equivalent viscous modal
     damping.
Method: Direct integration and modal superposition. For modal super-
     position, proportional damping or equivalent viscous modal damping
     must be used. For direct integration, discrete viscous dampers
     may be used.
Usage: Success was reported for a wide variety of forcing functions
     including random and seismic.
Availability: From the CDC Cybernet Service or from Dr. R. Rosen,
     Mechanics Research Inc., 9841 Airport Blvd., Los Angeles, CA 90045

Program STRUDL

Capability: Proportional damping and equivalent viscous modal damping
Method: Modal superposition
Usage: Success was reported for free vibration, transient forcing, and
     seismic excitation of damped structures.
Availability: ICES Users Group, Inc., Box 8243, Cranston, RI 02920.
     In addition, STRUDL exists in many private versions.

Reference [17] lists three programs which allow the solution of
lumped parameter dynamic models having Coulomb dampers. One program is
applicable to a single-degree-of-freedom model, one to a two- or three-
degree-of-freedom model, and one to a model with up to 65 degrees of
freedom. The programs also permit the use of viscous dampers, nonlinear springs,and gaps. The programs are written in FORTRAN and are
available on cards. Information on price is available from: Technology
Marketing Operation, General Electric Co., 1 River Road, Schenectady, NY
12345, USA.
     Reviewing the above summaries as a whole, several common features
can be discerned. If modal superposition is a desirable solution
method (e.g., the response is expected to be dominated by a few modes),
equivalent viscous modal damping ratios or a proportional damping matrix
is used. The use of modal superposition and complex eigenvalues and
complex eigenvectors is less common.
     If, on the other hand, discrete viscous or hysteretic dashpots are
desired, a nonproportional damping matrix is generated and the solution
typically proceeds by step-by-step direct numerical integration. In
those cases where the forcing is harmonic, several programs choose to
incorporate damping via a complex stiffness matrix.
     It appears from the survey that there are many general programs
available for solving damped response problems; nevertheless, there are
several areas in which additional research would be helpful. One of
the main difficulties is ascertaining the correct damping values to be

inserted into the program. It is clear that the establishment of a com-
pendium of damping values for a wide variety of structures and materials
would be a useful contribution. Further research is needed in modeling
systems to account for different values of damping in different elements
of the system. In this regard, the rapidly evolving techniques of substructures, or component mode analysis, should be helpful. Recent
attempts to use substructure analysis to determine overall structural
damping are given in Ref. [54-56]. Further work is also needed
for systems in which different types of damping mechanisms (e.g., viscous
and hysteretic) are acting separately or simultaneously.

Recent work [44] has shown the utility of damped forced modes in
the analysis of systems with hysteretic damping, while Ref. [57] has de-
lineated the theory of transient response of continuous systems with viscous damping. This chapter is an update of Ref. [58].

REFERENCES

1 Lazan, B. J., Damping of Materials and Members in Structural Mechanics, Pergamon Press, 1968.

2 Bert, C. W., "Material Damping: An Introductory Review of Mathematical Models, Measures and Experimental Techniques," J. Sound and Vib., Vol. 29, No. 2, 1973, pp. 129-53.

3 Ruzicka, J. E., ed, Structural Damping, A.S.M.E. Colloquium, 1959.

4 Blevins, R. D., Flow-Induced Vibration, Van Nostrand, 1977.

5 Zener, C., Elasticity and Anelasticity of Metals, University of Chicago Press, 1948.

6 Internal Friction, Damping, and Cyclic Plasticity, ASTM Special Technical Publication No. 378, 1965.

7 Kimball, A. L., and Lovell, D. E., "Internal Friction in Solids," Physical Review, Series 2, Vol. 30, 1927, pp. 948-59.

8 Ruzicka, J. E., and Derby, T. F., Influence of Damping in Vibration Isolation, SVM-7, Shock and Vibration Information Center, Washington, D.C., 1971.

9 Miller, R. K., "The Steady State Response of Systems with Hardening Hysteresis," ASME paper 77-DET-71.

10 Crandall, S. H., "The Role of Damping in Vibration Theory," J. Sound and Vib., Vol. 11, 1970, pp. 3-18.

11 Yamada, Y., "Time Dependent Materials," in Shock and Vibration Computer Programs, SVM-10, Shock and Vibration Information Center. Washington, D.C., 1975.

12 Scanlan, R. H., and Mendelson, A., "Structural Damping," AIAA Jour., Vol. 1, No. 4, pp. 938-39.

13 Caughey, T. K., and Vijayaraghavon, A., "Free and Forced Oscillations of a Dynamic System with Linear Hysteretic Damping (Non-Linear Theory)," Int. J. Non-Linear Mech., Vol. 5, 1970, pp. 533-55.

14 Bagley, R. L., and Torvik, P. J., "A Generalized Derivative Model for an Elastomer Damper," presented at 49th Shock and Vib. Sym., Oct. 1978.

15 Jones, D. I. G., "Low Cost Measurement of Material Damping Behavior," presented at 49th Shock and Vib. Sym., Oct. 1978.

16 Reed, R. R., "Analysis of Structural Response with Different Forms of Damping," NASA TN-D-3861, 1967,

17 Levy, S., and Wilkinson, J. P. D., The Component Element Method in Dynamics, McGraw-Hill, New York, 1976.

18 Ungar, E. E., "The Status of Engineering Knowledge concerning the Damping of Built-up Structures," J. Sound and Vib., Vol. 26, No. 1, 1973, pp. 141-54.

19 Thomson, W. T., Calkins, T., and Caravani, P., "A Numerical Study of Damping," Earthquake Eng'g & Structural Dynamics, Vol. 3, 1974, pp. 97-103.

20 Rayleigh, Theory of Sound, Vol. I, Dover Publications, 1945, p. 102.

21 Newmark, N. M., Blume, J. A., and Kapur, K. K., "Design Response Spectra for Nuclear Power Plants," Am. Soc. of Civil Eng. Structural Engineering Meeting, San Francisco, April 1973.

22 Hart, G. C., and Vasudevan, R., "Earthquake Design of Buildings: Damping," J. Structural Div. ASCE, Vol. 101, No. ST1, Jan. 1975, pp. 11-30.

23 Structural Analysis and Design of Nuclear Power Plants, (Draft for trial use and comment), Committee on Nuclear Structures and Mat'ls of Structural Div. of ASCE, 1976, Chapter 5, pp. 166-70.

24 Nelson, F. C., "Techniques for the Design of Highly Damped Structures," Shock and Vibration Digest, Vol. 9, No. 7, July 1977, pp. 3-11.

25 Rodgers, L., ed, "Conference on Aerospace Polymeric Viscoelastic Damping Technology for the 1980's," AFFDL-TM-78-78-FBA, July 1978.

26 Snowdon, J. C., Vibration and Shock in Damped Mechanical Systems, Wiley, New York, 1968.

27 Nashif, A. D., "Materials for Vibration Control in Engineering," Shock and Vibration Bulletin, part 4, 1973, pp. 145-50.

28 Crandall, S. H., and McCalley, R. B., "Numerical Methods of Analysis," Shock and Vibration Handbook, Vol. 2, McGraw-Hill, New York, 1961.

29 Wilkinson, J. H., The Algebraic Eigenvalue Problem, Oxford Univ. Press, 1965.

30 Meirovitch, L., Analytical Methods in Vibration, Macmillan Co., New York, Chapter 9, 1967.

31 Caughey, T. K., "Classical Normal Modes in Damped Linear Dynamic Systems," Jour. of Applied Mech., Vol. 27, 1960, pp. 269-71.

32 Wilson, E. L., and Penzien, J., "Evaluation of Orthogonal Damping Matrices," International Journal for Numerical Methods in Engineering, Vol. 4, 1972, pp. 5-10.

33 Lalanne, M., Paulard, M., and Trompette, P., "Response of Thick Structures Damped by Viscoelastic Material with Application to Layered Beams and Plates," Shock and Vibration Bulletin, Vol, 45. 1975, pp. 65-71

34 Warburton, G. B., and Soni, S. R., "Errors in Response Calcula-tions for Non-Classically Damped Structures," Earthquake Engr. and Struct. Dyn., Vol. 5, 1977, pp. 365-76.

35 Tsai, N. C., "Modal Damping for Soil-Structure Interaction," Journal of the Engineering Mechanics Division, ASCE, April 1974, pp. 323-41.

36 Whitman, R. V., "Soil Structure Interaction," Seismic Design for Nuclear Power Plants, ed. R. J. Hansen, M.I.T. Press, Cambridge, Mass., 1970, pp. 241-69.

37 Roesset, J. M., Whitman, R. V., and Dobry, R., "Modal Analysis for Structures with Foundation Interaction," Journal of the Structural Division, Proceedings ASCE, March 1973, pp. 339-416.
38 Frazer, R. A., Duncan, W. J., and Collar, A. R., Elementary Matrices, Cambridge University Press, 1957.
39 Beliveau, J. G., "Eigenvectors in Structural Dynamics," AIAA Jour., Vol. 15, July 1977, pp. 1039-41.
40 Foss, K. A., "Co-ordinates Which Uncoupled the Equations of Motion in Damped Linear Dynamic Systems," Jour. of Applied Mechanics, Vol. 25, 1958, pp. 361-64.
41 Hurty, W. C., and Rubinstein, M. F., Dynamics of Structures, Prentice-Hall, Englewood Cliffs, N.J., 1964.
42 Law, E. H., and Cooperider, N. K., "A Survey of Railway Vehicle Dynamics Research," J. of Dynamic Systems, Measurements, and Control, Transactions ASME, June 1974, pp. 132-46.
43 Fraeijs de Veubeke, B. M., "A Variational Approach to Pure Mode Excitation Based on Characteristic Phase Lag Theory," A.G.A.R.D. Report 39, April 1956.
44 Mead, D. J., "The Existence of Normal Modes of Linear Systems with Arbitrary Damping," Symposium on Structural Dynamics, Loughborough University of Tech., Vol. 1, 1970, pp. C.5.1-C.5.15.
45 Belytschko, T., "Transient Analysis," Structural Mechanics Computer Programs, ed. W. Pilkey, K. Saczalski, and H. Schaeffer, University Press of Virginia, Charlottesville, 1974, pp.
46 Chopra, A. K., "Earthquake Analysis of Complex Structures," Applied Mechanics in Earthquake Engineering, ASME, AMD-Vol. 8, 1974.
47 Bathe, K. J., and Wilson, E. L., Numerical Methods in Finite Element Analysis, Prentice-Hall, Englewood Cliffs, N.J., 1976, Chapter 9.
48 Clough, R. W., and Mojtahedi, S., "Earthquake Response Analysis Considering Non-Proportional Damping," Earthquake Engineering and Structural Dynamics, Vol. 4, 1976, pp. 489-96.
49 Chopra, A. K., and Gutierrez, J. A., "Earthquake Response Analysis of Multistory Buildings Including Foundation Interaction," Earthquake Engineering and Structural Dynamics, Vol. 3, 1974, pp. 65-77.
50 Cooley, J. W., and Tukey, J. W., "An Algorithm for the Machine Calculation of Complex Fourier Series," Mathematics of Computation, Vol. 19, April 1976, pp. 297-301.
51 Cooley, J. W., Lewis, P. A. W., and Wlch, P. D., "Application of the Fast Fourier Transform to Computation of Fourier Integrals, Fourier Series, and Convolution Integrals," IEEE Transactions on Audio and Electroacoustics, Vol. AU-15, June 1967, pp. 79-84.
52 Yeh, G. C. K., "Determination of the Damping Matrix in Dynamic Structural Analysis of a Reactor Containment," Proceedings of the First International Conference on Structural Mechanics in Reactor Technology, Paper J4/2, pp. 317-33.
53 Meirovitch, L., Elements of Vibration Analysis, McGraw-Hill, New York, 1975.
54 Klein, L. R., and Dowell, E. H., "Analysis of Modal Damping by Component Modes Method Using Lagrangian Multipliers," Jour. Applied Mechanics, ASME, June 1974, pp. 527-28.
55 Kana, D. D., and Unruh, J. F., "Structure Energy Method for Prediction of Space Shuttle Modal Damping," J. Spacecraft, Vol. 12, No. 5, May 1975.
56 Hasselman, T. K., "Damping Synthesis from Substructure Tests," AIAA Jour., Vol. 14, No. 10, Oct. 1975, pp. 1409-18.

57 Strenkowski, J., and Pilkey, W., "Transient Response of
Continuous Elastic Structures with Viscous Damping," <u>Jour. Appl. Mech.</u>,
Vol. 45, Dec. 1978, pp. 877-82.
58 Nelson, C. F., and Grief, F., "Damping," <u>Shock and Vibration
Computer Programs</u>, eds. W. and B. Pilkey, Shock and Vibration Information
Center, Washington, D.C., 1975, pp.603-24.

Subject Index

Index of Programs